Innovation and Discovery

Bath and the Rise of Science

Detail from an engraving of Lansdown Crescent, Bath, first published in 1841. This shows the telescope belonging to Henry Lawson FRS (1774–1855) on the roof of No.7. (*Bath in Time, Bath & North East Somerset Council*)

Innovation and Discovery

Bath and the Rise of Science

Foreword by Sir Patrick Moore and Dr Allan Chapman

Edited by Peter Wallis

Authors:
Colin Axon, Angus Buchanan, Stuart Burroughs, Mike Chapman,
Robert Draper, Trevor Fawcett, Peter Ford, Marek Lewcun, Robert Randall,
Francis Ring, Roger Rolls, Peter Wallis, Roger Watson, Matt Williams

Bath Royal Literary and Scientific Institution
&
The William Herschel Society

The editor and authors are pleased to dedicate this book to
Dr W. John Williams and Diana M. Stoddart
who showed us what to do

Bath Royal Literary and Scientific Institution,
16-18 Queen Square, Bath BA1 2HN, UK
Phone: +44 (0)1225 312084
Fax: +44 (0)1225 442460
http://www.brlsi.org

The William Herschel Society,
The Herschel Museum of Astronomy,
19 New King St, Bath BA1 2BL, UK
Phone: +44 (0)1225 446865
http://www.williamherschel.org.uk

Cover illustrations:
(*front*) Detail from *Section of the Strata through Hampshire and Wiltshire to Bath ...* by William Smith, 1807
　　　　(© *Natural History Museum*)
(*rear*)　Drill machine, from the Bath and West Society's *Letters and Papers* (1802)
　　　　(*Bath Central Library, Bath & North East Somerset Council*)
　　　　William Herschel in 1781
　　　　(*The Herschel Museum of Astronomy*)
　　　　A Map of the Scite of the dissolved Priory of Bath ... , surveyed for the Duke of Kingston in 1750
　　　　(*Bath Record Office, Bath & North East Somerset Council*)
　　　　Bridge over the canal in Sydney Gardens, Bath, erected by George Stothert in 1800
　　　　(*Photograph by Edith Wallis*)

First published in 2008 by Bath Royal Literary and Scientific Institution and The William Herschel Society in association with Millstream Books, 18 The Tyning, Bath BA2 6AL

Set in Bembo and printed in Great Britain by The Short Run Press, Exeter

ISBN 978 0 948975 82 0

British Library Cataloguing-in-Publication Data:
a catalogue record for this book is available from the British Library

Foreword

It is now 30 years since John Williams and Diana Stoddart published their book on science in Bath, and over the intervening period much fresh research has been done. This new study of Bath science, undertaken by a group of specialists in their fields, is likely to remain authoritative for a long time to come.

While many think of Bath in terms of ancient Romans, or of eighteenth-century architecture, music, fashion, and culture, the city has always had, as this book makes clear, a close and enduring connection with science, medicine, and technology. Indeed, Bath's very existence in the first century AD owed as much to the ingenuity of the Roman engineers who first drained the marshes as it did to the hot springs which were subsequently to provide the lifeblood of the city's medical history. Almost as soon as the post-Roman town began to emerge in the Middle Ages, it produced talented men who were active in science. Adelard of Bath, the twelfth-century astronomer and translator, was among them, while the Reverend Joseph Glanvill, a seventeenth-century Rector of Bath Abbey, was a Fellow of the newly-founded Royal Society.

Bath science really took off in the eighteenth century, for a variety of reasons. There was of course at this time a burgeoning culture of science across Europe, which developed in the wake of numerous discoveries made in geography, anatomy, and astronomy – to name just a few sciences – after about 1500. Great Britain had already become one of the key players in this new movement well before 1700, with such eminent figures as William Gilbert (magnetism), William Harvey (discoverer of the circulation of the blood), Robert Hooke (pioneer of the experimental method), and Sir Isaac Newton, whose writings so profoundly influenced the eighteenth-century approach to science.

As well as providing this succession of great discoveries, Britain's wider culture proved very conducive to scientific and technological innovation. Despite the poverty and despair highlighted by artists like William Hogarth and other social commentators, Britain (and England in particular) had the largest, richest, and most independent middle class in world history: a people who had both formed and been formed by a variety of circumstances peculiar to Britain and its emerging American colonies. These included a Parliament-based political and legal tradition, a popular monarchy whose powers were limited by statute, a free press, a tolerant state Church from which one had the right to 'Dissent', and a flourishing economy, with a great deal of spare cash being generated from overseas trade and industrial enterprise and by the already globally-dominant City of London.

So Georgian England had numerous comfortably-off middling country gentry, clergy, and professionals, with money to spend and leisure in which to enjoy its fruits. Moreover, since it was regarded as a gentleman's prerogative to act freely, an individual might spend his money as wisely or as foolishly as he chose. Besides sport, theatre, balls, and fun, such people actively pursued art, music, and science. Indeed, a gentleman's credibility rested on his knowledge of 'culture', and by 1750 this would include such things as Newton's Laws or how clocks worked, as well as architecture, perspective drawing, literature, racehorses, dogs, and boxing.

Bath was a magnet to such people. For the city was full of all manner of service-providers, from physicians to dancing masters. If a Bath resident or visitor had an interest in science, he might attend lectures put on by a growing circuit of itinerant lecturers who performed to paying audiences, as a sort of scientific theatre. Newtonian gravitation, optics, mechanics, and electrostatics were established eighteenth-century favourites, as were the steam engine, photography, and geology in the nineteenth. These lectures, moreover, were usually demonstrated with exquisitely-made instruments. Some lecturers, such as the London-based virtuoso Benjamin Martin in the earlier part of the eighteenth century, also sold instruments and wrote books for their audiences. Indeed, the market mechanism sounds remarkably modern!

Yet in addition to the scientific dilettanti, Bath had many residents and visitors who were involved with science more formally. Physicians and surgeons obviously constituted the largest group of such individuals, but then there were chemists, geologists, engineers, and archaeologists as well. One man's scientific life was changed profoundly in Bath: Sir William Herschel switched careers from music to research astronomy in the early 1780s and went on to win enduring fame. In the following pages you will meet a whole collection of ingenious scientific individuals who at one time or another lived and worked in Bath.

Remember that from the time of King Charles II to that of Queen Victoria science and invention were seen as part of a broad and integrated culture, and that in a Bath drawing-room or in the Pump Room you could have heard conversations about planets, fossils, medical therapies, or clever inventions intermixed with remarks about art, theatre, or the latest fashions. This is the scientific culture that this book is about.

We warmly applaud the editor and the authors for their achievement. So read on and enjoy yourself.

Sir Patrick Moore, CBE, FRS, FRAS
President, The William Herschel Society
Selsey, West Sussex

Dr Allan Chapman, FRAS
Vice-President, The William Herschel Society
Wadham College, Oxford

March 2008

Contents

The following abbreviations are used in this book:

BRLSI   Bath (Royal) Literary and Scientific Institution

DNB   *Oxford Dictionary of National Biography*, Oxford, Oxford University Press, 2004

FGS   Fellow of the Geological Society (London)

FRS   Fellow of the Royal Society

Acknowledgements

This book would not exist if Peter Ford had not suggested, in April 2005, that I might like to think about producing a new edition of the Williams and Stoddart book on Bath science and scientists. In the early stages, John Williams and Bob Draper also proved extremely supportive in developing my idea of a wholly new book with different chapters written by different experts.

I am extraordinarily grateful to all the authors for their friendly and enthusiastic cooperation, even when I inevitably found it necessary to pester them with urgent requests for hard work. It is also a pleasure to express my thanks for the extraordinary amount of new information that the authors unearthed: at times it seemed to me as editor that new information about Bath science and scientists was simply pouring out of the woodwork!

I am most grateful to Sir Patrick Moore and Allan Chapman, who provided the Foreword: Allan also contributed enthusiastically on many occasions during the production of the book. Publication would not have been possible without the participation of BRLSI and The William Herschel Society, and the exemplary expertise and professionalism of our publisher, Tim Graham of Millstream Books. The support of our sponsors is also gratefully acknowledged.

In administrative matters I was greatly helped by Francis Ring of The William Herschel Society, and also by Colin Axon, Peter Ford, John Garrett, Clyde Hunter, Roger Rolls, Fred Schlesinger and Julian Vincent. Angus Buchanan, Allan Chapman, Trevor Fawcett, Patrick Moore and Dava Sobel read the whole book in draft and many useful comments resulted.

Many others have provided invaluable help, support and encouragement along the way. My apologies to anyone inadvertently omitted from the following list: David Allen, Stephen Athearn, Rigmor Bastvik (Bodleian Library), Stephen Bird, Daniel Brown (Bath in Time), Charles Burnett, Stephen Clews (Roman Baths Museum), Roland Cross, Barry Cunliffe, Bob Draper, David Dunlop, Sheila Edwards, Susan Fox (Roman Baths Museum), Jill Frederick, David Gardener, Elizabeth Henry, Lee Hooper, Michael Hoskin, Colin Johnston (Bath Record Office), Michael King, David Knight, David Mitchell, John Mudford, Lucy Powell (Bath Record Office), Dennis Powney, Lucy Rutherford (Bath Abbey), Michael Tabb, Hugh Torrens, Rex Valentine, Bob Whitaker, Phil Willis.

My own personal thanks to BG, and most of all to EMW who made it possible.

Sponsors

Cross Manufacturing Company (1938) Limited
IPL Information Processing Limited

Dr David Dunlop
Don Foster MP
Mrs Richard W. Hamming
Mr and Mrs J. Herschel-Shorland
Michael King
Dr Richard Mawditt OBE
Dr Michael Rowe
Robert Whitaker MBE

Preface

As indicated in the Foreword, there are several reasons why Bath had the good fortune to become a centre for gentleman scientists of the eighteenth century and, incorporating the contributions of both earlier and later residents, there is ample scope for an informal book on science in Bath. Such a book was first produced in the nineteenth century when the Reverend Joseph Hunter FSA, a member of the Bath Royal Literary and Scientific Institution, produced his book *The Connection of Bath with the Literature and Science of England.*[1]

More recently, John Williams and Diana Stoddart, then working at the University of Bath, produced a modest hardcover book, *Bath – Some Encounters with Science,*[2] to mark the 1978 Bath meeting of the British Association for the Advancement of Science. Their book systematically describes scientists, scientific discoveries and scientific institutions associated with Bath and its neighbourhood.

The Williams/Stoddart book has long been out of print, and so much more has been discovered about Bath science since its publication that a new book is clearly overdue. The present book endeavours to fulfil that need by providing a collaboration between a number of qualified authors. While it is wholly new, this volume retains the flavour and intention of its 1978 predecessor, and in acknowledgement of their debt the editor and authors of this book dedicate it to John Williams and Diana Stoddart. The present work not only reflects greatly increased knowledge of Bath scientists collected since 1978 but its scope has been extended to include more fields of applied science such as archaeology, map-making and engineering.

Much care has been taken to ensure the completeness and accuracy of this book, with many parts of it reviewed by specialists in the subject-matter concerned. However, errors and omissions are inevitable in a project of this complexity, and as editor I am responsible for all that remain. All comments and corrections are welcome and should be sent to the Editor, *Innovation and Discovery*, Bath Royal Literary and Scientific Institution, 16-18 Queen Square, Bath BA1 2HN, U.K.

Peter Wallis
Bath, October 2008

Introduction

Bath and Early Science

Peter Wallis

The city of Bath has the only hot springs in the United Kingdom. From the very earliest times these would have attracted people seeking healing, and since the Romans were well aware of their putative healing properties, there would surely have been related medical activity. So it would seem appropriate to start a book on science in Bath with some reference to medical practice at the Roman baths.

Hard information on the subject is virtually non-existent. However as the result of an eighteenth-century discovery we can name a single medical practitioner associated with Roman Bath. In 1731 a greenish rectangular stone around 8 cm long and 1 cm square was found during the digging of a cellar in Bath Abbey church-yard. This was a Roman medicine-stamp, bearing on its long faces reversed inscriptions to be pressed into tablets of ointment. Roman medicine-stamps are quite unusual but a fair number[1] have been found in Britain. The four long faces of the Bath stamp identify eye-ointments available from one Titus Junianus.[2] One inscription somewhat arrogantly describes an ointment 'for such cases as have been given up by the physicians' suggesting perhaps that Junianus specialised in eye diseases which were common in Roman times.

Diagram of Junianus' medicine-stamp,
taken from *Aquae Solis, or Notices of Roman Bath*
by H.M. Scarth (1864).

Unfortunately Junianus' medicine-stamp was lost after passing into the possession of a Mr Mitchell of Bristol during the eighteenth century, but not before the inscriptions on its faces had been recorded and casts of three of them (also now lost) made for the Museum of the Society of Antiquaries. A similar medicine-stamp in the collection of the Corinium Museum at Cirencester refers to Minerva who, as a healing deity, was also associated with the hot springs at Bath.

Beginnings of Modern Science

Junianus is simply the first Bath medical practitioner we can name, because of this chance discovery of his medicine-stamp. As the size of this book suggests, numerous contributions to science and technology have been made by people living and working in Bath since then, and the city has also been home to some distinguished scientific institutions. This first chapter summarises a few generalities about the history of science and about the history of Bath, providing an overall historical context for the accounts that follow. Even the terms *science* and *scientist* would have been unfamiliar terms to many of those featured here – the English word science originally simply meant 'knowledge' when first recorded in the thirteenth century[3] and only gradually supplanted the earlier term *natural philosophy*, while *scientist* was a nineteenth-century introduction, frequently attributed to the polymath William Whewell, writing around 1840.

The earliest origins of science may be traced to many cultures, for example to the Hindu/ Arabic positional number system, but the development of modern science is most directly derived from the learning of the Greek and Roman world. This became centred in Alexandria, where the Greek mathematician Euclid settled around 300 BC. Others who studied there included Archimedes (287-212 BC) and the astronomer Ptolemy (c.85-c.165 AD).

Following the fall of Rome, intellectual activity continued throughout Europe but with imperfect knowledge of classical learning. Western European knowledge of Euclid's *Elements*, to take a single example, derived from the fourth-century writings of Boethius and did not convey any emphasis on the importance of proving theorems. The bulk of classical learning survived in two main places: Greek copies in Byzantium which largely became available to Western learning through twelfth-century Latin translations, and a collection of Arabic translations of classical texts that became available to Western learning after the fall of Toledo in 1085. Medieval education was largely the province of the church and based on the seven liberal arts of antiquity divided between the *trivium* of grammar, rhetoric and logic and, for more advanced study, the *quadrivium* comprising arithmetic, geometry, astronomy (which was largely astrological) and music (taught as a branch of mathematics).

The Ruin

With the decline of Roman administration in Britain, the eventual decay of Roman Bath (Aquae Sulis) is not unexpected. Centuries later, the presence of substantial remains seems to have inspired the creation of one of the few known Old English poems. *The Exeter Book*, a tenth-century manuscript in Exeter Cathedral Library, contains the largest known collection of such poems.

Among these is *The Ruin*.[4] In this contemplative poem an Anglo-Saxon poet describes the visible fragments of a once impressive place, musing on the fate and fortunes of its former inhabitants and contrasting time past and time present. While there is no direct evidence that the poem is a description of Bath,[5] references to stone walls, tiles, towers, arched roofs and foundations bound with iron all suggest the remains of a Roman city. Moreover, three particular features taken in conjunction fit Bath but no other known site in Britain, namely
- The hot spring rising into a walled reservoir;
- The extent and number of the baths;
- The round pool mentioned, which appears to be a reference to the circular bath lying to the west of the large rectangular Great Bath.

It is indeed a beguiling thought that we may well have an eyewitness account of the ruins of Roman Bath as they appeared after a few hundred years of decay.

The original text of *The Ruin* requires translation for modern readers. The prose translation by R.K. Gordon runs:

> Wondrously ornate is the stone of this wall, shattered by fate; the precincts of the city have crumbled and the work of giants is crumbling away.
>
> There are tumbled roofs, towers in ruins, high towers rime-frosted, rime on the limy mortar, storm-shielding tiling scarred, scorched and collapsed, undermined by age. An earthly grasp holds the lordly builders, decayed and gone, the cruel grip of the ground, while a hundred generations of humanity have passed away. Often has this wall, hoary with lichen, stained with red, lasted out one kingdom after another, left upstanding after storms: lofty and broad, it fell. Still the rampart, hewn by men, crumbles away … they were joined together … cruelly sharpened … shone … skilful work ancient structure … A ring with encrustations of

soil prompted the mind and drew forth a swift idea. Ingenious in the making of chains, the bold-minded men amazingly bound together the ribs of the wall with cables.

There were bright city buildings, many bathhouses, a wealth of lofty gables, much clamour of the multitude, many a mead-hall filled with human revelry – until mighty Fate changed that. Far and wide men fell dead: days of pestilence came and death destroyed the whole mass of those renowned swordsmen. Their fortresses became waste places; the city rotted away; those who should repair it, the multitudes, were fallen to the ground. For that reason these courts are collapsing and the wide red roof of vaulted beams is shedding its tiles. The site is fallen into ruin, reduced to heaps, where once many a man blithe of mood and bright with gold, clothed in splendours, proud and flown with wine, gleamed in his war-trappings, and gazed upon treasure, on silver, on chased gems, on wealth, on property, on the precious stone and on this bright citadel of the broad kingdom: and the stone courts were standing and the stream warmly spouted its ample surge and a wall embraced all in its bright bosom where the baths were, hot at its heart. That was convenient. Then they let pour ... the warm springs across the grey stone ... until the round pool hotly ... where the baths were. Then is ... It is a fitting thing how the ... city

Adelard of Bath

An important Bath connection with the early history of Western science is provided by Adelard of Bath (c.1080-c.1152)[6] whose special significance is as a pioneering translator of Arabic texts into Latin, making them accessible to European learning. Evidence for the details of Adelard's life is meagre, being based largely on autobiographical remarks. He certainly came from Bath, referring to the city several times in his writings.

Adelard would have grown up in Bath around the time that Bishop John of Tours[7] was the local bishop and the cathedral moved from Wells to Bath. A former physician from Tours, Bishop John initiated the building of a major Romanesque church in Bath, parts of whose foundations still lie beneath Bath Abbey and its vicinity. Bishop John is known to have enjoyed the company of scholars and under his leadership the monks of Bath became renowned for their learning. Adelard appears to have been educated initially in Bath, presumably in connection with this learned community. It was usual for scholars of the time to travel abroad for advanced study taking pupils with them. Adelard travelled to Tours, Bishop John's former home city, around 1100 with his 'nephew' (presumably a bright pupil) for more advanced study, based on the *quadrivium* in the manner of the times; his studies in Tours would thus have included music and astronomy. Subsequently he moved to Laon in France for a period, taking his 'nephew' and other students with him. Laon appears to have been a natural destination at the time as relatives of several of Henry I's key administrators were students there. Leaving Laon and his pupils behind and proposing to study Arabic learning, Adelard embarked on seven years of Mediterranean travels which were to take him to Sicily, Italy and Asia Minor. He praises William, Bishop of Syracuse, for his expertise in mathematics, and possibly learned Arabic while in Sicily. Adelard then embarked on a pioneering search for Arabic texts previously unknown to European learning.

Returning from his Mediterranean travels around 1116, Adelard is believed to have spent the rest of his life living and working in Bath, probably as a tutor to sons of the nobility. He was a prolific writer and scholar, and appears to have had numerous important pupils. His extensive writings fall into two broad classes – didactic literary works plainly written with a large audience in mind, and his important scientific translations from the Arabic.

Adelard's didactic works cover a remarkable range of topics, including contributions to medieval philosophy and education, instructions on the use of the astrolabe and a practical treatise on falconry. Among the most highly polished are those involving his 'nephew', which are of particular interest in the light they cast on his life and achievements.[8] The *De Eodem et Diverso*,[9] written before his extensive travels, takes the form of conversations between Philocosmia, advocating worldly pleasures, and Philosophia who defends scholarship, with Adelard's nephew as a silent auditor. An interesting feature of *De Eodem et Diverso* is that its treatment of geometry does not suggest any knowledge of Euclid: it reflects the classical learning that Adelard would have received at Tours and Laon. Adelard's subsequent *Questiones Naturales*,[10] apparently written soon after his return from his extensive travels, affords fascinating insights into scientific knowledge of the time. It consists of a series of questions about the natural world, presented as a dramatic work recreating a real conversation between Adelard and his 'nephew'.

By far the most important parts of Adelard's work, however, were his translations from Arabic into Latin of scientific texts previously unknown to medieval Europe. These represent major contributions to the development of Western learning. Most importantly, he was responsible for three Latin versions of Euclid's *Elements* circulated under his name (two of which are likely to be of his authorship). Before these Latin translations, Euclid's *Elements* was known in Europe only as a few isolated fragments that failed to convey the importance of proving theorems. Adelard's comprehensive translations thus introduced formal deductive reasoning to Western learning. Remarkably, the translations include interpretive material enlarging upon the text for an educated readership, so their preparation necessarily required considerable mathematical expertise.

Among Adelard's other translations from Arabic were works on astrology and astronomy, most notably the *Zij* (or astronomical tables) of al-Khwarizmi (*see Colour Plates I and II*). These tables are used for calculating the apparent positions of astronomical bodies at specified times and places, and were primarily of astrological use. Their importance to the history of Western science lies not only in the new astronomical knowledge they contained but also because they introduced to Europe the Hindu/ Arabic method of calculating with angles that superseded the Ptolemaic method using chords then in vogue. The translation includes what is probably the first appearance in a Latin text of a table of the trigonometric sine function (although Adelard does not use the actual term 'sine', which was introduced slightly later): tables of the tangent function also appear.

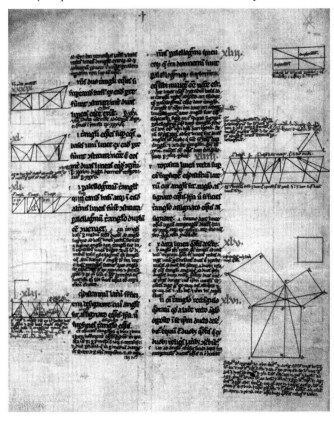

A page from Adelard of Bath's version of Euclid's *Elements* that appears to illustrate Pythagoras' theorem.
(*Bodleian Library, Oxford, Auct. F.5.28*)

Science and the Renaissance

Adelard was widely revered in medieval times for his introduction of Euclid into European education. His pioneering translations formed a part of the movement sometimes termed the 'Twelfth-century Renaissance', when European learning was revolutionised by the availability of classical texts through direct translations from the Arabic. However, this represented simply one component of the huge cultural transformation eventually known as the Renaissance, in which Western scholars rediscovered classical models of all kinds, initially to be unquestioningly venerated and subsequently to be taken as starting-points for development. The transformations effected by the Renaissance in European art and architecture are well known, while their effects on scientific endeavours are at least as important. What is frequently called the Revolution in Science, extending roughly from the fifteenth to the seventeenth centuries, reflected the general spirit of the Renaissance precisely, culminating in the experimental, sceptical approaches that characterise science today.

It may be helpful to attach a few dates to this general scenario. The beginnings of experimental science are frequently traced to the work of the English philosophers Roger Bacon and Robert Grosseteste in the early thirteenth century, the beginnings of modern science perhaps being taken to date from the 1543 publication of Copernicus' *De Revolutionibus*. This work attempted a complete replacement of Ptolemy's system of astronomy centred on a fixed Earth. In the same year Vesalius' *De Humani Corporis Fabrica* was published, overturning parts of the teachings on anatomy of the ancient physician Galen with observations based on human dissections and initiating an approach to anatomy that led directly to Harvey's seventeenth-century discovery of the circulation of the blood.[11] This general replacement of classical scientific models with more progressive ones was extremely gradual. To give examples based on Copernicus' work, both the idea that the Earth was not stationary and the idea of frictionless motion (i.e. of motion that did not require a force to maintain it) took many years to gain general acceptance. An important figure in these early developments is that of Francis Bacon (1561-1626), whose writings on scientific method were very influential on British scientists of the generations that followed.[12]

The beginnings of modern organised scientific practice date from the latter part of the seventeenth century. The experimental natural philosophy of that period was beginning to emerge as a collaborative effort, supported by the discussion groups that spawned the very first scientific journals. Groups of natural philosophers centred at Gresham College in London and at Wadham College, Oxford, were of particular importance in England, for they led to the birth, in 1660, of the Royal Society, which received its charter from Charles II in 1662. In the early days of the Royal Society, there were continuing tensions between the new empirical approach exemplified by current developments in experimental natural philosophy, and more conservative approaches to learning based on classical models. Only when the infallibility of classical models was widely called into question was it possible for modern experimental science to begin its rapid development.

Joseph Glanvill

Bath is connected with the tensions surrounding the early development of experimental science through the person of the Reverend Joseph Glanvill (1636-1680), who was appointed Rector of Bath Abbey in 1666 and lived in Bath until his death. A conspicuous churchman, Glanvill published prolifically on many subjects including religious practice, witchcraft, and paranormal phenomena. Most importantly, he is a pivotal figure in the history of

seventeenth-century science in England due to his advocacy of the value of experiment in natural philosophy. Born in Plymouth, Glanvill was educated at Oxford (BA Exeter 1655, MA Lincoln 1658) and ordained in 1660. Elected FRS in 1664, he was also the first secretary of a Somerset affiliate of the Royal Society established in 1659.

Glanvill's direct contributions to natural philosophy were quite modest. In issue No.19 of the *Philosophical Transactions of the Royal Society*, Robert Boyle published a list of inquiries concerning mining procedures and the characteristics of mining areas. Glanvill responded by producing two sets of replies[13] from miners and local residents relating to the Mendip lead mines near Bath. These replies are quite detailed and of some permanent value in the history of mining.[14] Subsequently Glanvill published a largely factual report on the hot springs at Bath[15] in response to queries by the natural philosopher Henry Oldenburg.

Engraving of Joseph Glanvill by William Faithorne. (*Bath in Time, Bath & North East Somerset Council*)

Many of Glanvill's writings appeared in several different forms during his lifetime and those on experimental natural philosophy are no exception. His ideas originally appeared in *The Vanity of Dogmatizing* (1661). This was originally intended to form the preface to a projected book on the immortality of the soul and is extremely wide-ranging. For instance it includes the story of the scholar gipsy. This was later used in the famous nineteenth-century poem by Matthew Arnold which refers to 'Glanvil [*sic*] and his book'. *The Vanity of Dogmatizing* contains much other material of no relevance here, but owes its importance in the history of science both to its attacks on the Aristotelian style of education then prevalent at Oxford and Cambridge and to its praise of the experimental approach to science exemplified by contemporary natural philosophy.

The Vanity of Dogmatizing proved controversial and Glanvill responded with a revised version, *Scepsis Scientifica* (1664), which included a long preface addressed to the Royal Society. Continuing controversy precipitated a third version, *Plus Ultra* (1668), whose writing was encouraged by Henry Oldenburg. *Plus Ultra*, an early attempt at a history of science, praised the experimental natural philosophy of the Royal Society as the most productive yet found.[16] By the time of Glanvill's last work on natural philosophy, *Against Confidence in Philosophy* (1676), the attack on Aristotelianism was no longer felt to be necessary: by 1676 it was clear that the natural science of the experimentalists had gained a permanent place at Oxford and Cambridge.

Glanvill died of a fever on 4 November 1680 and is buried in Bath Abbey. His memorial stone in the floor of the nave, although partially obscured by pews installed around 1860, can be clearly seen very near the north-west entrance currently used by visitors to the Abbey.

The Latin inscription refers to his Fellowship of the Royal Society.

Later Developments

Although experimental science had progressed very significantly by the late seventeenth century it remained far from modern in its form and preoccupations. Even the great Newton wrote more on alchemy than he did on natural philosophy, his alchemical writings being largely private. Moreover, scientific knowledge was not then organised into academic disciplines[17] in the modern way: for example, in the seventeenth century both physics and biology were among the concerns of natural philosophy, while chemistry was largely practised either by alchemists or by medical practitioners, who saw it as part of their field.

The crowning achievement of the seventeenth-century English natural philosophers was the 1687 publication of Newton's *Principia*. In the following century Newton became revered as a hero, especially in France, because of his solution to the riddle of the planets, showing that they obey the same laws as motions on the Earth.[18] Enlightenment attitudes of the eighteenth century encouraged the application of the Newtonian model to different scientific fields. This led very gradually over the eighteenth and early nineteenth centuries to the emergence of the different scientific disciplines we know today, a process so profound that it is sometimes[19] called the Second Scientific Revolution. Among the scientists whose work is discussed later in this book, we can identify two who were particularly important in the early development of their respective modern disciplines: Joseph Priestley's discovery of oxygen was a key event in what Butterfield[20] famously calls 'the postponed scientific revolution in chemistry', while William Smith's work was central to the development of systematic geology.

Inscription on the memorial slab in Bath Abbey for Joseph Glanville [*sic*], as recorded in a Victorian transcription of the Abbey monuments. (*Photograph by Alan Morley*)

Bath and Science

Apart from its hot springs, Bath was a relatively small and undeveloped English market town into Tudor[21] and Stuart[22] times, despite its status as a centre for therapeutic bathing. The first signs of a real change in fortune resulted from the vogue for therapeutic drinking, whose origins date from the very important installation of a new drinking pump in 1671; the subsequent visits of Queen Anne in 1702 and 1703 in many ways heralded the development of the spa in earnest.[23] This led directly to the rise of the city as a fashionable spa in the latter half of the eighteenth century, when it attracted the rich and the famous from all over the country. The consequent speculative development of the eighteenth-century city left Bath with the spectacular legacy of Georgian architecture for which it is renowned today.[24] The early nineteenth century saw a relative decline in Bath's fame and prosperity,[25] and although there were some notable Victorian and twentieth-century commercial developments Bath has never become a major industrial centre.

The chapters that follow describe the work of scientists who have lived or worked in the vicinity of Bath and some of the city's scientific institutions. The emphasis is on developments that pre-date contemporary academic science and commerce, so that overall there is a concentration on the Georgian period as a natural consequence of Bath's national importance as a fashionable spa at that time. Joseph Priestley (a Dissenting minister) discovered oxygen while he was employed at Bowood near Bath. Important medical advances pioneered in eighteenth-century Bath resulted from the presence both of the hot springs and of the physicians who consequently came to Bath to offer treatment. Bath is well-known as the home of William Smith's pioneering work on geology, precipitated by his civil engineering work in the area, but the city has also been home to a number of other notable geologists. A high point in Bath's eighteenth-century scientific history was the discovery of the planet Uranus by William Herschel: Herschel had come to Bath as a musician. There were a number of notable local contributions to systematic scientific natural history, and William Henry Fox Talbot pioneered early photography while he lived at Lacock near Bath. Further scientific developments resulted from the exploration of Bath's archaeology, from the need to map the city and its area (arising partly from William Smith's work), and from engineering and commercial activities in the city.

Scientific institutions in Bath owed their beginnings to the national vogue for popular scientific lecturing in the eighteenth century, which naturally found a ready audience in Bath among those whose presence related to the spa. A number of scientific societies and institutions were founded as a consequence, among them the three successive Bath Philosophical Societies and Bath Royal Literary and Scientific Institution (BRLSI). BRLSI was one of many such institutions founded around the country in the early nineteenth century, but had an unusual twentieth-century history, passing first into a moribund state and then, most unusually, being revived in the early 1990s due to a combination of initiatives by various groups of local residents mounted in response to various proposals by local government to disperse its assets completely: it was formally re-launched in 1993 and is now thriving. Among its numerous other activities BRLSI does much to support and encourage the interests of scientists now living and working in the area, while the British Association for the Advancement of Science has held three of its annual gatherings in Bath. Modern professional science is strongly represented in Bath, both by the range of related businesses in the area and by the presence of the University of Bath, which has developed a distinguished research reputation since receiving its charter in 1966.

Further Reading

Burnett, C., *Adelard of Bath, Conversations with his Nephew: On the Same and the Different, Questions on Natural Science, and On Birds*, Cambridge, Cambridge University Press, 1998

Butterfield, H., *The Origins of Modern Science*, Cambridge, Cambridge University Press, 1949; second edition, 1957

Cochran, L., *Adelard of Bath: The First English Scientist*, London, British Museum Press, 1994.

Gribbin, J., *Science: A History 1543-2001*, London, Allen Lane, 2002.

Kuhn, T.S., *The Structure of Scientific Revolutions*, Chicago, University of Chicago Press, 1962; second edition, 1970.

Part I
People

1: Airs and Waters
The Hot Springs and Bath Chemistry

Peter Ford and Roger Rolls

The fame of Bath stems from the city's hot mineral springs[1] which emerge from the ground at a temperature of about 46.5 degrees Celsius (117 degrees Fahrenheit). Between 65 and 75 AD the Romans restored the ancient and decaying Celtic shrine of Sulis, making it once again magnificent and sumptuous. They dedicated it to Sulis Minerva. It is perhaps significant that the shrine was named after the Roman goddess Minerva: she was the goddess of wisdom and war, also believed to possess the power to cure illness.

Over the last millennium, many explanations for the water's constitution and therapeutic potential have been proposed, reflecting contemporary beliefs about the nature of disease. Modern research goes some way to explain why a course of treatment in the baths might have helped patients who resorted to the spa in former centuries, and how spa treatment can benefit some conditions prevalent today. However, it was ancient theories which in the past provided doctors with a rationale for treatment.

Elements and Humours

For centuries, it was thought that disease was caused by an imbalance of four body fluids known as humours and called yellow bile, black bile, blood and phlegm. Like the four elements of the ancients, each humour had physical properties corresponding to its degree of heat and moisture: for example, yellow bile was hot and dry whereas phlegm was cold and wet. An excess of any of these humours related to a corresponding illness. Nature tended to cure disease by redressing the humoral balance, which explained why people often recovered from their illnesses spontaneously. Slight imbalances were thought to explain variations in personality. Terms we use today, such as being in a good humour, being sanguine or phlegmatic reflect this ancient belief.

Humoral theory can be supported by observation. When blood is placed in a glass vessel, it settles into distinct layers, the thickness of which may vary when disease is present. For example, the white cell layer (anciently identified as phlegm) thickens during infections and other inflammatory conditions, whilst the red cell layer (identified as blood) diminishes if the person is anaemic. The yellow component, now known as serum, could have been confused with bile, and when blood coagulates the clot which forms in the bottom of the vessel is dark enough to resemble black bile.

The job of physicians was to set up favourable conditions to aid recovery by advocating treatments to rebalance the humours. An excess of phlegm was implicated as a cause of many disorders. For example, too much phlegm in the eye could cause cataract (literally a waterfall of phlegm). Phlegm was implicated in forgetfulness, deafness, sterility, miscarriages, gout (literally a drop of phlegm), dropsy, stroke, and many other diseases known today to have no connection with the secretion of mucous. William Turner, who wrote one of the earliest printed books about the use of spa waters, listed nearly 90 disorders which he considered would benefit from mineral water treatment.[2] Cold moist disorders required hot drying remedies. The Bath waters are certainly hot and because of their mineral content they taste 'dry'. They also promote excretion. For the seventeenth-century physician, Bath spa treatment was therefore a logical choice where an excess of phlegm was implicated as the cause of an illness.

Chemical Cures

The increasing interest in alchemy during the sixteenth century, stimulated by the writings of the itinerant Swiss physician Paracelsus (1493-1541), led to a gradual rejection of the humoral theory of disease. The body was likened to a complex chemical laboratory where a large number of minerals reacted to form salts and other compounds in a sort of fermentation process. Just as metals can corrode, so minerals in bodily tissue can putrefy and lead to disease. Similarly, as apples can be cooked, or fermented and distilled to alcohol, so food can be concocted (cooked) in the stomach and fermented and distilled into constituents of the body. The human body reflects the external terrestrial and celestial worlds: in other words, the 'microcosm' is a mirror of the 'macrocosm' and health is preserved when there is harmony between the two.

Alchemical physicians were particularly interested in the mineral constituents of thermal water and believed that if they analysed them it would be possible to make artificial waters usable as medicines. If applied externally they could pass through the pores of the skin and modify the internal chemistry. One of the first analyses of the Bath waters was performed by Dr Edward Jorden (1569-1632) who practised as a physician in Bath and whose book, *Discourse of Naturall Bathes and Minerall Waters, etc.*, served as a standard work during the seventeenth century.[3] Jorden's analytical process involved distillation of the mineral water and recrystallisation of its residue so that he was able to identify the crystals which formed. He also used a precipitation method, identifying bases and acids by what appears to be an early example of an acid base indicator:

> I have observed that the Salts are proper to blue colours, and the other to red: for example, take a piece of Scarlet cloth, and wet it in Oil of Tartar (the strongest of that kind) and it presently becomes blue, dip it again in Oil of Vitriol, and it becomes red again.[1]

The red dye was possibly cochineal or Brazil wood.[5]

Physicians believed the three principal constituents of the Bath waters were nitre, sulphur and bitumen. Although nitre now refers to naturally occurring potassium nitrate, the word was originally applied to sodium carbonate. (The related word natron is still sometimes used for this substance.) Sulphur and bitumen were thought to be present in the waters because people believed them to be heated by underground fires of brimstone akin to volcanic activity. However, the Rector of the Abbey Church, Joseph Glanvill, presented a paper to the Royal Society of London in 1669 in which he suggested that the high temperature of the spring water resulted from reaction which generated heat when two streams with different mineral content mingled together – an erroneous opinion for which he subsequently apologised.[6]

Glanvill's treatise is one of many dissertations on the Bath waters compiled by various authors, mostly physicians, which appeared throughout the seventeenth and eighteenth centuries.[7] Views differed over whether or not sulphur and bitumen were constituents. Despite these disagreements, most eighteenth-century doctors attributed the curative properties of the water to their chemical constituents. One problem with the mineral waters became apparent as a result of chemical analysis: most were so dilute that very large doses had to be prescribed to produce their effect.

An alternative theory, known now as iatromechanics, became popular at the end of the seventeenth century and often features in eighteenth-century publications about the Bath waters. The body was thought of in mechanical terms with its vessels and nerves acting like a hydraulic system. Disease resulted from variations in the elasticity of the body's solid parts, thereby interfering with the movement of body fluids. The fluids themselves might thicken from accumulation of viscous particles, causing stagnation and congestion. Mineral water was believed to enter the circulation, dissolve these viscous particles in the blood and soften the solid parts. The mineral content still had relevance because doctors thought that the waters could stimulate fibres and nerves. They could also cleanse the kidneys, bladder and womb. To prevent the water from washing impurities from the stomach into the blood and from overheating the system, the patient had to be prepared by purging, bleeding and induced vomiting.

Drinking mineral water was only recommended from the mid-seventeenth century onwards after pumps were installed on the edge of the baths and it became possible to safely imbibe uncontaminated water. General medical opinion before this time held them to be unsafe.[8]

Later in the century, Dr William Falconer and colleagues identified *fixed air* (later known as carbon dioxide) and other gases in the water, suggesting that the dissolved gases might be the vital healing agent.[9] Moreover, even in the eighteenth century, some doctors were sceptical that there was anything special about the waters, attributing improvements in patients' health to temporary changes of air, diet or lifestyle.[10]

Modern Analyses

Since 1823 there have been at least ten major studies of the composition of the Bath waters whose increasing sophistication reflects the progress made in analytical chemistry during that time. The chief constituents are ions of calcium, magnesium, sodium, sulphate and chloride. Despite statements made by earlier authors, neither free sulphur nor bitumen is actually present. It was the residue resulting from a growth of algae on the surface of the water in the baths which led to this mistake as, when dried, it burned with a blue flame similar to that of blazing sulphur.

The amount of dissolved solid in the Bath waters is approximately 2.2 grams per litre of water, about 16 times less than that found in seawater (approximately 35 grams of dissolved solid per litre). Beginning in the latter half of the nineteenth century, spectroscopic techniques of increasing accuracy have been employed to examine the waters and these have revealed the presence of many trace elements. One popular theory suggested that one or more of these elements might act as enzyme catalysts, stimulating healing processes in the body, but this remains unproven.[11] One of the trace elements is the precious element silver, estimated to be present in a concentration of about 0.001 milligram per litre. The flow rate of the mineral springs is approximately one million litres per day and this corresponds to about one gram of silver, which is far too low to be extracted commercially. However, with approximately 2.2 grams of dissolved solid per litre of water, the total quantity of solid brought to the surface during one year is quite considerable. At the 1864 British Association meeting in Bath, the famous geologist Sir Charles Lyell stated that in a year the total amount of dissolved solid in the mineral springs could form a column some nine feet (three metres) in diameter and 140 feet (42 metres) high.[12]

By the mid-nineteenth century both gases and chemical constituents were losing credibility as healing agents and physicians felt that the effects of the waters were mostly due to their hydrostatic properties and heat. The vogue for plain water bathing was popularised in mainland Europe by Vincent Priessnitz and Father Kneipp, and so called hydropathic institutions based on their principles began appearing in various parts of Britain.

In the first years of the twentieth century two discoveries drew worldwide attention to the mineral springs at Bath. These were the discovery of the presence of helium in 1901 and then, at the very end of 1903, the announcement of the discovery of radium. The former discovery was made by two eminent scientists, Sir James Dewar, Fullerian Professor of Chemistry at the Royal Institution in London, and Robert Strutt, the eldest son of the more famous John William Strutt, the third Lord Rayleigh. An article in *The Daily Telegraph* for 12 April 1901 stated:

that rare element Helium which was first found in the sun by spectroscope, and then by Professor Ramsay in the mineral cleveite is, say *The Lancet*, the costliest substance known. It has been found recently in the gases given out by the Hot Springs at Bath, and there Professor Dewar is collecting it to submit the element to high pressures and low temperatures. It costs £200 per cubic foot to collect, or more than a million times the price of coal gas.[13]

When the King's Spring was explored by divers in 1968,[14] it was necessary first to remove a wooden structure around eight feet square, said to be due to Dewar. A hood at the top of this connected to a galvanised iron pipe feeding cubicles where people could 'breathe the elixir of life'! Presumably Dewar used this structure to collect gases for study.

For Dewar and Strutt to obtain the helium gas was no mean feat since it constitutes less than three parts in 10,000 in volume of the gases emanating from the hot mineral water. The two chief constituents are nitrogen, which is some 96% and then carbon dioxide with approximately 3.5%. Helium gas obtained from the Bath hot springs played an important role in Dewar's attempts to liquefy it. Dewar was an outstanding experimental scientist who played a prominent role in the liquefaction of gases. In 1898 he became the first person in the world to liquefy hydrogen, which boils at a temperature of some 20 degrees Celsius above the absolute zero of temperature (-273C). At the time Dewar thought that hydrogen was the gaseous element with the lowest boiling point, although it rapidly became apparent that the boiling point of helium was even lower. Dewar's attempts to liquefy helium were frustrated because the helium he obtained from the Bath Spa water was contaminated with argon and neon, which kept blocking the tubes and valves of his apparatus. Dewar never succeeded and the Dutch scientist Heike Kamerlingh Onnes became the first person to liquefy helium in 1908 using pure helium gas obtained from monazite sand. His achievement initiated the study of matter close to the absolute zero of temperature, an important branch of physics ever since.[15]

The discovery of radium in the hot mineral springs at Bath seemed to cause an even greater stir. On 30 December 1903, Robert Strutt wrote to a Mr Cotterell, who was a member of the Hot Mineral Bath and Pump Room Committee:

I understand that the Baths Committee will be holding a meeting shortly, and shall be obliged if you will convey my best thanks to them for their kindness in allowing me to have samples of the iron deposits left by the waters of the hot springs. My experiments have led me to some conclusions which, I hope, interest the committee. I have found the deposit contains Radium in appreciable amounts, though I am sorry to say, not enough to pay for extraction ...[16]

This discovery by Strutt came only a few years after the French scientists Pierre and Marie Curie had first discovered this unusual and remarkable element, and news of its presence in the mineral waters of Bath was received with great enthusiasm by the local population. *The Bath Herald* wrote:

Notwithstanding, they might pride themselves in the knowledge that this rare element, on which so much has been written, and which so recently caused a sensation in the whole scientific world, existed in the hot springs of Bath and in no other springs in the United Kingdom.[17]

The magazine *Punch* celebrated the event with the delightful cartoon shown overleaf, the glow around 'Monsieur Radium' illustrating the fact that salts of radium glowed in the dark. Widespread national interest in the fact that radium was present in the mineral springs at Bath occurred after the earlier result was confirmed in 1912 by Sir William Ramsay. At the time Ramsay was working at University College, London, and was perhaps the most eminent chemist in the country, having become the first British recipient of the Nobel Prize for chemistry in 1904 (the same year that Robert Strutt's father, the third Lord Rayleigh, achieved the same distinction for physics). Ramsay has a local connection. In 1880 he was appointed Professor of Chemistry at the University College, Bristol, and the following year became Principal of the College. During his time there he regularly gave evening lectures both at Bath and at Trowbridge nearby.

The discovery that the spa waters are radioactive rekindled ideas that they contained a labile curative principle, and for a time radiation was thought to explain their health-giving properties. Radiation certainly had dramatic biological effects which was more than could be

BEAU NASH AND THE FOREIGN INTRUDER IN THE "PUMP ROOM."

DISGUST OF BONE-ASH (CALCIUM PHOSPHATE) ON FINDING THAT THE LITTLE PARVENU UPSTART, MONSIEUR RADIUM (DISCOVERED BY MADAME CURIE) IS ALSO PRESENT IN THE THERMAL SPRINGS OF BATH.—IN SPITE OF THE MOST STRINGENT AND EXCLUSIVE RULES TOO!

["The Hon. R. J. STRUTT has detected the presence of radium in the waters of Bath." "The reason why the presence of radium is easily detected in spite of the smallness of the proportion present, is that *the tests are so exceedingly sensitive.*" "Calcium is predominant in the thermal springs of Bath."—*Daily Papers.*]

A *Punch* cartoon from c.1904 showing the disgust of Richard 'Beau' Nash that radium is present in the thermal springs of Bath.

said for the chemical components of the water. Such was the enthusiasm for radioactivity at this time that a Bath baker even offered 'radium bread' for sale!

In a brochure, proudly entitled *The Radium Waters of Bath*,[18] which the City Corporation published in the early 1920s, health seekers were exhorted to expose themselves to the highest levels of natural radiation possible by entering the Radium Inhalatorium – a room in the new Queen's Bath fitted out with apparatus for delivering radon gas evolved at the source of the spring. In fact the radiation level of Bath mineral water is relatively low; the waters of several continental spas, for example those at Bad Gastein, Baden-Baden and Carlsbad, contain significantly higher concentrations of radium and radon, though still not sufficient to pose any risk.

Modern research suggests that any medical benefits from spa treatment can be attributed to the hydrostatic effects of the water, although most studies have been done in tap water. A study to compare the physiological effects of tap water and Bath water immersion was carried out in Bristol[19] during the 1980s but no difference in effect was noticed, although the Bath water had to be reheated after transporting it from its source. Immersion in any type of water up to the neck exerts a hydrostatic pressure on the body, forcing water out of the tissues and into the blood stream. As a result the central blood volume increases, triggering the release of hormones which cause the kidneys to excrete more water and salt: urine output may increase more than threefold after one hour of immersion. There are also significant changes in urinary electrolyte excretion. Regular immersion in water can also bring about an acceleration of lead excretion which may explain the success of Bath spa treatment at a time when lead poisoning was common. This was caused by lead contamination of commonly imbibed drinks like fortified wines and cider, the production of which involved using lead vessels. Lead poisoning was probably responsible for many of the conditions encountered in patients visiting Bath in the seventeenth and eighteenth centuries, particularly the Devonshire colic, gout and muscular weakness.[20]

As well as scientific studies on the medical applications of spa water, there has been considerable interest in the source of the springs themselves. Mainly through geochemical studies it is believed that the water for the springs originates from rainfall on the Mendip hills some 20 kilometres (12.5 miles) distant. It then percolates downwards from the surface and circulates in the Carboniferous Limestone to a depth of roughly 2.7 to 4.3 kilometres (1.7 to 2.7 miles) where the water gets heated to a temperature of about 80 degrees Celsius. The temperature of the water decreases as it is forced upwards to discharge at Bath at a temperature of 46.5 degrees Celsius (117 degrees Fahrenheit). It is believed that the water does not mix appreciably with any groundwater close to where it discharges. It is not certain how long the water takes to flow from the Mendips to discharge at the mineral spring at Bath, although it has been suggested that the journey might take something like 4,000 years.

Early Encounters with Air

Two men associated with Bath – John Mayow and Joseph Priestley – stand out as contributors to understanding the chemical constituents of air. John Mayow (1641-1679) was an Oxford physician and chemist who, during the summer bathing season, practised at Bath in the early years of the Restoration. Mayow was born at the manor house of Brae near Looe in Cornwall. He studied law and medicine at Wadham College, Oxford, and became a member of the Oxford Philosophical Club which had been started by the Reverend Dr John Wilkins, Warden of Wadham who moved to London to become in 1660 a founding member of the Royal Society.

Mayow was one of the first to begin to understand the mechanism of respiration. He described how the lungs are inflated by the action of the diaphragm and the intercostal muscles and how air thereby comes into contact with blood and releases something into it which he called 'aerial nitre'. He supposed that expiration carried away vapours produced by the heating of the blood. Mayow was a major figure in the Restoration school of Oxford experimentalists who took Harvey's discovery of the circulation of the blood as the basis for further experimental investigations. He supported Richard Lower's theory that blood carried the aerial nitre to the muscles, where a chemical reaction (fermentation) with combustible matter (sulphur) contained in muscles caused them to move.[21] He was only 38 when he died in London at an apothecary's house, 'having a little before been married, not altogether to his content'.[22] He is buried in St Paul's Church, Covent Garden.

John Mayow. Frontispiece from *Tractatus Quinque Medico-physici*, Oxford, 1674.

25

Mayow paved the way for later observations which led to the discovery of oxygen. By trapping a mouse inside a glass bell jar inverted over water he noticed that the amount of air in the vessel diminished as the animal breathed. He also observed in a separate experiment that an object burning in the bell jar had the same effect. These two experiments allowed Mayow, together with his Oxford colleagues Robert Hooke and Robert Boyle, to make the connection between combustion and respiration. By 1674 they understood that only a part of air was necessary to support life and this was the same part which supported combustion. Another century was to pass before the nature of these gases was understood after discoveries by Priestley and Lavoisier.

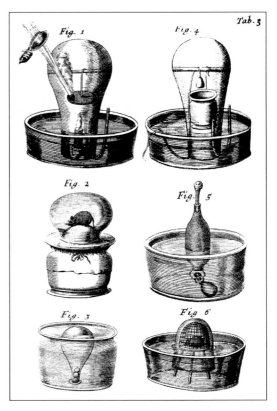

Mayow's experiments with respiration and combustion, from *Tractatus Quinque Medico-physici*, Oxford, 1674.

Joseph Priestley (1733-1804)
Born in Birstal Fieldhead near Leeds on 13 March 1733, Joseph Priestley was the eldest son of a cloth-dresser. His mother died when he was seven years old and it was mainly his aunt who brought him up. He showed early academic promise and it was decided that he should be educated for the ministry. At the age of 17 Priestley entered the Dissenting academy at Daventry and, on completing his studies there, became a preacher first at Needham Market in Suffolk and then at Nantwich in Cheshire. Due to an unfortunate stammer, he was not particularly successful at either place. However, at Nantwich he opened a school which proved so successful that in 1761 he was asked to become a language tutor at the recently opened dissenting academy at Warrington. The following year Priestley married Mary Wilkinson who was the daughter of Isaac and sister to John and William Wilkinson, all three men being prominent iron masters in the eighteenth century. William had been a student of Priestley both at Nantwich and at Warrington. It was while he was at Warrington that he began his scientific work as well as becoming ordained for the ministry. In addition, in 1764 he also obtained an LL.D. from the University of Edinburgh in recognition of his work on education. However, early in 1767 he resigned his teaching position at Warrington partly due to financial difficulties arising from his growing family. Priestley then became minister at Mill Hill Chapel in Leeds, which had an important Presbyterian congregation. While at Leeds he became a Unitarian and began writing controversial theological works as well as carrying out some of his most important scientific investigations.

In addition to his scientific work Priestley spent much of his life both as a teacher and a preacher. He was a true polymath writing books and articles on theology, history, education, aesthetics and politics as well as science. During his lifetime he was as well known for his views on theology and politics as for his work in science.

Priestley's Early Scientific Work

Joseph Priestley's scientific interests began around the middle of the 1760s. While in Warrington he began to write his *History and Present State of Electricity, With Original Experiments.* The aim of the book was to give a systematic account of earlier discoveries as well as ongoing work so as to provide pointers for the future direction of research. While compiling the book he received help and corresponded with several people including Benjamin Franklin,[23] William Watson,[24] and John Canton.[25] While writing the book Priestley carried out several experiments, among them an ingenious demonstration of the inverse square law of electrostatics. This is generally known as Coulomb's law but Priestley's work predates that of Coulomb by nearly 20 years. The book was first published in 1767 while he was still living and working in Leeds and it proved to be remarkably successful. During Priestley's own lifetime it went through five editions and was translated into Dutch, French and German. His increasing scientific reputation, stemming mainly from his work on electricity, led to him being elected FRS in

Engraving of Joseph Priestley by Thomas Holloway, after the portrait by William Artaud, dated 1794. (*Science Museum, London*)

1766. In addition to his book on the *History and Present State of Electricity, With Original Experiments*, he also wrote the *History of Optics* (1772). Priestley was a founder member of the Leeds Library becoming both Secretary and later President. In 1989 the Leeds Library spearheaded the setting up of the Association of Independent Libraries to which BRLSI also belongs. The Leeds Library holds important archival material on Priestley's time there.

Priestley's Experiments with Gases

While he was in Leeds, Priestley began his most important scientific researches, namely those connected with the nature and properties of gases. The term 'air' was then a general word used to describe a gas. Initially Priestley examined the 'air' given off by the fermenting liquors from the local brewery, which was next door to his house. He established that this was 'fixed air' (carbon dioxide) and a bizarre consequence of this is that Priestley can claim to be the father of the soft drinks industry: he found a technique for dissolving carbon dioxide in water to produce a pleasant 'fizzy' taste and advocated the health benefits of drinking it. Priestley received the Copley Medal of the Royal Society in 1773 in large part for this work, and over a hundred years later Mr Bowler of Bath profited from this when he formed his own soft drinks industry.

Priestley then began a systematic examination of other forms of 'air' given off when different substances were heated. To achieve this he developed a novel piece of equipment comprising a trough full of mercury over which could be placed inverted glass vessels to catch any gases. The substance to

Joseph Priestley's laboratory at Bowood House from *Experiments and Observations on Different Kinds of Air* (1774). (*Science Museum, London*)

be heated was placed in a further glass vessel, which had a curved stem leading to the surface of the mercury. His discoveries in this period included the isolation of nitric oxide and ammonia.

The most creative period scientifically for Priestley was when he was in the service of William Petty, 2nd Earl of Shelburne, as his librarian and tutor for his children in 1773–80. While he was living at Shelburne's country estate, Bowood House, not far from Bath, he discovered oxygen. In a classic series of experiments, Priestley used his 12-inch 'burning lens' to heat up mercuric oxide and observed that a most remarkable gas was emitted. In his paper published in the *Philosophical Transactions of the Royal Society* in 1775 he refers to the gas as follows:

> this air is of exalted nature...A candle burned in this air with an amazing strength of flame; and a bit of red hot wood crackled and burned with a prodigious rapidity, exhibiting an appearance something like that of iron glowing with a white heat, and throwing sparks in all directions. But to complete the proof of the superior quality of this air, I introduced a mouse into it; and in a quantity in which, had it been common air, it would have died in about a quarter of an hour; it lived at two different times, a whole hour, and was taken out quite vigorous.[26]

Priestley's discovery of oxygen aroused a great deal of interest in the scientific community. In a letter to Benjamin Franklin he wrote rather wittily: 'Hitherto only two mice and I have had the privilege of breathing it'. The discovery was crucial to the beginnings of modern chemistry although apparently Priestley did not fully appreciate this. He referred to the new gas as 'dephlogisticated air', in accordance with the phlogiston theory of combustion then prevalent among chemists.

The Greek philosopher Aristotle maintained that there were only four elements: earth, air, fire and water. Such was his reputation that this viewpoint continued right up to the end of the seventeenth century when it first began to be seriously challenged. Fire was considered to be especially interesting in that it was the only one of the four elements which did not appear to support life. The phlogiston theory, the word being derived from the Greek word for 'burning', was put forward to try and understand the nature of fire. It was initially introduced in the latter part of the seventeenth century by Johann Becher and developed by Georg Stahl at the turn of the eighteenth century. The basic idea was that when a substance burned, phlogiston was released; the more phlogiston that the substance contained, the faster and stronger was the burning that took place. If for example one burns a metallic element such as magnesium, it burns brilliantly to form an ash. According to the prevailing wisdom in the early eighteenth century, burning the magnesium released the phlogiston resulting in the formation of the ash,

Satirical cartoon of 1791 showing Priestley as Dr Phlogiston. (*The Trustees of the British Museum*)

which was regarded as the fundamental material. Nowadays our thinking is almost the complete opposite, that it is the oxygen in the air which combines with the metal to form magnesium oxide.

Paris

The modern viewpoint of chemistry began to take shape after Priestley accompanied the Earl of Shelburne to Paris and there met with the great French chemist Antoine Lavoisier. Priestley described his experiments, which had resulted in the production of dephlogisticated air. Lavoisier was immensely interested in Priestley's work and began to carry out similar experiments. Lavoisier had already appreciated that air was not an element, as Aristotle had stated, but instead a mixture of gases. He realised that Priestley had discovered the active component of air – the part which supported life and burning. Lavoisier heated mercury in a fixed volume of air. He observed that the volume of air decreased by a fifth and that the remaining volume would extinguish a lighted taper and cause mice to suffocate. He called this residual gas azote, which is Greek for 'without life' and the French word for what we now call nitrogen in English. The mercury, giving rise to the decrease in volume, had been transformed to mercuric oxide. Lavoisier then carried out a further experiment, which was almost identical to that carried out earlier by Priestley, in that he heated the mercuric oxide and obtained mercury as well as recovering the volume of gas, amounting to one fifth of the total, which had been lost when the mercury was originally heated. The new volume which was created supported life and burnt vigorously and Lavoisier called this oxygen. Carrying out quantitative experiments, in which he measured the actual volume of gas lost or gained, was crucial to Lavoisier being able to provide a modern interpretation of the experiments. This was a decisive advance over the qualitative investigations made by Priestley. Lavoisier was finally able to debunk the ideas of the phlogiston theory by carrying out careful experiments to show that the ash remaining after a metal was heated is heavier than the original metal. This is consistent with the modern idea that a metal combines with oxygen to form an oxide while a loss of weight would be expected if the ash formed as a result of the release of phlogiston.

Photosynthesis

Although oxygen was by far his most important discovery, Priestley also used his equipment to isolate and identify other gases such as ammonia, sulphur dioxide, nitrous oxide and nitrogen dioxide. He was also able to carry out some of the earliest experiments leading to the recognition of photosynthesis, which is essential for plant life: in 1771 he burnt a candle inside his apparatus until the gas contained there was no longer able to support combustion. He then introduced a green plant into the container and found that a few days later the ability to support combustion had been restored. In 1779 a highly versatile Dutch scientist, Jan Ingenhousz, extended Priestley's work by showing that the green plant must be exposed to sunlight if the combustible material, by that time identified as oxygen, was to be restored. In addition, Ingenhousz also showed that the green tissues of the plant were necessary for the process to occur. He established that green plants breathe out oxygen under sunlight conditions, which is then breathed in by animals. Ingenhousz was a frequent visitor to the Earl of Shelburne's Bowood House estate near Calne and died there in 1799.

Priestley's Later Years

By 1780 the cordial working relationship between Priestley and the Earl of Shelburne had cooled somewhat and Priestley decided to move with his family to Birmingham. He became preacher at the New Meeting House, which was one of the most liberal congregations in England. His time in Birmingham was among the happiest in his life. Priestley soon became actively involved with the Lunar Society – a small group of academics, scientists and industrialists with wide-ranging interests who were prominent in driving forward the Industrial Revolution in England. The society was so named because its members met at full moon thereby facilitating travel home in the dark after the meetings. Fellow members of the Lunar Society included Matthew Boulton, Erasmus Darwin (grandfather of Charles and also a pioneer in the theory of evolution), James Watt and Josiah Wedgwood.

Although Priestley played a prominent role in the Lunar Society, his interests turned increasingly towards theology. He became an active Dissenter with outspoken criticism of the established church. These were dangerous times to be alive with the French Revolution (1789-91), which Priestley supported, sending shock waves and fear around Europe. In 1791, on the second anniversary of the storming of the Bastille, a 'Church and King' mob in Birmingham destroyed the New Meeting House as well as Priestley's own house and laboratory. He barely escaped with his life and most of his equipment and records were lost. Priestley briefly joined a Dissenting group in London at Hackney but after renewed vitriol against him and his family he emigrated to the United States of America in 1794.

Priestley was offered the chair of chemistry at the University of Pennsylvania, founded by Benjamin Franklin, but declined the offer and instead settled in Northumberland, Pennsylvania, in an area intended for British émigrés fleeing political persecution. Priestley's final years were sad and lonely: his favourite son died in 1795 and his wife a year later. Priestley himself died in America on 5 February 1804 aged 71 and was buried in Northumberland where his house has now been turned into a museum.

Priestley carried out his most important scientific work while living at Bowood House. During his time there, he became an active member of the Agricultural Society in Bath as well as a founding member of the first Bath Philosophical Society. Priestley was a friend of William Herschel and the younger William Watson, both of whom lived in Bath at that time and also became founding members of the Bath Philosophical Society. Priestley possessed enormous technical skill and ingenuity as well as possessing great originality of thought. He was a man of rare insight and talent who contributed significantly to the foundations of modern chemistry.

Conclusion

Scientific studies of the hot springs have provided interest in several distinct areas, for example the composition of the waters, the history of their medical use, and the story of the studies of gases using those originating in the hot spring. It is indeed a strange curiosity that Priestley's fundamental discoveries in chemistry while working at Bowood, near Bath, also involved the chemistry of gases.

Further Reading

Mayow

Proctor, Donald F., *A History of Breathing Physiology – Lung Biology in Health and Disease*, New York, Marcel Dekker, 1995.

Priestley

Anderson, R.G.W. & Lawrence, Christopher, eds., *Science, Medicine and Dissent; Joseph Priestley (1733-1804)*, London, Wellcome Trust/Science Museum, 1987.
An excellent account of the life of Priestley, especially his connection with the Lunar Society, is given in the *The Lunar Men* by Jenny Uglow, London, Faber & Faber, 2002. For an interesting discussion of Priestley, Lavoisier and the phlogiston theory see the chapter on Lavoisier in *On Giants' Shoulders* by Melvyn Bragg, London, Hodder & Stoughton, 1998.

2: Looking for Evidence
Medicine in Georgian Bath

Roger Rolls

For centuries the hot springs at Bath have attracted innumerable health seekers. They arrived, often after long and arduous journeys, in the hope that a few weeks sojourn at the spa would provide a cure for their illnesses. In their wake, medical practitioners of all descriptions frequented the city trying to secure a foothold in the lucrative health business. Until the middle of the eighteenth century, physicians who underwent a university education based their rationale for treatment on the recommendations of classical teaching. Medical theories expounded by Galen in the second century AD were still underpinning treatment in the first half of the seventeenth century. It was only then that physicians began to move away from the idea of humoral balance and consider the idea of the physical state of tissues and the freedom of movement of liquids through the body's natural channels. Consideration was also given to chemical reactions which might occur within the body, particularly fermentation and putrefaction. Observations and practical experience began to displace outmoded dogma and doctors started to question the efficacy of traditional treatments. Transition to a more scientific approach to medicine was largely promoted by small groups of doctors who recognised that any departure from traditional therapy would only be acceptable if evidence could be presented of superior alternative treatment. To achieve this, it was necessary for a doctor to keep meticulous records of his clinical observations and then analyse the observations in a quantitative way. It is perhaps surprising that Georgian Bath, a town given over to fun and frivolity, gossips and gourmandisers, scandalmongers and social climbers, should have attracted serious-minded practitioners whose prime desire was to demystify medicine rather than pander to a myriad of health freaks and hypochondriacs whilst fleecing the pockets of the desperately ill.

The Oxford Influence

Even before the eighteenth century there are several examples of Bath physicians who kept meticulous records. Dr Robert Peirce (1623-1710) and Dr Thomas Guidott (c.1638-1706) recorded hundreds of clinical descriptions, many of which were observed to improve with Bath mineral water treatment.[1] Both were graduates of Oxford University where there was a group of young men who, questioning traditional dogma, were keen to investigate the natural world and propose novel theories which they could verify by experiment: men like Robert Hooke, Christopher Wren, Richard Lower and Thomas Willis. These men, who were among the founders of the Royal Society, were undoubtedly influential in engendering a spirit of enquiry in their contemporaries who practised at Bath. This is certainly true of Thomas Guidott and John Mayow (1641-1679), both of whom were curious about the chemical nature of the mineral water and conducted quite sophisticated experimental analyses, although they came to different conclusions.[2]

Clinical practice was also undergoing change as a result of an inquisitive attitude towards diseased organs. Robert Peirce and the other medical practitioners at Bath with whom he jointly consulted were eager to perform autopsies to assess the cause of death. Peirce describes five autopsies in his memoirs,[3] three of which are explained in considerable detail. Peirce also made some attempt to classify the types of clinical problem which responded well to spa treatment, rejecting the notion that spa therapy was a panacea for all ailments. Such conclusions could only be achieved by observing many hundreds of different conditions and recording their outcome even though the first attempt to provide some primitive statistical analysis of benefit did not take place until the following century.

Reasoning from Data

Whereas most doctors who practised in Bath were attracted by the hot mineral springs, William Hillary (1697-1763) set up his own cold water spa at Lyncombe, now a suburb on the south side of the city. An iron-containing mineral spring was discovered accidentally in the grounds of Lyncombe House and Hillary exploited its therapeutic potential by publishing *An Enquiry into the Contents and Medicinal virtues of Lincomb Spa Water near Bath* (1742).

After a short period of practice in Ripon, Hillary moved to Bath in 1734 and remained in the city until 1746 when he emigrated to Barbados. Whilst in Bath, he published a treatise on smallpox in which he postulated that outbreaks of epidemic disease correlated with changes in the weather. His interest in infectious disease continued during his time in the West Indies, and in 1759 he published one of the first books in English to deal specifically with tropical diseases[4] in which he describes what may have been tropical sprue, a disease interfering with absorption of nutrients from the bowel and thereby causing progressive weight loss. He also witnessed the tsunami which hit the coast of Barbados on All Saints' Day 1755 as a result of the Lisbon earthquake and calculated that it had travelled across the Atlantic at over 400 miles per hour.

Hillary's work demonstrates his enthusiastic belief in the value of a scientific approach to medicine. His bedside descriptions of disease and his condemnation of preconceived ideas are an indication of the emerging scientific attitude to clinical medicine where rationalism and enlightenment displace doctrine and dogmatism. He wrote that.

> it is by this Method of reasoning from Data, founded upon observations and real Facts, that the Healing Art must be improved and brought to a state of Perfection.[5]

Statistical Analyses

Most practitioners, even those like Peirce and Hillary who remained in active practice for many years, did not have the opportunity on their own to accumulate sufficient data for numerical analysis. It was only with the opening of the Bath General Hospital[6] in 1742 that an ample number of patients became available for this kind of study. As an early publicity broadsheet for the hospital explained:

> a few years will furnish more histories of cases, which may be depended upon, (if the physicians keep due registers of the sick under their care) than any man's private practice could have done in an age.

This opportunity was first used in Bath by Dr Rice Charleton (1723-1788) (*see Colour Plate III*), an honorary physician to the General Hospital, when he examined the records of all patients seen there between May 1751 and May 1764. In his *Inquiry into the Efficacy of Warm Bathing* (1770), he identifies 1,053 cases of palsy which he divides into 12 types. He analysed their outcome, presenting his findings as a numerical table. Charleton's method of determining efficacy by numerical analysis, albeit defective in its lack of control subjects, is the first stage in what was to become the standard procedure for evaluating medical therapies[7] and puts Bath into the forefront of a movement now known as evidence-based medicine.

Charleton was an Oxford graduate but by 1780 the influence and power base of Oxbridge medical graduates and Church of England followers in Bath was waning. The most influential physicians in the second half of the eighteenth century were, like William Hillary, from Dissenting backgrounds and graduated from the newly established Scottish universities. These men were prepared to challenge established religious, political and medical beliefs and were not always popular for doing so. One such man was Dr William Falconer.

Response to Treatment

William Falconer (1744–1824) moved to Bath in 1770 from his family home in Chester. He had received his medical education at Edinburgh University which at the time had the most enlightened and advanced medical school in Britain. The newly appointed Professor of Medicine, William Cullen, departed from tradition by lecturing in English rather than Latin and teaching clinical medicine in the presence of living patients.

Dr William Falconer. (*Bath Reference Library, Bath & North East Somerset Council*)

Falconer was a man of great literary distinction, publishing many books and papers on diverse subjects including classics, theology, natural history and medicine. He wrote essays on the analysis and therapeutic use of the Bath waters and published theories about the effects of climate, diet and life style on health, mood and mortality. His *Dissertation on the Influence of the Passions upon Disorders of the Body* (1788) won the Fothergill gold medal of the Medical Society of London in 1796. As an early member of the Bath and West of England Society (founded 1777), he became interested in the occupational health of farm labourers, and his design for farm cottages appears in the Society's papers.[8]

Falconer was an honorary physician to the General Hospital, an institution which maintained meticulous records of all cases admitted, including a brief case description and the final outcome of treatment. Outcome was classified as one of five categories: cured, much better, better, no better and dead. The assessment was made by a committee who examined the patient before discharge. In his investigation into the efficacy of Bath mineral water treatment and its effects on chronic rheumatism, gout, and 'ischiatic complaints of the hip' (a mixture of conditions including referred spinal pain, sciatica and hip joint arthritis), Falconer used these records to make numerical analyses of the outcome for large numbers of patients. He then indicated the probability of the success of the waters by giving simple ratios of those who had benefited compared with the total admitted. By these means he was able to determine the type of condition best suited to Bath water treatment and establish whether there was a difference between men and women in their response to treatment.

Falconer's spa treatment analyses are probably the most detailed published attempt in the eighteenth century to quantify efficacy. However, they lack what is nowadays termed a 'control', for example the ability to discover whether treatment with spa water is superior to ordinary water. This was perhaps surprising, given that several eighteenth-century physicians, including the novelist Tobias Smollett (a doctor himself) had suggested that there was little difference between the two.[9] It is even more surprising given that Falconer was involved in conducting one of the earliest known controlled therapeutic studies – the rhubarb trial.

Rhubarb Trial

Rhubarb was widely used in the eighteenth century as a laxative. Its medicinal properties lay in the root of the pale broad-leaved plant known as *Rheum palmatum* which was imported from the Middle East. By the end of the eighteenth century, the increasing threat of war with Napoleon led to escalation in the price of imported drug materials. Even in those days, hospital administrators were mindful of saving money, so the Committee of the Bath General Hospital must have been gratified to learn that some of their medical staff were investigating the possibility of a cheaper source of drugs. One of their physicians, Dr Caleb Hillier Parry (1755–1822), wanted to discover whether there was any reason to pay for the expensive imported Turkish variety rather than using home-grown rhubarb.[10] Parry compared the effects of the two varieties on several hospital patients, 'crossing-over' the type of rhubarb given to each individual patient at different times and then comparing the symptoms a patient experienced whilst eating each type of rhubarb. Both types proved equally efficacious, thereby heralding two concepts which remain of paramount importance in hospital practice today: the comparative clinical drug trial and the policy of economic prescribing. The research was published in 1786, not in a medical journal as it would be today, but in the proceedings of the Bath and West of England Society of which Falconer and Parry were members. The Society's aim was to promote improvement in agriculture and rural arts by encouraging experimentation; unwittingly it encouraged experimentation in medical treatment. Parry's work represents one of the earliest examples we have of a 'cross-over' therapeutic trial, a technique which is now used widely in the evaluation of new drugs.

Parry, like Falconer, attended Edinburgh University and came from a non-conformist background. His father was a Dissenting minister at Cirencester and Caleb had attended the local grammar school there. Edward Jenner, the pioneer of smallpox vaccination, was also a pupil at the school and despite the difference in their age their friendship developed and continued throughout their adult lives.

Bath was still the most fashionable provincial city in England and by the time Parry arrived, elegant new buildings designed by the Woods and others had spread well beyond the confines of the old medieval town. Visitors far outnumbered residents. Amongst these, a large proportion came for health reasons, providing ample business for doctors. Parry found himself in competition with a multitude of well-established practitioners and his practice was slow to build up. This gave him an opportunity to develop his other interests – geology, ballooning and farming – and to make contact with people of inquiring disposition through the Bath and West of England Society and the first Bath Philosophical Society (founded 1779).

By 1786, Parry's practice was enlarging and his income steadily increasing. He was elected to serve as honorary physician to the Bath City

Bust of Dr Caleb Hillier Parry.
(*BRLSI collection*)

Infirmary and Dispensary (the forerunner of the Royal United Hospital) and later to the Bath General Hospital. Parry kept meticulous records of his patients but his case descriptions, which included exophthalmic thyrotoxicosis[11] and megacolon,[12] remained unpublished until after his death.[13] As a result, an Irish physician Robert Graves got credit for being the first to describe exophthalmic thyrotoxicosis. This condition, popularly known as Graves' Disease, should have been called Parry's Disease.

Parry was a remarkable physician for his time and often deduced general pathological principles from human and animal observation and experiment. In a collaborative observation with Edward Jenner he was able to recognise that narrowing of the coronary arteries was the cause of angina. In his quest for an understanding of clinical medicine, Parry was very willing to collaborate with his colleagues. The rhubarb trial was part of a team effort with Dr William Falconer and Dr Anthony Fothergill. This willingness for collaboration is further illustrated by Parry's involvement in a small medical society which he and Edward Jenner formed so that its members could meet regularly to present papers to each other. The Fleece Medical Society, named after the Gloucestershire inn in which the members met, was one of the earliest provincial medical societies in the UK.

Metallic Tractors

The first Bath Philosophical Society was disbanded in 1787, after the deaths of its founder, Edmund Rack, and another medical member, a retired physician from Liverpool called Matthew Dobson (1732-1784) whose major medical achievement was to prove that the urine of diabetic patients contained sugar.[14] The Society was further depleted by the departure of some of its members (Priestley moved from Bowood to Birmingham in 1780 and Herschel moved from Bath to Datchet in 1782).

Dr John Haygarth.
(*Private collection*)

In 1798, an attempt was made to restart the Society by Dr John Haygarth (1740-1827), a remarkable physician who did much to eradicate smallpox from Chester and who laid the foundations of infectious disease control. After many years as physician to the Chester Infirmary, where he had first met William Falconer, Haygarth retired to Bath probably as a result of his continuing friendship with his old friend and colleague. Haygarth acquired a house at No.15 Royal Crescent and later secured a second house on the eastern outskirts of Bath at Lambridge. Edward Jenner had recently published his famous paper on vaccination, and despite much initial scepticism and derision from members of the medical profession and the general public, Haygarth was a firm supporter of Jenner's discovery. Together with Thomas Creaser, a local surgeon, Haygarth helped to set up a vaccine institute in Bath to promote this new method of smallpox immunisation. This is thought to have been the first vaccination clinic in England.[15]

In 1799 Haygarth and Falconer carried out another comparative clinical study on patients in the General Hospital. This study was conducted to evaluate an invention by an American physician, Dr Elisha Perkins of Connecticut. Perkins had patented a device consisting of two small pointed rods made from secret alloys, one being the colour of brass and the other of silver. When applied to the skin and stroked downwards and outwards, these *metallic tractors* were supposed to bring benefit to patients suffering from gout, rheumatism, headaches, epilepsy and several other disorders. The tractors were distributed in England by Charles C. Langworthy, a Bath medical man who combined a flourishing practice in the city with the superintendence of a mental asylum at Kingsdown, near Box.[16]

'The tractors,' wrote Haygarth, 'have obtained such high reputation at Bath, even amongst persons of rank and understanding, as to require the particular attention of physicians.' To this end, Haygarth made two wooden replicas the same shape as the metallic tractors and painted them in resembling colours. He collected together five patients at the hospital where on 7 January 1799, the wooden tractors were employed. All five patients except one assured him their pain was relieved and three were much benefited by the first application of the remedy. One felt his knee warmer and could walk much better. Another had relief of pain for nine hours until retiring to bed. A third experienced a tingling sensation for two hours. Yet 'the wooden tractors were drawn over the skin so as to touch it in the slightest manner. Such is the wonderful force of imagination.' On the following day, the Perkins tractors were used with almost identical results, 'distinctly proving to what a surprising degree mere fancy deceives the patient himself.'[17]

Reviving the Dead

Nowadays most people are aware of the possibilities of emergency resuscitation even if they have not learned to do it themselves. Paramedics and ambulance crews are frequently called upon to administer what is termed cardio-pulmonary resuscitation, a technique which in part originates from the work done by two physicians living in Bath during the latter end of the eighteenth century, Dr Thomas Cogan and Dr Anthony Fothergill.

Thomas Cogan (1736-1818) was the son of a Northamptonshire doctor. At the age of 23 he embarked upon a career as a Dissenting minister but later switched to medicine and qualified from Leiden University in 1767. Around that time a Frenchman was causing great interest amongst members of the Académie des Sciences in Paris through his accounts of successful resuscitation techniques which he had witnessed whilst travelling in Switzerland. It was not long before these ideas were adopted in major European cities and in the same year that Thomas Cogan qualified as a doctor (1767), the very first society for restoring apparently drowned persons was established in Amsterdam. By 1773 this society had collected

THOMAS COGAN, M.D.
Living Founder of the
Royal Humane Society.
1816

Bust of Dr Thomas Cogan.
(*Wellcome Institute for the History of Medicine*)

sufficient data to publisha paper on resuscitation which Cogan, by then practising in London as an obstetrician, translated into English and, with the help of a medical colleague, he founded the Royal Humane Society of London.

In 1784 Anthony Fothergill (1737-1813), who was a friend of John Haygarth, moved to Bath and rented rooms in Walcot where his 'reputation became great and his income splendid'. Like Cogan he was interested in the treatment of drowning[18] as well as collaborating with other Bath doctors on research projects concerning lead and copper poisoning whose results were published as a series of letters to the Bath and West of England Society.

When the Bath Casualty Hospital first opened in 1788, Fothergill and Cogan's ideas were successfully deployed in reviving people who had fallen into the river and drowned, although there was still a good deal of scepticism about the methods used, even from doctors. The techniques employed were remarkably modern in their approach. The lungs were inflated with a pair of bellows via a flexible tube inserted in either the nose or the mouth (*see Colour Plate VII*). Fothergill advised trying dephlogisticated

Silhouette illustration of Dr Anthony Fothergill who pioneered the use of oxygen in resuscitation. (*Wellcome Institute for the History of Medicine*)

air (oxygen), newly discovered by Joseph Priestley at Bowood House, near Calne, where the chemist had his laboratory. In addition to the bellows, a static electrical generator was used to apply shocks to the chest and the victim was gradually warmed by applying sheep's bladders filled with hot water or, if available, by a bed occupied by two buxom maidens between whom the drowned person was sandwiched. Finally, tobacco smoke was puffed into the bowel through an ivory enema tube. This was done in the belief that the intestines were the last part of the body to die, a misconception which had arisen following the earlier observation that the bowels of criminals who had been hanged, drawn and quartered continued to writhe long after all motion had ceased in the victim's voluntary muscles.

Thomas Cogan lived in Bath during his retirement and, in 1805, founded the Bath Humane Society which established a number of *stations* at regular intervals along the river and the Kennet & Avon Canal. These were equipped with the bellows apparatus needed for resuscitation, packed neatly into velvet-lined wooden cases. At least two of these sets survive, one in the BRLSI collection and the other at Blaise Castle Museum, Bristol. The Society also provided drag poles for use at the stations and latterly life belts. In recent times, the Society has concentrated on encouraging life saving in schools.[19]

Thomas Cogan moved to London in 1810 after his wife died. Dr Fothergill never married and left Bath in 1803, retiring to Philadelphia from where he toured extensively around the United States, eventually returning to London where he died in 1813, leaving an estate valued at £60,000 most of which went to charities in Bath, London and Philadelphia. As for the tobacco enemas, they were ultimately abandoned after the royal surgeon, Sir Benjamin Brodie, tried one on his dog. The dog expired within a few minutes of its administration.

Surgical Pioneers

In the days before anaesthetics and antiseptic technique, surgery was not only a high risk procedure but also an excruciating experience which would only be contemplated if the patient's condition was itself life-threatening or more painful than surgical intervention. Successful surgeons were fast surgeons and thereby minimised the chances of shock and supervening infection. However, the range of surgery was seriously limited and until the nineteenth century, major operations such as couching for cataract and lithotomy for bladder stone had remained virtually unchanged since Roman and medieval times. Bladder surgery was carried out by touch rather than via an optical instrument as it is nowadays. The ability to look into bodily orifices has become a commonplace procedure in contemporary medicine, mainly due to optical fibres which allow the transmission of light along the inside of long flexible instruments known as endoscopes. The first endoscopes were rigid and it was difficult to rely on daylight to illuminate as far as the end of the instrument.

One of the earliest instruments to use artificial illumination was invented by a Bath surgeon, Archibald Cleland (c.1700-1771), who in 1739 submitted his design to the Royal Society. The instrument was essentially an early otoscope, and illumination was provided by a candle mounted behind a condensing lens which could concentrate a beam of light into the ear canal. Cleland was a man of great practical ingenuity, and was the first British surgeon to pass a catheter into the eustachian tube.[20] He was appointed as one of the surgeons to the Bath General Hospital in 1742 but was later dismissed from this post for improper behaviour. Many believed his removal from office had been engineered by rivals who were jealous of his success, as there was scant evidence for his impropriety.[21]

Very little major surgery was carried out at the Bath General Hospital which, despite its name, was not really a general hospital. It was established to cater for poor patients who required mineral water therapy and by the nineteenth century it was more appropriately known as the Mineral Water Hospital.[22] Early developments in surgical technique were associated more with other hospitals in the city. The Bath Casualty Hospital, founded in 1778, provided the earliest accident and emergency service. In 1826, this institution united with the Bath City Infirmary and Dispensary, and the ensuing Royal United Hospital still serves the city today in its capacity as a district general hospital. In 1811 an eye infirmary was established in Bath which survived as a separate institution until its absorption into the Royal United Hospital just over a century and a half later. In their early years, these hospitals had an honorary team of surgeons who published a flurry of papers in medical journals of the early nineteenth century. John Smith Soden (1780-1863) was an early exponent of vascular surgery[23] and was also renowned for his skill in treating cataract. Soden had an extensive medical library, estimated to contain 220 books, which was ultimately presented to Bristol University and has been absorbed into their collection of historic medical works.

Several Bath surgeons appointed to the Bath City Infirmary and Dispensary developed a reputation for treating rectal strictures and were possibly the earliest specialists in this field. William White (1762-1826), John Sherwen (1748-1826) and Charles Hicks (fl.1812) all described this condition which was usually caused by cancer of the rectum. The condition could be temporarily ameliorated by dilating the stricture with metal bougies[24] or wax candles. Most patients ultimately succumbed and often died in extreme discomfort. What was needed was a way of bypassing the obstructed bowel.

A Bath surgeon called Daniel Pring (1789-1859) was one of the first to solve this problem by pioneering colostomy surgery on a patient called Mrs White. In 1820, he became the second British surgeon known to have performed the operation.[25] Pring described in detail the formation of a

Pencil drawing of Daniel Pring. (*Bath Reference Library, Bath & North East Somerset Council*)

sigmoid colostomy and the patient's recovery.[26] He recognised the post-operative stoma complications like skin ulceration and prolapse and promoted the use of ostomy appliances and stoma care. Pring thought his patient's colostomy was of such great benefit that it had

> afforded her a moral, as well as a physical advantage; for she is now at no loss for an interest, and is provided with something to think of for the rest of her life.

Generally, few surgeons of this period were courageous enough to perform bowel surgery. They were reluctant to enter the peritoneum for risk of causing fatal sepsis. Knowledge of bacteria, antiseptics and the importance of asepsis was yet to develop, and even after the advent of anaesthetics, colostomy surgery was not looked upon favourably and was reluctantly performed until after the First World War.

New Technology

John Ewart and James Nooth were both honorary medical staff of the Bath City Infirmary and Dispensary. Ewart was the son of a Scottish minister and one of 11 children including a diplomat and an engineer. James Nooth was the son of an apothecary at Sturminster Newton. During his years in Bath, his reputation as an able breast surgeon allowed him to accumulate data on over a hundred cases of breast cancer and he recognised the advantages of early treatment by local excision to achieve a cure. His brother, John M. Nooth, achieved fame as the inventor of an apparatus for making *fixed air*, the name given to carbon dioxide by Joseph Black in 1756. A few years later Joseph Priestley advocated using carbon dioxide to treat certain diseases, particularly those of a 'putrid' nature, by imbibing water impregnated with the gas. Ewart and Nooth observed the effect of the gas applied directly to the ulcerated malignant tissue of patients suffering from advanced breast cancer.[27] The disease is now seldom witnessed at such an advanced stage.

Ewart, Nooth and William White, another Bath surgeon, constructed an apparatus in which a gas generator was connected by a tube to a bisected bladder which occluded the breast so that no external air could reach the tissues. After several prolonged applications of carbon dioxide, the ulcerated areas improved and the patients were relieved of pain. Only three cases were reported, two by Ewart and a third by Nooth who also gave an update on the outcome of one of Ewart's cases. The treatments were merely palliative but the work illustrates the enthusiasm for experimental techniques using newly discovered substances with possible therapeutic application. Nooth also demonstrated an awareness of the ethics of medical research in an intriguing experiment to prove that cancers are not contagious.

> Being anxious to know what effects [cancerous] matter would produce if inserted by inoculation into the arm of a healthy person, (but not being entitled to make that experiment on any human being except myself,) I conveyed a minute portion of it into a small incision on my arm; two hours afterwards I felt the part uneasy, with a strong pulsation. On the following

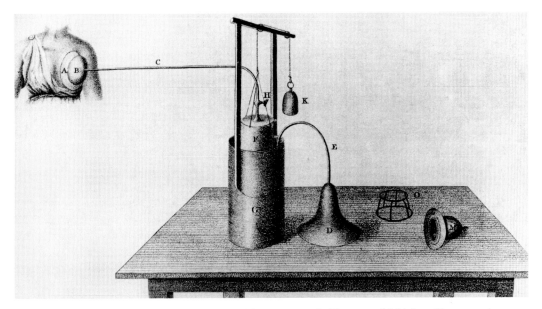

Nooth's breast cancer apparatus. From *Observations on the Treatment of Schirrhous Tumours and Cancers of the Breast*, Bath, 1803. (*Bath Reference Library, Bath & North East Somerset Council*)

day, it was more uneasy, and much more inflammation appeared than generally attends so small a wound inflicted by a sharp instrument; on the third, it remained nearly in the same state; on the fourth day the wound became easier, and the inflammation and pulsation began to subside. A few days afterwards a large dry scab was formed which I removed, and found the sore perfectly healed. Not choosing to rely on a single experiment, as a sufficient proof that a cancerous disposition could not be conveyed into the habit, I repeatedly inoculated myself from the year 1777, without ever producing any effects dissimilar to those in the first experiment. I am convinced, that those persons who give their attendance to cancerous subjects, are not so liable to get this cruel disease by absorption, as has been too generally supposed.[28]

Self-experimentation is less popular with today's doctors but is sometimes still practised. Nearly two centuries after Nooth's experiment, Dr George Kersley (1906-1993), a pioneering rheumatologist at Bath's Royal National Hospital for Rheumatic Diseases, injected his muscles with irritants so that he could observe how the tissues reacted.[29]

Conclusion
Between 1780 and 1820, Bath provided a meeting place for many enterprising and innovative medical practitioners. Nearly all had moved to Bath after initially practising elsewhere. Most were imbued with a revolutionary spirit, not only in medicine but also in the spheres of religious and social reform. By collaborating in research projects and discussing ideas with each other, they helped turn the tide of medical knowledge away from didacticism and dogma by contributing to the early development of modern medicine through careful observation, experimentation and record keeping.

Further Reading
Booth, Christopher, *John Haygarth: A physician of the Enlightenment*, Philadelphia, American Philosophical Society, 2005
Glaser, Sholem, *The Spirit of Enquiry – Caleb Parry, M.D., F.R.S.*, Stroud, Alan Sutton Publishing, 1995
Tröhler, Ulrich, *To Improve the Evidence of Medicine*, Edinburgh, Royal College of Physicians, 2000

3: Of Canals and Quarries
The Bath Geologists

Matt Williams

The geological setting of Bath and surrounding area has had a marked influence both on its cultural development and on the advancement of the study of British geology. The most important geological feature that has influenced the history of Bath's settlement is undoubtedly its hot spring. This significant surface discharge of heated water is unique in the United Kingdom, approximately 1,250,000 litres at 46.5°C flowing daily from the King's Spring, the largest of the three.[1] It seems likely this is what first attracted settlement by the Romans. The rise in the prosperity of Bath in the eighteenth century was also significantly influenced by the presence of the hot springs; in fact the influx of wealthy people into Bath became, for a while, self-perpetuating and it was this popularity that attracted many of the men who became involved with the scientific life of the city. The fossiliferous Middle Jurassic rocks of Bath and the variety of Triassic and Jurassic strata in the region provided stimulating material for those with the means and the intellect to study them. The scope and import of the discoveries made by the most influential of Bath geologists has shaped the science to this day.

William Smith was, of course, Bath's most famous and influential resident geologist. In this account of Bath's geologists and their work, Smith is somewhat underemphasised. This is not to understate the importance of his achievements, but because many entire books have now been devoted to William Smith,[2] other important early geologists of the Bath area are relatively less known.

John Walcott (1754–1831)
If one were to regard anyone as Bath's first geologist (the birth of a field of scientific enquiry is seldom so easily defined) it would probably be John Walcott. Walcott was born in Ireland (probably in Cork) in 1754,[3] and lived in Bath from 1766 to 1783. He was a keen naturalist, a founding member of the first Bath Philosophical Society and a member of the Agricultural Society. In 1779, while still a young man, Walcott published his only geological work *Descriptions and Figures of Petrifactions found in the Quarries, Gravel Pits etc. near Bath*.[4] The book describes and illustrates 68 different fossils or, as he described them:

> remains of animals lodged in stone; and found in almost every part of the environs of Bath, in
> so great abundance that every ploughed field produces a plenteous harvest of them.

In homage to his work, James Sowerby later described a fossil that had been illustrated in Walcott's *Descriptions …* and named it *Spirifera walcotti*.[5] It is interesting to speculate that if Walcott had given names to the specimens he described in this book he might have gained more recognition for his work and perhaps would have been considerably better known to this day. Ironically Walcott was a great proponent of Linnaeus's work. Walcott's work also extended to botany and zoology and he published books on such topics as British plants and birds.

It was probably through meetings of the various scientific and philosophical organisations of which Walcott was a member that he met and influenced the physician Dr Caleb Hillier Parry[6] who became a keen amateur geologist. It is possible that at the Agricultural Society he also met

A plate from Walcott's *Descriptions and Figures of Petrifactions found in the Quarries, Gravel Pits etc. near Bath*; the items illustrated include echinoderms (echinoids, crinoids and blastoids), a hybodus shark spine, and the vertebrae and possibly a limb bone of an Ichthyosaur.

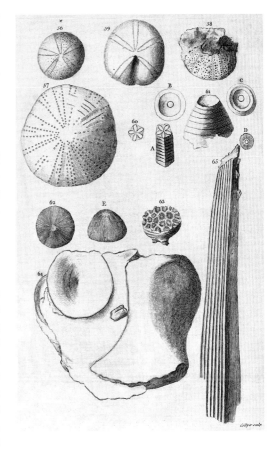

and influenced the work of William Smith. Certainly Walcott's publications on fossils did inspire Smith's work, as Smith himself acknowledged.[7] Walcott also spent some time in Teignmouth (where he studied fish) and at Highnam Court, Gloucestershire,[8] but he did eventually return to Bath where he died, on 5 February 1831, in Great Pulteney Street.

William Smith (1769-1839)

Undoubtedly the most famous geologist connected with Bath was William Smith, whose pioneering work on stratigraphy and mapping has earned him a prominent position in the history of science. Smith, the son of a blacksmith who died when William was just eight years old, was born in Churchill, Oxfordshire, on 23 March 1769.[9] At the age of 18 Smith was employed by a local surveyor, Edward Webb, who required him to travel extensively in neighbouring counties. In the autumn of 1791 Smith first came to North Somerset, lodging at Rugborne Farm, near High Littleton, only ten miles from Bath. Among his duties on this visit he was involved in a survey of the coal mines of the area. The steeply dipping and heavily faulted coal measures are overlain by gently dipping red Triassic marls, followed by Rhaetic marls and then by the distinctive limestone of the Jurassic Blue Lias. Although Smith could not have used the names of these geological periods (they had not yet been coined) he did recognise the importance of this sequence, having seen the same strata in that order in Worcestershire. Later he was to write:

> my subterraneous survey of these coal veins, with sections which I drew of the strata sunk through in the pit, confirmed my notions of some regularity in their formation.

Smith's next engagement was to carry out a survey for a group of local landowners who were considering the construction of a canal linking the coal pits of North Somerset to the Kennet & Avon Canal (then partially completed). The preliminary survey encouraged colliery proprietors from the Dunkerton and Radstock area to form the Somersetshire Canal Company in 1793 and on 17 April 1794 the Somersetshire Coal Canal received the royal assent, after Smith himself had given evidence before Parliament in its support.[10] The following year Smith was appointed Resident Engineer on the project and moved to Cottage Crescent (now Bloomfield Crescent) in Bath. The Crescent consisted then of seven houses, of which Smith's was the central one. Of the fine view this house commanded Smith later wrote:

The eye roved anxiously over the interesting expanse which extended before me to the Sugar-loaf Mountain in Monmouthshire, and embraced all the vicinities of Bath and Bristol; then did a thousand thoughts occur to me respecting the geology of that and adjacent districts ...[11]

Later, in 1794, Smith took a tour of the North accompanying two prominent local coal owners, Richard Perkins and Samborne Palmer, as far as Newcastle-upon-Tyne and returning via Shropshire and Wales. The purpose of this trip was to study various techniques in colliery and canal construction, but Smith was also able to note the similarity of certain strata to those he was familiar with in the South of England. The progression of excavations for the Somersetshire Coal Canal during 1795 helped Smith to consolidate his developing ideas about the regularity of sequences seen in strata and his observations that fossils, as well as being interesting curios, were useful for differentiating strata of similar lithology (rock type). This observation was primarily of economic interest to Smith, for it meant that many geological problems could be

Bust of William Smith.
(*Oxford University Natural History Museum*)

solved with greater efficacy. One example of this was that the variety of dark clay layers associated with coal measures could be differentiated with real accuracy for the first time. Recognition of this fact enabled Smith to establish his prospecting work. Also around this time he started employing a technique of mapping in which different geological units were delineated by different colours.

In June 1799 Smith was involved in a disagreement with his employers over the failure of a caisson lock in the new canal and the future of the use of such structures, which it seems that he did not support: Smith's employment was terminated. Smith had joined the Bath Agricultural Society in 1796 and there he met the Rev Benjamin Richardson and later the Rev Joseph Townsend, who both encouraged his pursuit of geology. It was to Richardson that Smith dictated his *Order of the Strata round Bath* one day in June 1799 at Townsend's house at No.29 Great Pulteney Street. This lists the successive strata and their accompanying fossils. As John Phillips, Smith's nephew, recorded in Smith's memoirs:

One day after dining together at the house of Rev. Joseph Townsend, it was proposed, by one of the Triumvirate that a tabular view of the main features of the subject, as it had been expounded by Mr. Smith, and verified and enriched by their joint labours, should be drawn up in writing. Richardson held the pen and wrote down from Smith's dictation the different strata according to their order, commencing with the chalk and numbered in continuous series down to the coal, below which the strata were not sufficiently determined.[12]

Although he had been developing his ideas for some time prior to 1799, that year marked an important turning point for Smith. The same year he completed a geological map of the countryside within a five-mile radius of Bath. Having bought a home known as Tucking Mill in 1798, he became an independent land surveyor with his assistant Jeremiah Cruse, operating from a rented house, No.2 Trim Street. Smith now travelled widely around Britain seeking commissions, undertaking work over the next decade as varied as the construction of sea defences on the South Wales and the east coast of England, coal prospecting in Somerset, Yorkshire and Lancashire, and land drainage throughout England and Wales. All the while he was gathering data on the geology of the regions through which his travels took him. By the time Smith moved his office from Bath to London in 1803, transporting his fossil collection there the following year, he had already attracted interest in his proposed *Geological Map*, including that of the wealthy President of the Royal Society, Sir Joseph Banks.[13]

In 1804 Banks opened a subscription for Smith's map project with £50 towards its publication. Unfortunately for Smith the subscription drew little income. Despite the support shown to him by Banks, the import of Smith's work was not fully appreciated and the Geological Society (founded in November 1807) offered little or no help, proposing in 1810 to publish their own *Geological Map*. It was not until 1812 that Smith could negotiate an offer with London map engraver and publisher John Cary for the publication of his map. Three years later, in 1815, *A Delineation of the Strata of England and Wales, with part of Scotland* was published at a scale of five miles to the inch, in full colour and dedicated to Banks who had been so supportive of his work (*see Colour Plate V*). This was the first large-scale geological map of any country and its publication is rightly regarded as a defining moment in the history of geology.

For William Smith the publication of his map must have been gratifying but it did not bring him as much recognition as he might have deserved, nor did it save him from his worsening financial difficulties. Around 400 copies of the map may have been sold[14] but despite a price of five guineas(£5.25) the proceeds only just covered the cost of production. The fee he was able to charge for his surveying work did not adequately cover the costs of his travels and researches. He unsuccessfully tried to sell his Tucking Mill home near Bath and now embarked on a venture that was to prove his downfall. Smith chose to invest in a railway and sawmill for the quarrying of Bath stone from Kingham Fields Quarry;[15] ironically Smith, a surveying geologist, had invested in a quarry in which the stone was of poor quality. Having borrowed money for this failed venture Smith was now forced to sell his library and his fossil collection, and finally to part with Tucking Mill (a home for which, it is apparent, he had great affection); it was insufficient to save him, however, and in June 1819 he was sent down for just under ten weeks at the King's Bench Prison in London.

Smith never returned to live in Bath and spent his last 20 years of life in Yorkshire accompanied by his mysterious wife[16] and his nephew John Phillips who had become a geologist of some import himself. Here Smith taught various geological pupils and continued to revise parts of his map, never losing interest in the subject. Not until 1831, when the Geological Society of London awarded him the Wollaston Medal, was Smith officially recognised for his contributions to the science. The following year the medal was presented to him at the Oxford meeting of the British Association for the Advancement of Science and Smith was granted a pension of £100 per annum in a Royal Warrant signed by William IV. Smith fell ill while travelling to the Birmingham meeting of the British Association in 1839 and died at the age of 71 on August 28 in Northampton. He is buried in St Peter's church in Northampton: his sandstone gravestone has lost nearly all its markings but there is a memorial bust inside the building.

The memory of William Smith has further been honoured in the naming of a Stage of geological time, the geological timescale being divided into *Systems*, whose major subdivisions are called *Stages*. The name *Bathonian*[17] is given to a Stage of the Jurassic System and corresponds to a time very roughly around 160 million years ago. It was first applied in 1843, by the Belgian geologist Jean-Baptiste Julien Omalius d'Halloy (1783-1875), to divide off those rocks best seen around Bath first separated by William Smith and comprising all the rocks from the Inferior Oolite[18] up to the Cornbrash.

William Lonsdale (1794-1871)

William Lonsdale, the first of several eminent geologists associated with BRLSI, was not as influential a character as William Smith but led a distinguished career in which his contribution to the institution of British geology was considerable. Born to a moderately wealthy family in Bath on 9 September 1794, he was the youngest of five children. He obtained a commission in the army in 1810 as an ensign in the 4th (King's Own) Regiment.[19] During the next five years he served in the Peninsular War (receiving the Peninsular Medal and a clasp for the Battle of Salamanca) and was also present at the Battle of Waterloo, the only officer in his regiment to escape unwounded (receiving a Waterloo Medal). Shortly after Waterloo his battalion was reduced in size and Lonsdale was placed on half pay. He never again undertook military service and in 1815 he moved to stay with his mother in Batheaston.[20]

By Lonsdale's own account he was introduced to the subject of geology by overhearing two ladies in a Bath Library discussing a fossil found locally. His curiosity roused, he started looking into the subject of geology and gathering his own collection. By 1825 he had sufficient authority as a geologist to be appointed curator responsible for the setting up a museum at the newly opened BRLSI, to which he donated 800 geological specimens and 290 fossils.[21] Lonsdale was elected as its honorary curator the following year and remained in the post until 1829. Most of Lonsdale's specimens are still housed at BRLSI and his fossils are still associated with his own handwritten labels. The BRLSI proceedings from this period give the impression that Lonsdale was instrumental in persuading a number of persons to deposit or donate parts of their collections with the Institution, forming the basis for a later substantial museum collection. It is known, for instance, that Lonsdale was responsible for classifying and arranging collections of minerals donated by Sir Richard Colt Hoare and Francis Basset, Lord de Dunstanville.[22]

One of the fossils curated by William Lonsdale in BRLSI's collections, this specimen of *Spirifera walcotti* (now *Spiriferina*) is connected to many of Bath's famous geologists: named by James Sowerby after John Walcott, this specimen was collected from the Lower Lias of Camerton by Rev Benjamin Richardson whose collection was arranged by William Smith. (*BRLSI collection*)

Lonsdale quickly gained a reputation for being a tireless worker and a painstaking curator, apparently walking from Batheaston to Terrace Walk every day and working ceaselessly, often without a midday meal, until his return home in the evening.[23] It was not long before Lonsdale's skills in classification and organisation attracted the interests of London's premier geological organisation, the Geological Society of London. On 15 May 1829 Lonsdale was elected FGS and later that year he was appointed as the curator and librarian of that same organisation. Lonsdale never forgot his association with Bath and BRLSI, despite his busy post in London, regularly donating publications of the Geological Society to the BRLSI library.[24]

The manner in which he undertook the work allotted to him in London earned Lonsdale the respect and friendship of many eminent geologists of the day, including Sir Henry de la Beche and Sir Roderick Impey Murchison. He was encouraged by these and other geologists to examine and publish on the oolitic districts of Bath[25] and later, at the request of the Society's Council, of Gloucestershire.[26] During his time in the employ of the Geological Society, Lonsdale received the Wollaston Fund (a research grant from that organisation) on four occasions, and also received the Wollaston Medal for his studies of fossil corals from the Silurian and Devonian of England, the Tertiary of America and the Palaeozoic of Russia:[27] he later donated his medal to BRLSI.

The Wollaston Medal awarded to Lonsdale by the Geological Society of London in 1846. (*BRLSI collection*)

Lonsdale's study of fossil corals from the limestone of Devon enabled him to distinguish a system of rocks dated between those of the Carboniferous and Silurian periods.[28] Both Murchison and Adam Sedgwick supported Lonsdale's view and after great controversy a geological period known as the Devonian was formally established. Lonsdale made a further major contribution to geology with his observations on the Cretaceous chalk. One of the earliest geologists to employ microscopy for the study of rocks, he noted that chalk was composed predominantly of the fossil remains of micro-organisms,[29] a fact that, while it is astounding in itself, has contributed to the understanding of geological time and of the deposition of sediments.

Following his resignation from his post with the Geological Society of London in 1842 due to ill health, Lonsdale visited Devon for the sea air and then returned to the region of his birth, staying in Melksham and at various places in North Somerset, eventually settling in Bristol. Lonsdale maintained links with BRLSI throughout his life and donated copies of his papers to the BRLSI library. Lonsdale's collection was stored in BRLSI in a room that bore his name throughout his life, and although this was moved into storage in the basement in the 1890s his name was never forgotten by the Institution. Early in 2006 a room on the first floor of BRLSI's Queen Square premises was renamed the Lonsdale room.

William Lonsdale died in his house in City Road, Bristol, on 11 November 1871 and is buried in Arno's Vale Cemetery, Bristol. In his presidential address to the Geological Society of London in 1872 Joseph Prestwich commended his contributions to geology and, commenting on the time he devoted to his fellow researchers, said:

The unseen hand and thoughtful head may be felt and recognised in many of the important papers which then appeared in our *Transactions*. Added to a great knowledge of geology and palaeontology, William Lonsdale was endowed with extreme caution and had a keen sense of the importance of using, in scientific papers especially, as few words as possible, whence in many cases (he made) a free use of scissors and brush whenever allowed, in fact, generally freely granted by many of the then leaders in geology, in consequence of their high opinion of the sound judgement and discrimination of their able secretary.[30]

Charles Moore (1815-1881)

Charles Moore, to whom part of William Lonsdale's collection has in the past been mistakenly attributed, remains one of Bath's most important geologists and certainly its most prolific collector of fossils. Born in Ilminster, Somerset, in 1815, to John and Hannah Moore, Charles was the second son of a family that grew to three sons and three daughters. As a child he attended the Commercial School until 1827 when he entered the Free Grammar School for a further year.[31] Later in his life, Moore reflected that his interest in geology began whilst still at school:

Charles Moore with his hand resting on one of his 'fish nodules'. (*BRLSI collection*)

> my half-holidays were often spent collecting the Ammonites with which the beds in the Upper Lias in the neighbourhood of Ilminster abound, for the purpose of rubbing down to shew their sparry chambers.

On leaving school Charles began work with his father in the business of a bookseller and for some time it appears his pursuit of geology abated.

Moore first came to Bath in 1837 when he began working for William Meyler, a well-known bookseller in the Abbey Churchyard and the publisher of the *Bath Herald*. Moore returned to Ilminster in 1844, following his father's death, to run the family business on behalf of his older sister Sarah. During his time in Bath, Moore noted that walks through quarries in the neighbourhood had rekindled his interest in geology. In Ilminster this interest grew and he began to build up a substantial collection of fossils from the Middle and Upper Lias of the region. While in Ilminster Moore also worked as an agent for emigration to Australia: many of his fossils were stored wrapped in emigration papers. It was during the nine years he remained in Ilminster that he made his first 'geological friends'. These included J. Chaning Pearce of Bradford-on-Avon, with whom he corresponded by letter before the two of them met, and Thomas Davidson FRS, a brachiopod expert who was to become Moore's lifelong friend. Davidson offerred Moore advice on his papers, and used his specimens for his own researches; he may also have been a source for some of Moore's later geological correspondence.

One of Moore's collecting localities during this time in Ilminster was Strawberry Bank. From here he collected the most spectacular fossils in his collection from a single 15cm-thick horizon that he named the 'saurian, fish and insect bed' (the Toarcian, falciferum zone in the Jurassic Upper Lias of that area). The discovery of this 'saurian, fish and insect bed' is a remarkable tale.

> An old school house [near the Commercial school-house, in which he had passed his early days[32]] was being renovated, and two boys were amusing themselves with a pebble or nodule they had found in the rubbish. This, in rolling from one to another, separated and by a lucky chance the pieces were looked at and preserved. In the centre and naturally at the point of separation, was a beautiful fish of the extinct genus Pachycormus.[33]

Over the following years Moore collected hundreds of vertebrate fossils from Strawberry Bank, most of which are articulated specimens: he recovered fish from at least four genera, three near complete Ichthyosaurs, and numerous isolated bones representing probably two genera and 22 specimens of crocodilomorph that Moore called Teleosaurus. These were formally described by Eugène Eudes-Deslongchamps, to whom he was probably introduced by the aforementioned Davidson,[34] as belonging to the genus Pelagosaurus. Moore's Pelagosaurus fossils, which are at BRLSI, constitute the world's largest collection of this genus. Moore also recovered invertebrate fossils: numerous cephalopods with their ink sacks preserved, at least five genera of marine arthropod, and specimens which he describes as 'insects' and 'fruit'. The insects are of particular interest, if Moore was using the term in its modern scientific usage rather than referring to arthropods in general. He refers to approximately 1,000 specimens of insects, none of which is to be found in the BRLSI collections. Rev Henry Winwood gave these specimens along with various others to Taunton Museum in 1905[35] as revealed by the discovery of packages of fossils wrapped in paper and labelled in Winwood's handwriting in Somerset County Museum's stores (Taunton) in 1975. These specimens have not yet been studied or even unwrapped and if they did prove to be insects would be of considerable interest to the scientific community (Upper Lias insects being a scarce resource for study indeed). Even discounting these potentially exciting specimens Moore's Strawberry Bank collection should be regarded as one of the most spectacular vertebrate assemblages in England, both in terms of its diversity and the exceptional preservation of the specimens.

Fossil fish specimens from Moore's 'saurian, fish and insect bed' (Upper Lias, Strawberry Bank, Ilminster, Somerset). *Top left*: *Pachycormus esocinus*, the specimen also seen on the table in the previous photograph [M1308 in the BRLSI collections]; *top right*: *Leptolepis constrictus* [M1267 in the BRLSI collections]; *bottom*: *Lepidotus elvensis* [M1289 in the BRLSI collections]. The scale bars are in centimetres. (*BRLSI collection*)

In 1853 Moore moved back to Bath, where he resided for the rest of his days. Soon after his return he married Eliza Maria Deare, only daughter of the wealthy James Deare of Widcombe.[36] Both Charles and Eliza were aged 39. Little is known of how the marriage came about but it certainly gained Moore the financial independence he must have craved. Only a year earlier Moore had written to the renowned naturalist and palaeontologist Richard Owen to ask for a testimonial that might enable him to gain an official position as distributor of stamps for the county, a post he was unsuccessful in securing. Prior to his marriage Moore had been primarily occupied by his business concerns and had little time to describe the specimens he had collected, relying on his better-advantaged peers. Now he was able to give up his business and devote himself to the study of geology, his immediate success being indicated by his election as FGS the following year.

In the first year of his marriage, Moore joined BRLSI and offered it the opportunity to house his already extensive palaeontological collection which they accepted. This offer was not without condition however: always looking towards the benefit of his fellow men, Moore insisted that his collection should be exhibited as a free museum, open to the public five days a week throughout

A composite of three photographs (calotypes) taken of Charles Moore's palaeontological collection displayed as a free public museum at BRLSI around the 1860s. (*BRLSI collection*)

the year. Arranged stratigraphically in glass-topped cabinets with his larger specimens mounted on the walls after the fashion of the day (part of the Sedgwick Museum in Cambridge has been preserved as an example of such an approach to display), the collection became a draw for visitors to the Institution. Displaying Moore's collection was undoubtedly to BRLSI's benefit, though having a dedicated room to house his ever-growing collection was also a huge advantage to Moore himself. The collection grew with great rapidity once Moore had the facility of space provided by BRLSI. Within three years he already had 23 large wall-mounted Ichthyosaurs and despite the large room given over to Moore it eventually became necessary to expand the space for display by the construction of a raised iron gantry around the room, completed in 1876.[37]

The founding of a public museum was just one of Moore's many efforts towards the social improvement of Bath. During his first residence in the city Moore attended the Trim Street Chapel, a Unitarian Congregation (the liberal denomination of Christianity that Moore had been baptised into as a child), where he was an active member and regular Sunday School teacher. On his return to the city he was able to take an even more involved role, playing the flute and leading the choir for many years. Moore was a devout Christian, never seeing a conflict between science and his faith and

> a constant attendant at the Chapel, morning and evening in all weathers ... The same energy he showed in all his pursuits in life was conspicuous in his politics. Wherever there was a party conflict, Charles Moore was always in the thick of the fight, and always on the Radical side.[38]

This is not the place for a full examination of Moore's social and political life but it should be noted that alongside his many scientific achievements he was elected town councillor for the ward of Widcombe and Lyncombe in 1858, ran for Treasurer of the city in 1867 and was made an alderman in November 1874. As with William Smith we cannot discuss all of Moore's many findings but some of his most interesting work can be mentioned.

While he was still residing in Ilminster, Moore had made a significant discovery which he published once afforded the leisure to do so.[39] Moore had collected extensively from the *Avicula contorta* zone with the intention of determining its relative age (in stratigraphical terms a zone, or bio-zone, is a stratigraphical division marked by the presence of a distinctive fossil, in this case a foraminifera). After many years of describing sections from small quarries and a canal cutting, and having collected many new fossil species, Moore had the evidence he needed that the *Avicula contorta* zone overlays the White Lias. Moore was able to advocate the adoption of a European term, the 'Rhaetic Formation' for these beds. The Rhaetic beds in Britain (part of the Rhaetian Penarth group, no longer recognised as a formation) have remained important in geological research and a hot topic in palaeontology ever since.[40]

Perhaps Moore's most significant contribution to palaeontology was his introduction of the study of fossils from infilled fissures in the carboniferous limestone extracted mechanically and followed by the systematic extraction of specimens, a technique now known as bulk picking.[41] This technique is now used by palaeontologists studying microfossils throughout the world, powerful binocular microscopes and fibre optic lighting making the task considerably easier on the eyes than it must have been in the mid-nineteenth century. The bulk picking technique was essential to Moore's work on the early Jurassic fauna of Holwell quarry. His findings have influenced the study of fossilised microvertebrates to this day.

In 1858 Moore discovered Rhaetic fossil material in the Mendip hills, a region previously thought to contain rocks of exclusively Carboniferous age. By chance Moore spotted yellowish rock amongst a heap of quarried blue Carboniferous Limestone as he passed by on the road to Wanstrow. Once he had examined the fossils it contained he became determined to track down the quarry from which that stone had been extracted. Moore recognised the fossils he had identified as being not of Carboniferous but of Rhaetic age. He searched the local quarries without success for some time but eventually came upon a quarry in the region of Holwell that contained fissures within the Carboniferous Limestone infilled with the same yellow sediments. One fissure, infilled with a mottled red and yellow marl, was particularly fossiliferous and Moore was convinced that all the sediment should be collected and its remains extracted and studied. He persuaded a local farmer (who initially suggested that Moore could find better gravel nearer home) to bring the material by cart to his home in Bath for a fee of 55 shillings (£2.75p).[42] For the next three years much of Moore's time was employed in picking through approximately three tons of this sediment.

Among the specimens Moore extracted from this material were around 70,000 small shark teeth identified by Moore as belonging to Lophodus but now known to belong to the two species *Lissodus minimus* and *Polyacrodus holwellensis*. Less visually impressive but more important are the type specimens of what Moore called *Microlestes moorei*, early mammals now assigned to a group known as the *Haramiyids* (in this case of the genus *Thomasia*).[43] These specimens were particularly important at the time as prior to this only one poorly preserved mammal tooth was known from sediments so old. Moore said he found 29 of these early mammal teeth,[44] though after he had sent nine of them to the famous palaeontologist O.C. Marsh at Yale in 1881 and three had been exchanged with the Natural History Museum in London after his death[45] there remained only 15 specimens (one of which has been replaced by a fish tooth). This leaves three unaccounted for. In all, Moore recovered specimens from 14 or 15 genera of fish, one of mammals and eight or nine of reptiles from this one fissure.

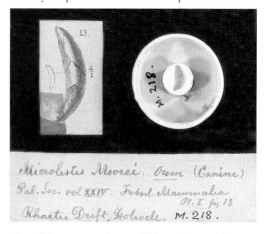

One of the type specimens of *Thomasia moorei* (Owen, 1871), in this case a canine, named by Richard Owen after its discoverer (the genus was renamed as *Microlestes* as *Thomasia* had already been assigned to a beetle) [M218 in BRLSI collection] (BRLSI collection)

Moore was one of the first geologists to recognise the importance of what he called 'abnormal deposits' – sedimentary rocks found out of stratigraphical context – which he used to deduce the age of the White Lias,[46] the Sutton Stone and the Southern Down series of South Wales.[47] While he often misunderstood the reason for their occurrence, attributing the uplift of the Mendips and the formation of fissures to volcanic intrusions rather than to tectonics and the action of water (which he considered an insufficient agent), most of Moore's conclusions from his interpretation of these deposits have been upheld. The study of such deposits remains invaluable to palaeontologists and geologists to this day.

Moore and the Rev Henry Winwood were local secretaries at the 1864 BA meeting in Bath (*see chapter 14*). Moore had first met Winwood the previous year and together they had ensured Bath's nomination to host the meeting. Moore and his work were already known to many of the geologists attending this meeting. He had published numerous well-received papers and attended previous meetings of the BA. Having talked at the 1860 meeting in Oxford on his discoveries from Holwell quarry he had been commended on his work by none other than Charles Lyell and William Pengelly,[48] two of the most eminent geologists of their day. Lyell had even come to Bath to be guided around the region by Moore in 1863.[49] The 1864 meeting was particularly successful for Moore: not only did he play a major role in its organisation but he also delivered

Detail of a photograph showing Charles Moore (left of centre, wearing a top hat and leaning on an umbrella) at Holwell quarry during the British Association meeting of 1864. To his left, also carrying an umbrella, is the famous missionary and explorer Dr David Livingstone who was only in Britain for a year before returning for the last time to Africa. (*BRLSI collection*)

a talk describing his fossils from Strawberry Bank, his discoveries from Holwell quarry and his findings of fossils from the drift deposits around Bath. Moore had prepared a guide to his collection that was made available to the delegates visiting his museum at BRLSI[50] and he led a field excursion to Frome and the Mendips. During the excursion he explained the geology of the region and took the participants to Holwell Quarry, where he presumably gave an account of his discovery of the fissure fill. Of Moore's talk the President of the Geology Section, Professor John Phillips, said

> that they had heard one of the most interesting and instructive addresses that could possibly be given to the British Association.[51]

In total Moore published 65 scientific papers, mostly concerned with local palaeontology and to a lesser extent with stratigraphy and geochronology. He became an expert on fossil brachiopods (marine bivalved invertebrates), naming several new species, though never becoming what by modern standards would be considered a specialist. He even worked and published upon fossil material that had been sent to him from Australia, via contacts he had made when working as agent for emigration to the colony.

Sometime in the early 1870s Moore was trapped by a rock fall in a cave at Murder Combe in the Mendips; his health never truly recovered. Moore said of himself in a letter to Richard Owen (August, 1878) that he was 'a sad invalid without the prospect (having lost one lung) of ever being sound or fit for much hard work again', yet he remained active and regularly published new findings. In November 1881 Moore was working on his most recent research interest, the attempt to extract fossils of cellular strands from Precambrian rocks he had obtained from Canada. Laminae in these rocks, discovered by the Canadian William Dawson and named by him *Eozoon canadense* (dawn animal from Canada), were thought by many researchers in the mid to late nineteenth century to be the earliest traces of life, though they are now known to occur in heavily metamorphosised rocks and not to be organic in origin. To exclude any possible source of contamination from experiments (he was afraid dust or artificial fibres might be mistaken for the fossil strands for which he was searching) Moore conducted these experiments with Winwood in an unheated room bare of any furniture. Winwood recalled in his account of Moore's life that he was

> particularly struck with the zeal of the man who, labouring under a most distressing cough at the time, and being asked whether he did not feel the cold (I was chilled to the backbone during the time of the investigation in the Lonsdale room at the Institution), replied, 'No, I don't, but suppose my enthusiasm has kept me warm.' These were the last words I ever heard him utter; in a fortnight after this he was gone.[52]

Moore died on 8 December 1881, leaving his estate and collections to his wife. Eliza Moore offered the main part of her husband's collection to BRLSI, who after having the British Museum value the collection at £1,100, paid for it by subscription. The Moore collection has remained largely intact and, with the exception of some of the largest specimens, it is still stored at BRLSI where it is used by researchers and occasionally exhibited.[53]

Henry Winwood (1830-1920)

After Moore's death, the Rev Henry Hoyte Winwood was appointed curator of the Moore collection. He studied at Exeter College, Oxford, where he took a BA in 1852 and an MA in 1855. In the year he obtained his MA he was also ordained (becoming curate of Farlingdon in Hampshire) and a year later received priest's orders.[54] He came to Bath in 1858 where he was soon involved with the Somersetshire Archaeological and Natural History Society (of which he later became vice-president), the Bath Natural History and Antiquarian Field Club (Bath Field Club) and BRLSI. Winwood had a private income through his family inheritance and was married to Anna Cecilia Mary Day in 1856. His wealth allowed him the leisure to study the geology of the region. In 1865 he was elected FGS, possibly in recognition of his

Reverend Henry Hoyte Winwood.
(*BRLSI collection*)

work for the British Association meeting the year before. He was active in the Geological Society throughout the rest of his life, serving on the Council of that organisation for 20 years and being twice elected vice-president.[55]

Alongside the botanist C.E. Broome, Winwood was made honorary curator of BRLSI's geological collections in 1882. Winwood revised Moore's handbook to the geological collection at BRLSI for a second annual meeting of the BA at Bath in 1888.[56] At the meeting he spoke on a geological section between Tytherington and Thornbury to which he led a field excursion the following day. It seems Winwood had taken on the role that Moore once would have fulfilled as the principal authority on the local geology. That Moore had influenced the direction of Winwood's research is clear from the talks he gave to the Bath Field Club, many of which focused upon Rhaetic exposures in the region.

R.D. Oldham, then president of the Geological Society of London, said of Winwood following his death that 'his published writings are no measure of the services he rendered to geology and the society'.[57] Indeed Winwood made no spectacular discoveries and wrote no landmark papers (though he regularly published in respected journals) but he improved the organisation of the Moore collection dramatically, publishing a comprehensive guide to the geology museum in 1900 in a revised edition of his handbook. The same charitable attitude extended to his work in society, donating money to many worthy causes (including BRLSI) and serving as a governor of the Royal Mineral Water Hospital in later life.[58] Winwood died on Christmas Day, 1920.

Conclusion

In the preface of his *Descriptions and Figures of Petrifactions Found in the Quarries, Gravel-pits, &c., near Bath* Walcott encourages

> those who have taste and leisure to collect the works of their Creator, to make further researches: in this pursuit they cannot fail meeting such new subjects, as will gratify their curiosity, and excite their admiration.[59]

It is, no doubt, coincidental that Lonsdale, Moore and Winwood all seem to have followed his advice. What is certain, however, is that in the days before the specialist professional geologist it was those amateurs who had the means and time to do so that advanced the science so significantly. We too often forget that to be called an amateur was once a compliment, suggesting, as in the ultimate Latin source *amātor*, a devoted lover or enthusiastic pursuer of an objective. The early geologists of Bath (excepting Smith whom Hugh Torrens calls the ultimate professional, in trying to earn a living thereby[60]) were *amātor* above all else.

Further Reading

For a lay person's introduction to the geological history of Britain see Toghill, P., *The Geology of Britain*, Ramsbury, The Crowood Press, 2002. A more regional overview can be found in Hardy, P., *Geology of Somerset*, Bradford-on-Avon, Ex Libris Press, 1999. Good histories of geology are hard to come by but try Gohau, G., *A History of Geology* (revised and translated by Albert Carozzi and Margueritte Carozzi), New Brunswick, NJ, Rutgers University Press, 1991. More information about the life and work of William Smith can be found in Torrens, H. (ed.), *Memoirs of William Smith. LL.D., author of the 'Map of the Strata of England and Wales' by his nephew and pupil John Phillips, F.R.S., F.G.S.,* (first published in 1844), reissued Bath, Bath Royal Literary and Scientific Institution, 2003. A good review of the work of Charles Moore can be found in Copp, C.J.T., Taylor, M.A. & Thackray, J.C., 'Charles Moore (1814-1881), Somerset Geologist', *Proceedings of the Somersetshire Archaeological and Natural History Society*, 140, 2000, pp.1-36.

4: Telescopes and Astronomy
The Herschels in Bath

Francis Ring

By their very nature, developments in the arts and the sciences are different. The contribution of a Picasso or a Beethoven is distinctive and more a reflection of individual genius than of external factors. In the field of science this is not the case. Here the channel along which a particular topic develops is largely predetermined by contemporary techniques and theories. Yet great scientific insights, just like those in music, often depend on extraordinary lateral thinking. The discovery of the planet Uranus by William Herschel, a German musician living in Bath, was an amazing event. Herschel had received no formal training in science, yet was able to change the established knowledge of the heavens – an intriguing aspect of scientific advancement. Although an amateur, hitherto unknown to the scientific world of the late eighteenth century, he tenaciously applied himself to the systematic study of telescopes and astronomy. William was supported by his sister who had joined him from Hanover. Caroline Herschel, who had had less formal education, later became the first female to receive a pension as recognition of her achievements in astronomy. The experiences of brother and sister in Bath changed the course of both their lives, and gave them a firm place in history for their remarkable discoveries.

Early Years
Friedrich Wilhelm (William) Herschel (1738-1822) was born in Hanover on 15 November 1738. His father, Isaac Herschel, was a musician in the band of the Hanoverian Guards. In May 1753, during the Seven Years' War in Europe, William joined his father's regiment, aged 14, and already a regular musician, became an oboist in the regimental band. In 1756 the regiment was posted to Maidstone in England. From Maidstone they marched to Coxheath, where the Hanoverian troops were encamped. William, his father and his eldest brother Jacob made several valuable acquaintances with families that were fond of music. This first visit to England gave William the opportunity to establish musical contacts that were to prove useful in later years. He also clearly possessed abundant charm and social sensitivity that enabled him to become accepted so quickly. He was an avid scholar, and learned the English language sufficiently well to read John Locke's influential *Essay Concerning Human Understanding* (1690).

Moving on to Rochester in Kent, he made more friends, just before orders came to return to Germany. The regiment had to return to Hanover after a disastrous campaign against the French, where the regiment surrendered, and the French occupied Hanover for two years. Because William was young and non-combatant he wanted to leave the army. He had not been sworn in, and in their defeat the army had little thought or care for their musicians. In October 1757 he left for England with help from his parents, arriving at Dover practically penniless. His brother Jacob, who had been discharged from the band and was in hiding, accompanied him. The two brothers met at Hamburg and travelled together to Dover, and on to London. They went at once to a music shop and offered to copy music. An opera given to William was delivered so rapidly and expertly that they both had a constant supply of paid work until more profitable employment could be found.

In August 1759 the French were finally overthrown by the victory of Minden. Isaac Herschel then obtained his discharge and returned to Hanover to rejoin his family. Jacob also returned to

Hanover soon after peace was declared, to resume his place in the court orchestra. William, however, decided to remain in England and seek his fortune as a musician.

After a difficult few years, during which William became head of a small military band for the Earl of Darlington in Yorkshire, he was appointed director of public concerts at Leeds, where he remained for four years. During this time he worked hard, writing music, though he confessed that it was a pity that music was not more difficult as a science. His love for activity made it essential that he should remain busy; idleness he found made him sick. He studied the theory of music, and of harmony in particular. The close connection between music and mathematics drew his interest. Early in 1766 Herschel moved to Halifax, where he quickly became a popular organist at the parish church. However, this move was soon followed by the offer of a post of organist at the new fashionable Octagon

William Herschel in 1764,
shortly before he came to Bath.
(*Mr John Herschel-Shoreland, Herschel Family Archive*)

Chapel then being built in Bath. He arrived in Bath in December 1766, and within his first few weeks had given a concert in the Pump Room, mainly of his own compositions. He was offered a place in the established band, which played for subscription concerts and balls.[1]

Bath at that time had only four parish churches, inadequate for the ever-increasing number of residents and spa visitors. The Octagon Chapel had been built in 1765-1767 as an auxiliary private chapel on land belonging to a local apothecary, William Street, in Milsom Street. A young preacher, Reverend Dr John de Chair, was co-proprietor. The invitation came to William from de Chair's wife Julia. William first set up a joint household at Beaufort Square with a former acquaintance, Mr Bulman, for whom he had secured the post of Clerk to the Octagon. The organ at the Octagon, opened in 1767, was built by Johann Sneztler, one of whose organs William had played at Halifax parish church.

William's musical activities, composing, performing, teaching, and conducting choral works, suggest that his life in Bath was very busy.[2] However, as before, he was not content to fill his time only with music. His interest in mathematics led him first to optics, and then to astronomy. By the time he had brought his sister Caroline to Bath from the family home in Hanover in August 1772, his interest in astronomy seems to have been firmly established.

Mr. HERSCHEL's
Oratorio-CONCERT
At the NEW ROOMS,
WEDNESDAY, APRIL 15, 1778.

FIVE SHILLINGS.

Caroline, 12 years younger than William, had (like other members of her family) a considerable talent in music. She was somewhat shy and self-conscious when she arrived in Bath, with limited knowledge of English. However, her brother encouraged her to embark on a singing career, and her name appears on posters still surviving as soloist in Handel's *Messiah*, conducted by her brother. After a successful Bath concert, Caroline was approached with an invitation to sing in Birmingham, but refused on the grounds that she would only ever sing when her brother was the conductor.[3]

Caroline also shared William's growing interest in astronomy. By this time she had become William's housekeeper and assistant. The Bulmans had left Bath and William's term as organist at the Octagon had ended upon his appointment as concertmaster in both Bath and Bristol.

Several important books, one of which was Colin Maclaurin's *A Treatise of Fluxions*, influenced William Herschel. Maclaurin, a disciple of Newton, was one of the great English mathematicians of the eighteenth century. Of even greater influence was Robert Smith's *A Compleat System of Opticks*. This two-volume work published in 1738 not only furnished the reader with an extensive account of the theory of optics, but also suggested construction methods for telescopes and microscopes. There could barely have been a book better suited to Herschel's needs, for he was now firmly resolved to try his hand at constructing telescopes.

Telescope Making

William Herschel's great reputation as an astronomer has in some measure overshadowed his almost equal fame as a master of practical optics. In context, it is interesting that in the mid-eighteenth century, commercial telescopes were available from manufacturers such as James Short, but were expensive. Short (1710-1769), a pupil of the Edinburgh professor Colin Maclaurin, had acquired a considerable reputation as a telescope maker. He produced a large number of telescopes during his lifetime and amassed a fortune in the process. Short was reluctant to explain his techniques of mirror making; he left no account of his methods and is said to have destroyed all his tools before his death. Yet James Short did become FRS, and was even a candidate for the post of Astronomer Royal.

Later, Dr John Mudge, a Plymouth physician, acquired a reputation for mirror making, though Herschel subsequently surpassed him. By now it was 160 years since Hans Lippershey had constructed a simple telescope in Holland in 1608. Galileo, Professor of Mathematics at Padua, took up Hans Lippershey's idea and built his own model to the same pattern. These were all refracting telescopes, in effect long tubes housing glass lenses. There were some major disadvantages in this system. First, there was the problem of chromatic aberration, which results from light at different wavelengths coming into focus at different focal points. This results in colour fringes on the object under investigation. To minimise the problem, refracting telescopes had to be very long, often as much as 50 feet in length. This problem was solved by the invention of the achromatic or compound lens.

The Scottish scholar James Gregory produced a reflecting telescope in 1663, using mirrors instead of lenses. This was a great improvement in that, because the mirror was parabolic, the reflected rays were brought to a focus at one point. A concave secondary mirror reflected the rays back through a central hole in the large parabolic magnifying mirror, to an eyepiece. Isaac Newton produced another design in 1668, using a parabolic main mirror at the end of the tube, and a flat secondary mirror to deflect the magnified image through an eyepiece at the side of the tube. Short's telescopes were mainly of the Gregorian design, and much of his success resulted from his use of metal rather than glass mirrors. He used 'speculum metal', an alloy containing copper, tin and small amounts of arsenic or antimony. This alloy could be ground and polished, but was more brittle than glass. (Silver coating on glass, as a means of mirror construction, was not achieved until 1855.[4])

These were the kinds of astronomical telescopes available to Herschel
when he set about manufacturing
his own. Herschel purchased a set
of secondhand mirror-making tools
from a frustrated amateur who had
advertised in the local newspaper.
Undoubtedly the main problem in
making a reflecting telescope was
ensuring the success of the mirror.
Herschel found this more difficult
than expected. After many failures he
succeeded in producing a reflector with
a mirror about five inches in diameter

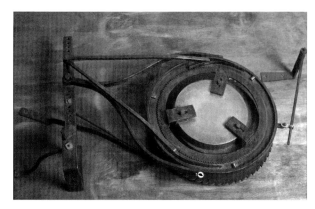

A polishing machine for speculum metal.
(*The Herschel Museum of Astronomy, Bath*)

and a focal length of 5½ feet. 'On March 4th 1774, this new instrument was turned to the Great
Nebula in Orion, and Herschel's real career was well and truly launched'.[5] Evidence of his activity
and approach to telescope making can be found in his notes for a lecture given to the Royal Society
on 11 June 1795:

> When I resided at Bath I had long been acquainted with the theory of optics and mechanics,
> and wanted only that experience which is necessary in the practical part of these sciences. This
> I acquired by degrees in that place, where in my leisure hours, by way of amusement I made for
> myself several 2 feet, 5 feet, 7 feet, 10 feet and 20 feet Newtonian telescopes, besides those of the
> Gregorian form of 8 inch, 12 inches, 18 inches, 2 feet, 3 feet, 5 feet and 10 feet focal length. My
> way of doing these instruments at that time, when the direct method of giving the figures of
> any of the conic sections of specula was still unknown to me, was, to have many mirrors of each
> sort cast, and to finish them as well as I could, then to select by trial, the best of them which I
> preserved; the rest were put by to be re-polished. In this manner I made not less than 200 7 feet,
> 130 10 feet, and about 80 20 feet mirrors not to mention those of the Gregorian form, or the
> construction of Dr Smith's reflecting microscope of which I made a great number.[6]

His telescope mounting techniques were described in a similar manner, being made by way of
amusement. He clearly enjoyed the challenge of designing suitable mounts for his telescopes. There
is little doubt that Herschel's skill and patience as a telescope maker were phenomenal, matched
only by his skill as an astronomer. Unlike his predecessors he was aware of the effects of aperture,
and wanted to penetrate the heavens further than anyone before. Crucial to William's lateral
thinking was how he was motivated to sweep the heavens, and the need for a large aperture. This
was an original concept at that time in astronomy. Eighteenth-century astronomy was concerned
with angular measurements and planet scrutiny. The stars and open star fields in themselves were
open territory in 1770.

The archived papers of the Herschel family (The Herschel Archive, The Royal Astronomical
Society, 2005) contain many letters and papers giving details of William Herschel's telescopes.
He provided a large number of telescopes to the wealthy and famous around the world, and in
many cases illustrated with detailed drawing exactly how the telescope should be assembled. A
good example is the 25-foot telescope built for the King of Spain after Herschel had left Bath. The
drawings were so good that the King had them coloured with watercolours, and beautifully bound
in leather. These volumes survived, though the original telescope did not. They are kept in the Old
Royal Observatory in Madrid. The detail was such that a modern reconstruction of the telescope,
made using the drawings, was completed in 2005: it is housed in a special building near the Madrid

Observatory. A small facsimile of these drawings is in the Herschel Collection in Bath, by courtesy of the Spanish Royal Observatory.

The special alloy used for the casting of a speculum mirror had to be polished in a meticulous way. Herschel did this by hand, using a method not dissimilar to that used by modern astronomers in preparing glass mirrors. The glass piece is ground with an abrasive mixture of sands, powdered earth and water until a curve of sufficient depth is produced. (Herschel has not recorded the material or substance used for polishing, and it is unlikely that he would have had carborundum – silicon carbide – in his time.) The roughly ground mirror is then smoothed by grinding with progressively finer grades of abrasive until the surface becomes free from pits and scratches. The final polishing makes use of materials such as jeweller's rouge or cerium oxide. This process involved a wide number of different strokes. At this stage frequent testing is required. The surface must now be changed from spherical to parabolic, which is accomplished by changing the type of polishing stroke.

Herschel once carried out this process for 16 hours without once removing his hands from the mirror, his sister Caroline feeding him. The result was that he learnt to produce mirrors with the exact properties he required. In 1782 one of his telescopes, taken for comparison with other instruments used by the Astronomer Royal at the Royal Observatory, proved to be superior to all others.

Advances in Astronomy

Herschel wanted to know how the heavens were (as he said) 'constructed'. He appears to have recognised at an early stage that the investigation of distant objects would require a telescope of considerable light-gathering power. In other words, the telescope must both magnify and collect sufficient light for the magnified image to be observed. He achieved both of these requirements, and developed a special lamp micrometer of his own design.

Herschel first turned his attention to the question of stellar distances. Following up on a method already suggested by Galileo, he embarked on a study of 'double stars'. If the fainter member of such a pair was so distant that it could be considered a stationary point for practical purposes, then the apparent annular movement of the brighter (and presumably, nearer) star might be measured from the angle of parallax. There is no known star with a parallax greater than one second of an arc, which was the smallest angle that astronomers could measure in 1780. This is equivalent to the angular size of a disc 1cm in diameter at a distance of over two kilometres!

Unfortunately there is a fundamental flaw in this method. This is the assumption that all stars are of similar brightness and that a faint star must subsequently be farther away than a bright one. The astronomer John Mitchell had pointed out in 1767 that it was not so, and that many double stars were simply pairs of stars revolving around each other, but Herschel chose to ignore this view. He accepted that some stars might be a bit bigger or smaller than others – in the same way that some oak trees, cats or horses varied in size, on the argument that there are generic sizes for objects. The history of science reveals many occasions where great scientists have refused to accept new ideas, even in the face of unambiguous evidence. Isaac Newton himself refused to believe in Robert Hooke's theory of 1665 describing a wave theory of light in preference to the corpuscular theory. Newton's optics were inspired by his reading of Hooke's 1665 *Micrographia*, which he acknowledged to the Royal Society in 1672, but later rejected. Hooke's wave theory had a two-colour model of light, being a mix of red and blue, but not seven or more real colours. In this particular instance, Newton's actions only resulted in the delay of the general acceptance of the new theory. In Herschel's case, although he failed in his parallax experiments, they led him to something far greater.

A far more successful investigation was the study of the distribution of stars in space. His technique here was 'star gauging', where he would direct his telescope towards one part of the sky after another and count the number of stars that could be seen in the field of view for each position. It became apparent that stars were far more numerous in some directions than in others. Herschel was able to confirm Galileo's pronouncement that the Milky Way consisted of myriads of faint stars and concluded that our galaxy was nearly flat with our sun near its centre. In this he was essentially correct. Although Thomas Wright of Durham had reached the same conclusion in 1750 in *An Original Theory or New Hypothesis of the Universe*, Herschel extended the idea and carried out measurements to substantiate the theory. From the motion of only seven stars he established that the sun was moving in the direction of the constellation of Hercules. This was later proved to be correct. Herschel claimed that he only learned of Wright's work after making his own discoveries.

The First Bath Philosophical Society

William Herschel was not scientifically isolated in Bath. One of the great influences on his work was Dr William Watson FRS, a local physician. Watson met Herschel in the street outside his house (No.5 Rivers Street) when Herschel was using his telescope there. They became lifelong friends. It was Watson who introduced Herschel to the exclusive Bath Philosophical Society just then being formed (late 1779). Herschel proved a lively and active member of this Society, presenting 26 papers in the three years that he remained in Bath. The Royal Society subsequently published some of those papers in *Philosophical Transactions*. There can be little doubt that Herschel's transition from musician to astronomer and scientist was greatly assisted by the regular meetings of the local society. Not only Dr Watson (son of the Watson who had been honoured for his publications in electricity) but also Joseph Priestley, who had discovered oxygen and investigated other gases, were fellow-members of this select group of Bath intellectuals. Herschel was immensely intelligent and a fast learner, having picked up fluent English and shown great interpersonal skills. As a self-taught astronomer, he had not received formal training in scientific discipline. He rapidly developed the skills necessary to report his work in a convincing way at regular meetings of the Bath Philosophical Society. In the climate of learning and new science in Bath at that time, Herschel had his place in the demonstration and discussion of many aspects of the late eighteenth-century science.

Edmund Rack, the secretary of the Bath Philosophical Society, recorded that on 14 January 1780, he went

> to J Bryants Esq. to see some curious electrical experiments made on his new machine by Himself, Arden & Herschel, some of them were quite new and astonishing, such as firing pistols, cartridges etc. and lighting candles by the electrical sparks.[7]

Unfortunately there is no record of this machine, but it indicates the excitement from experiments that demonstrated growing awareness of electricity, which at that time was widely demonstrated as 'Electro-staticks'.

Dr William Watson constantly encouraged Herschel, helped him to deal with critics, and later introduced him to the Royal Society in London. This also brought him to the notice of King George III, which as a result was to change his future life and prospects by bringing him into royal employment as King's Astronomer.

In December 1781 Watson presented Herschel with the first extensive catalogue of nebulae, compiled by Charles Messier of Paris, 'the ferret of comets'. The contemporary view held that nebulae were 'nothing but light coming from an extraordinary great space in Ether; through which a lucid medium is diffused, that shines with its own lustre'. Herschel considered Messier's work, and consequently in 1783 began what proved to be a 20-year period of searching for nebulae. In total he discovered over 2,500 and established the existence of several classes of these distant bodies. Later with his 20-foot telescope he resolved many groups of individual stars, pointing to systems similar to our own galaxy, the Milky Way. Herschel believed that nebulae were vast distant star clusters – like the one in Hercules – though he later recognised 'true nebulosity' or 'glowing chevelures' or 'hairyness'. Herschel also concerned himself with globular clusters, beautiful objects consisting of tens of thousands to hundreds of thousands of stars. Our own galaxy contains about 100, several of them discovered by Herschel himself. It was not until 1917 that Harlow Shapley correctly deduced that these were the elements that formed the framework of our own galaxy.

In 1793, Edward Pigott (1753-1825), an itinerant astronomer from York, stayed in Rivers Street, Bath, for a time. Using a portable transit by Sisson, he had been studying variable stars since 1781. While in Bath he described two stars of variable brightness, one in Sobieski's Shield with a period of 63 days, and the second in the Northern Crown, which changed from invisibility to magnitude 6.7. William Herschel had prepared a useful catalogue of the Comparative Brightness of the Stars from which it became possible to note future changes in brightness in the listed stars.

William Herschel's major contribution to astronomy was his *On the Construction of the Heavens*, or development of the celestial system, in which he aimed to explain the variety of celestial phenomena he observed. This work, finally published between 1811 and 1814, shows Herschel's brilliance at its highest level. From essentially static evidence he contrived to build up a dynamic picture of the sequence of changes in the developmental process. He envisaged a chain of development similar to the biological sequence of growth, maturity, decay and death, a concept that proved to be fundamentally correct. However, Herschel's concept was essentially a steady state cosmos – age, decay, re-assembly to new stars, etc. – rather than a developmental process.

The Discovery of a Planet

Wiliam Herschel's best-known discovery was his identification of Uranus. This was an observation of great significance, doubling the size of the known solar system. On 13 March 1781, between 10.00 and 11.00pm, he was observing a small group of stars in the constellation of Gemini, using his 7-foot telescope in the garden of his house at No.19 New King Street, Bath (which now houses The Herschel Museum of Astronomy). He noticed that one of the stars showed a blurred appearance rather than a pinpoint of light. This could only be a comet or a new planet. In his subsequent report to the Bath Philosophical Society, he described the object as a comet. Events moved rapidly, and by April the Astronomer Royal, Neville Maskelyne, became aware of this discovery. On 26 April Herschel's friend Dr Watson read Herschel's paper at the Royal Society in London. William wanted to call his new planet *Georgium Sidus*, after the Hanoverian King, but this name did not survive in favour of Uranus, after the mythological names of other planets. The name Uranus[8] was adopted following a suggestion by the German astronomer Johann Elert Bode (1747-1826).[9]

However, English publications were still referring to *Georgium Sidus* as late as 1846. Herschel was quick to accept that his object was a planet, and in a letter to a friend, Dr Hutton, he wrote:

> It has generally been supposed that it was a lucky accident which brought this star to my view; this is an evident mistake. In the regular manner I examined every star of the heavens, not only of that magnitude but many far inferior, it was that night its turn to be discovered. I had gradually perused the great Volume of the Author of Nature and was now come to the seventh planet.

It is of some interest to note that in discovering Uranus, Herschel had also unwittingly contributed to the later discovery of the eighth planet, Neptune.[10]

The seven-foot telescope designed and built by
William Herschel and used in the discovery of Uranus.
(*The Royal Astronomical Society, London*)

No.19 New King Street, Bath.
(*The William Herschel Society*)

He attempted to measure the apparent diameter of Uranus, and gave a preliminary value of 4.18 seconds of arc, though later gave the value to be 3.9. Today it is accepted that the mean apparent diameter of Uranus is about 3.6 seconds of arc, so this was an astonishing achievement given the limitations of Herschel's equipment.[11] It is also of interest to note that modern astronomical software allows us to reproduce a false image of the night sky in Bath on the famous night in 1781. Uranus became visible after 8.00pm and was out of sight soon after 11.00pm, so Herschel's timing was critical that night! The anniversary of 13 March 1781 was commemorated in Bath exactly 200 years later, by the opening to the public of The William Herschel Museum at No.19 New King Street, which celebrated its 25th anniversary in 2006.

The scientific establishment of the new object's status as a planet, rather than a comet, was left to professionals, and the German astronomer Bode in Berlin in mid-1782 made the confirming observation of the planet. William Herschel had already been awarded the Copley Medal of the Royal Society in November 1781, and had been elected FRS (*see Colour Plate IV*). It is interesting to note that of the eight Fellows who supported his nomination, three – William Watson, Charles Blagden (friend of Henry Cavendish) and John Lloyd – were members of the Bath Philosophical Society. The historical discovery of the new planet is commemorated at No.19 New King Street, on a bronze plaque marking the fact that he was living there in 1781. There is also a plaque donated in 2000 by the Institute of Physics recording Herschel's later discovery of infrared radiation in 1800, and Caroline Herschel's 250th anniversary (b.1750), a seeker of comets.

Herschel had lived in several different houses during his years in Bath. He was at No.7 New King Street from 1770, records showing that this was at a rental of 30 guineas a year. At a later date he moved to the Walcot Turnpike. It was on a plot of land near this house that he erected the first of his reflecting telescopes. Presumably he liked the dark sky at Walcot, there being no further habitation before Batheaston at that time. It was however less convenient for the concerts and centre of Bath, and he therefore returned to the city centre. W. Hervey wrote in 1782:

> After the play I went with Mr Herschel, who plays at the playhouse on the harpsichord, to his house in New King Street, where through his telescope, which magnifies 460 times, I saw the double star Castor, the treble one in Zeta Cancer, the new planet (Uranus) in Gemini. In his papers on Saturn I saw there were two belts on the body of the planet.[12]

This confirms that during his later years in Bath, William Herschel kept his musical activities and astronomy going simultaneously.

Departure from Bath

William moved to London for a period from May 1782, staying with the Watson family. During that summer Caroline had stayed in Bath with her brother Alexander, and copies of letters sent to her by William are held in the collection at the Herschel Museum of Astronomy in Bath. In July 1782 Herschel wrote that he was invited to demonstrate his telescope to King George III, a remarkably learned man, who had a notable interest in scientific novelty. George III founded the observatory at Kew, and established the modern royal collection. He had many scientific friends, and Herschel was to become one of this privileged circle. The King was delighted with the telescope demonstration, and both Jupiter and Saturn could be seen. William was granted a pension in recognition of his achievements, which enabled him to give up his musical employment. As there was no available astronomical post, he was awarded a civil list annual sum of £200, which would enable him to devote more time to astronomy. This involved some commitment to the royal family in the form of astronomical entertainment when required. It was, however, a substantial drop in income, for he was earning over £400 a year in Bath. As William could no longer continue to live in Bath, he left on 1 August 1782 for Datchet. Bath had lost its scientific genius, and notable musician. By now William was 44 years old, and embarking on a new career as an astronomer to the court.

One event that occurred shortly before the move away from Bath is worthy of mention. Herschel had planned to build a 30-foot telescope and in order to do this he had to have a furnace large enough to melt 538lbs of metal for a 36-inch mirror. This represented a very large mass of molten metal for an amateur's furnace to handle. Smaller mirrors had been made with moulds, usually of horse dung, but for such a large mirror there was a problem. The dried dung had been pounded in a mortar and sieved; Caroline reported that it was an endless piece of work. Alexander, her brother, also helped out in this special task. First attempts failed: the mould leaked and the mirror cracked. After modifying the mirror alloys, the metal was heated again in the furnace. However, on this occasion the furnace leaked and molten metal ran across the flagstones cracking them. All present fled for their lives into the garden. After the opening of the Herschel Museum in 1981, strange pieces of metal slag were found in the garden near the house, subsequently found to be speculum metal. With so many mirrors being made in that small area, it is not surprising that some remains survived and were uncovered in 1981 just before the house opened as a museum.

Caroline Herschel (1750-1848)

Much is now known about Caroline Herschel, who lived with her brother William from August 1772 until she married at Slough in 1788. Caroline's diaries and letters were published in 1879 by Mrs John Herschel, under the title *Memoir and Correspondence of Caroline Herschel*. The William Herschel Society reprinted this in 2000.[13] There are many other references to Caroline in *The Herschel Chronicle* written by Constance Lubbock, William's great granddaughter, in 1933. The Herschel Society has also reprinted this volume in recent years.[14] A modern and detailed review of the life of Caroline Herschel has been provided by Michael Hoskin.[15] Caroline clearly shared her brother's interest and was more than an assistant. In later years, even after William's death when she returned to her native Hanover, she published valuable papers and a catalogue of stars. At the age of 96, she received the gold medal for Science from the King of Prussia. 'She was not, and did not pretend to be a woman of genius. She had few personal ambitions, and devoted her life to her family and above all to her brother. We remember her today in the way she would have wished: by the glory of reflected light,' says Sir Patrick Moore.[16] After she had left Bath, William encouraged his sister to sweep for comets on her own: and between 1786 and 1797 she discovered eight new comets which are listed in an appendix to *Caroline Herschel, Reflected Glory*. In 1787 her astronomical achievements were recognised by the King with an award of £50 per annum.

At the age of 50, William married Mary Pitt, the wealthy widow of a former neighbour. This must have been a bitter blow to Caroline, who for 16 years had been William's housekeeper, and in charge of the expense account. She had no financial needs, and in that position it was almost as if she had been William's wife. Suddenly now she was redundant, having spent years working for only her board and lodging. The £50 pension awarded to her by the King enabled her to live independently, and she found a place to live at walking distance from her brother's home.

Caroline died at Hanover in 1848 and was buried near her father in the Gartenkirkhof. Her tomb, with the inscription written by Caroline herself reads:

Here rests the veil of Caroline Herschel,
Born at Hanover, March 16th 1750,
Died January 9th 1848.

The gaze of her who passed to glory was, while below, turned to the starry heavens; her own discoveries of Comets and her share in the immortal labours of her brother, William Herschel, bear witness of this to future ages. The Royal Irish Academy of Dublin and The Royal Astronomical Society in London numbered her among their members. At the age of 97 years 9 months and 24 days she fell asleep in happy peace and in full possession of her faculties; following to a better life her Father, Isaac Herschel, who lived to the age of 60 years 2 months 17 days and lies buried near this spot since 25th March 1767.

Despite her limited education she achieved much, which at this period in history was extremely unusual. She devoted her life to her brother and his interests. But for his turning to astronomy while in Bath, Caroline Herschel would have led a very different life.

Caroline Herschel in old age.
(*The Herschel Museum of Astronomy, Bath*)

Alexander Herschel (1745–1821)

Johann Alexander Herschel,[17] seven years younger than William, was born in 1745. He shared both musical and mechanical talents with his elder brother. He became first oboist in Prince Charles' regimental band. In 1770, he left Hanover for Bath with his brother Jacob, having received leave of absence from the court orchestra for two years. In fact he stayed in Bath for 46 years, long after William and Caroline had departed for Slough. He became a member of the Orchard Street Theatre band, continuing to perform there for most of his time in Bath. He became a noted musician on the oboe, clarinet and violin. Despite his musical ability, Alexander was prone to depression and referred to by William as a Dick Doleful! However, it was his mechanical skills that proved to be of special benefit to the work of his brother William. When William moved out from the centre of Bath to a house near Walcot Parade, this was conveniently next to a builder's yard where labourers were available when required. The house was too small to accommodate Alexander, who lodged in the town, but came daily to spend time with William and Caroline, or to work in the workshop. Alexander, like his brother, earned his living as a musician at that time, and was away every summer in these activities.

The telescope-making business for William developed after his famous discovery of Uranus in March 1781. In 1782 the King placed an order for five 10-foot reflectors. Alexander was by now also making reflectors, which enabled him to make an income outside the music season and become part of the production team. When William and Caroline moved from Bath to Datchet, Alexander stayed with them for two months, helping to get the house into habitable condition. He continued to reside at No.19 New King Street, where the two brothers had tried unsuccessfully to make a three-foot mirror. Left in Bath alone, his family were concerned about his welfare, and he had not met a suitable partner for marriage. His brother Dietrich tried to interest him in a vacancy in the court orchestra in Hanover, and William and Caroline had urged him to consider work in London, and be nearer to them. However in July 1783 he married a widow, Margaret Smith, at Walcot Parish Church in Bath. From Caroline's comments we learn that this was not a happy union. When William left Bath he evidently missed Alexander's workmanship in telescope construction.

Alexander's skills also extended to clockmaking. William purchased a timepiece by Thomas Field, but Alexander's clock was also used, William noting differences in timing accuracy between them in 1783. Alexander Aubert presented a third clock made by John Shelton to William, and in 1786 Caroline mentioned the winding of all three. She herself was given Alexander's clock for her comet sweeps. Later in 1833 it was recorded that the clock stood in John Herschel's laboratory inscribed 'Alexr Herschel fecit'. Another clock made by Alexander for Caroline was for outdoor use, with a loud tick per second, and became known by the family as the 'monkey clock'. William also used it for timing his polishing strokes in making speculum mirrors.

Alexander continued to spend time during the summer months with William, and evidently his wife accompanied him. He showed great expertise in working on the lathe and in turning brass for eyepieces and screws, etc. No telescopes made by Alexander are known to exist today. Once he had moved from No.19 New King Street, he no longer had a foundry and facilities for making telescopes on his own. His annual visits to Slough were devoted almost entirely to working on William's instruments. He was considered eccentric, and even more so after his wife died in 1788. His visits to Slough became longer – up to three months – though his music teaching continued, even through a period of ill-health. With his financial problems, Alexander seemed no longer attracted to Bath and he returned to his native Hanover in 1815, dying there in March 1821 at the age of 75.

John Herschel (1792-1871)

William's only child, John, who had a brilliant career after his Cambridge days, performed an experiment after his father's death to make the first infrared image by evaporography. His important publication in *The Philosophical Transactions of the Royal Society* in 1840 was another milestone in new technology by a member of the Herschel family. Thus the unusual events of 1800 and 1840 gave father and son a reputation as pioneers of the modern techniques of thermography and thermal imaging.

John Herschel was born in Slough on 7 March 1792, and became an accomplished scientist in his own right. His activities ranged from chemistry, geology and pioneering photography to astronomy. He knew and communicated with Henry Fox Talbot at Lacock Abbey, near Bath, himself a pioneer in photography. John Herschel certainly was the first to propose the use of silver bromide for printing photographs and produced the 'hypo fixer' used for many years by generations of photographers. He was also successful with the use of dyes in primitive colour photography, and his method for blueprinting used in engineering continued in use for many years. John added considerably to his father's achievements in astronomy, but he is less well known, due to his father's brilliance. He took one of his father's telescopes to Cape Town in South Africa to study the southern skies. His work there complemented his father's extensive studies in the northern hemisphere and together they improved the star charts and widened the knowledge of cosmology. A lifelong friend from his Cambridge days, Charles Babbage, is now considered by many to be one of the significant pioneers of the modern computer. John was touring in Europe on a scientific expedition with Babbage when William Herschel died in 1822.

His father was already 55 years old when he was born, and John grew up at Observatory House in Slough. His publications in the pages of the *Philosophical Transactions of the Royal Society* have, like his father's, made a significant contribution to science. He was knighted, and for a time became Master of the Royal Mint. A meeting of the Royal Society was held in 1992 to commemorate the bicentenary of his birth, where the many facets of his scientific interests were presented.[18] Again, the family history shows that John turned to astronomy in his father's advancing years, and that he, too, has been credited with a significant contribution to astronomy. Had his father remained a musician and composer, and William stayed in Bath, the history of this extraordinary family might have been very different.

Infrared Radiation

After William Herschel had left Bath, his time, first at Datchet and later at Slough, was marked more by a steady development of his work than by sensational discoveries. However, there was one important event in 1800: the discovery of 'dark heat' or infrared radiation as it is now called. The account of how this happened exemplifies both Herschel's innate sense of curiosity and his scientific ability. Wanting to examine some sunspots, he placed coloured glasses behind the eyepiece of his telescope and noticed that the coloured glass became warm. To test whether rays of each of the spectral colours heated bodies to the same extent, he carried out an experiment. Using a hole cut in an otherwise blacked-out window he caused a beam of light to pass through a prism, creating a spectrum of light on a tablesurface. He placed thermometers at each visible

Herschel's apparatus that led to the discovery of infrared radiation in 1800. (*The Herschel Museum of Astronomy, Bath*)

colour to record the heat, if any, of each colour. To his surprise, the greatest heat was found outside the visible spectrum, in fact beyond the red. He used a number of expressions for this – ranging from 'dark heat', to 'invisible light'. In subsequent experiments he went on to show that the characteristics of infrared radiation are similar to visible light, in that it can be reflected and refracted.[19]

The 40-foot Telescope

After years of planning that began in Bath, William finally obtained the necessary finances to build his dream telescope. This was a 40-foot wooden structure erected at Slough and could be seen for miles around. However it was never the success that he wished for, being affected by winds, but it did bring him fame, being the largest telescope of its time.[20] His son John dismantled the telescope in 1839, to the sounds of a requiem composed by John to the tune 'Old Hundredth', sung by the family assembled in the great tube. For some years the mirror was housed in the family home, Observatory House at Slough. It is now at the Old Royal Observatory, Greenwich, and a number of Herschel telescopes are stored at the Science Museum in London. Many other examples of Herschel's telescopes can be found around the world, and have been documented by Andreas Maurer[21] from Switzerland; the details are held in The William Herschel Museum in Bath.

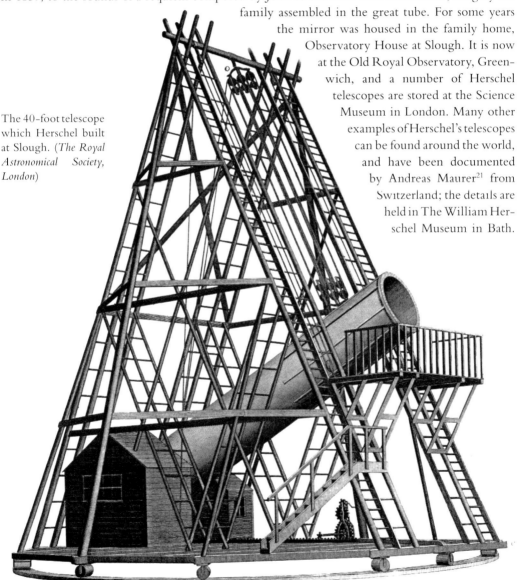

The 40-foot telescope which Herschel built at Slough. (*The Royal Astronomical Society, London*)

Closing Years

In 1816 William Herschel was knighted, and in 1821, when too infirm to be active, he was appointed the first president of the Astronomical Society of London, now the Royal Astronomical Society. The Society still has the Herschel 40-foot telescope in its logo, in honour of its first distinguished President.

William died on 25 August 1822, at the age of 84 years, and was buried at the church of St Laurence, Upton, Slough, where he and Mary Pitt were married. A memorial stained glass window was installed in the church in February 2001 depicting a telescope and planets, including Uranus. This is one of the more modern and artistic memorials to the great William Herschel. His epitaph at the church, translated from the Latin, reads:

> William Herschel, Knight of the Guelphic order.
> Born at Hanover, he chose England for his country.
> Amongst the most distinguished astronomers of his age
> He was deservedly reckoned.
> For should his lesser discoveries be passed over
> He was the first to discover a planet outside the orbit of Saturn.
> Aided by new contrivances which he had himself both invented and constructed
> he broke through the barriers of the heavens
> And piercing and searching out the remoter depths of space
> He laid open to the eyes and intelligence of astronomers
> The vast gyrations of double stars, To the skill
> With which he separated the rays of the sun by prismatic analysis into heat and light,
> and to the industry
> With which he investigated the nature and position of nebulae and of the luminous
> apparitions beyond the limit of our system, ever with innate modesty tempering his bolder
> conjectures, his contemporaries bear willing witness.
> Many things he taught may yet be acknowledged by posterity to be true, should astronomy
> be indebted for support to men of genius in future ages.
> A useful, blameless and amiable life distinguished not less for the successful issue of his
> labours than for virtue and true goodness was closed by a death, lamented alike by his
> kindred and by all good men in the fullness of years on the 25th day of August, the year of
> salvation 1822, and the 84th of his own age.

William Herschel and Romanticism

Because of its powerful imaginative potential, Herschel's work on the immensity of space contributed to the prevailing intellectual climate of the wider Romantic Age.[22] Romantic thinkers were fascinated in general by the pushing back of boundaries, whether in the context of motion, of politics or otherwise. Herschel's cosmology was about perceiving the universe as no one had ever seen it before. This concept of cosmological vastness took people's breath away. In this respect his ideas were much at one with Romanticism, resonating with such typically Romantic notions as the longing for the infinite and the desire to enlarge the horizons of culture. Oddly enough, William Herschel – far from a Romantic himself – tapped into some of the most powerful intellectual currents of his age.

The William Herschel Society, Bath

During the period between 1965 and 1975, World War II reparations were planned for the inner city of Bath. New King Street, built in the eighteenth century, was being considered for demolition in the modern plan. Local residents, led by Miss Phillipa Savery, a Bath businesswoman, protested that New King Street, with its terraced Bath stone houses, was of special historical interest. No.19, in particular, had been the home of William Herschel when the famous discovery of the planet Uranus was made in 1781.

Miss Savery contacted Patrick Moore, the well-known British broadcaster and author in astronomy, and after a meeting in Bath, Herschel's house was finally saved. Two retired doctors in Bath, Leslie and Elizabeth Hilliard, subsequently purchased the house. At the proposal of Patrick Moore, the William Herschel Society was formed in 1977, and registered as a charity. Its aim is to raise money, to promote the life and times of William Herschel and family, and be responsible for the Herschel House property.

The house opened to the public as a Museum on 13 March 1981, exactly 200 years after Herschel's discovery of the planet. Patrick Moore, the founding president, and the late Caroline Herschel, a direct descendant, inaugurated the Museum, and Patrick Moore gave a public lecture on 'The Herschels of New King Street, Bath'. In the first few years the Society grew rapidly in membership as many visitors to the Museum joined to give their support. Today, there is an international membership, regular public lectures and meetings are held, and the Society publishes a journal, *The Speculum*. In addition the Society is a trustee organisation among others for the Herschel House Trust that now secures the building for future generations.

Patrick Moore and Caroline Herschel at the opening of the Herschel Museum in 1981.

Conclusion

William Herschel remains an important figure in the development of modern astronomy. His 15-year stay at Bath was a turning point in his career and a very active and creative period of his life. Caroline Herschel has been honoured and recognised as one of the first women in science and astronomy, all the more remarkable in a woman who had extremely limited education. Had her brother not brought her to England, her story would have been completely different. John Herschel, polymath and Cambridge graduate, changed course from teaching undergraduates to becoming an astronomer, initially with his father. Alexander Herschel, although at first occupied with some short-term telescope sales, remained in Bath, after William moved to Datchet, primarily as a musician. All these family members were touched by, and influenced by their ultimately famous brother and father. Bath had proved to be the crucible of change for the Herschel family, giving them a significant place in the history of science and astronomy in particular.

Further Reading

Lubbock, C.A., *The Herschel Chronicle*, Cambridge, Cambridge University Press, 1938; reprinted Bath, The William Herschel Society, 1997

Herschel, Mrs J., *Memoir and Correspondence of Caroline Herschel*, London, Murray, 1879; reprinted Bath, The William Herschel Society, 2000

Hoskin, M., *The Herschels of Hanover*, Cambridge, Science History Publications, 2007

5: Bath Naturalists
Apothecary to Zoologist

Robert Randall

Monastic communities were well known for their great knowledge of medicinal and culinary plants. The written word was also very important to them and so their accumulated knowledge was often written down. The earliest evidence of anyone noting localities for plants comes from Henry Daniel, a fourteenth-century Dominican friar whose manuscript list of plants includes a record of Meadow Saffron from Bruton, Somerset.[1]

Herbals and a Beginning to the Study of Natural History in Britain

The first printed evidence of the study of natural history is in the form of early 'herbals'. These were reference books describing wild and cultivated plants and listing their properties, either as noxious weeds or as plants with culinary, medicinal or other uses. William Turner (1509/10-1568), a physician and Dean of Wells from 1550, was the first to publish a herbal in English including original observations.[2] In *A New Herball* (1551-1568)[3] Turner described 238 native plants for the first time; some of the rarer ones he collected from the vicinity of Bath and Bristol. He was the first to provide English names for many plants, and some of his names (e.g. Spindle-tree, Toad-flax, Willow-herb, Wood-sorrel and Bittersweet) are still in use. For the rarer species he provided localities where he had seen them, e.g. 'Middow Saffrons ... Colchicum ... I have sene it growe in the west cuntrie besyde Bathe'. In doing so he provided the first botanical record for the Bath area.

More direct links between Turner and Bath come through the donation to the library of BRLSI by Thomas Kerslake in 1879[4] of Turner's *Common Place Book*, in two manuscript volumes, c.1560.[5] One of these deals with religious matters, the other includes a dictionary of diseases and their remedies. These books are now held in Bath Central Library. Also in the library is Turner's *Booke of the Nature and Properties of the Bathes in England* (1562),[6] which was amongst the books in the library of Capt. J.J. Chapman when it was given to the city in 1845.[7]

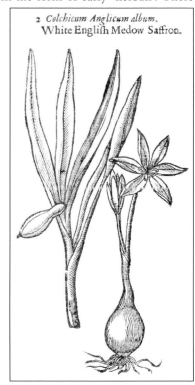

Meadow Saffron (*Colchicum autumnale*) as illustrated in Gerard's herbal, p.157.
(*BRLSI collection*)

The Flemish physician, Matthias de l'Obel (1538-1616),[8] in whose honour the genus Lobelia was named, became 'botanographer' to James I. L'Obel was the first to arrange plants into natural orders and a number of names used by him were taken up by Linnaeus. It is thought that he practised for a while at Bristol. His *Stirpium Adversaria Nova* (1570) includes the first local record of Herb Paris: 'Solanum tetraphyllum, sive Herba Paris ... Bathoniae Helvetiorum ...'[9]

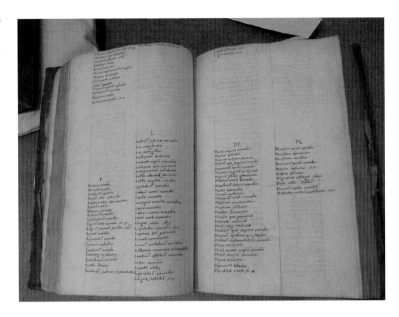

Part of the summary of ailments and remedies included in William Turner's *Common Place Book.* (*BRLSI collection*)

He later returned to Bristol with the European botanist Clusius on the high road from London via Marlborough, Chippenham and Bath. They visited the hot springs and stayed with Edward Saintloo at Chew Magna.

Henry Lyte (1529?-1607)[10] of Lytes Cary, Somerset, was a courtier in the last days of Elizabeth I. His *Niewe Herball* (1578)[11] was an English version, with additional commentary, of the 1557 French translation by Clusius[12] of a 1552 herbal[13] by the Dutchman Dodoens. The rapidity of publication of these translations gives some idea of the importance of such works at that time. Lyte's herbal includes several Somerset records and describes many native plants not mentioned by Turner. A later edition of Dodoens' book[14] inspired the publication of the more famous work by John Gerard. The London publisher and bookseller, John Norton, had commissioned the physician Robert Priest to produce an English translation from the original Latin and had purchased 1,800 original woodcuts for the plates. Unfortunately Priest died before the work was finished so Norton asked Gerard to complete the task. John Gerard (or Gerarde) (c.1545-1612)[15] was a member of the Barber-Surgeons Company who kept a botanical garden at Holborn. *The Herball or Generall Historie of Plants* (1597) contained the first local records for a number of plants, including Moonwort: 'Botrychium: Lunaria or small Moonewort groweth ... about Bathe in Somersetshire in manie places ...'[16]

Thomas Johnson (c.1597-1644)[17] edited the second edition of Gerard's herbal,[18] which included more local records. Johnson's *Mercurius Botanicus* (1634) included the results of botanical explorations in the vicinity of Bath and Bristol and was published with a tract on Bath and its hot springs. In the former he records the first unambiguous record of the Hairy Spurge (*Euphorbia villosa*): 'Esula major Germanica. Ad. Lob. Ger. Quacksalver's Turbith. By a woodside some mile south of Bathe'.[19] The only British records for this species are from Bath. It is possible that L'Obel was already aware of this plant. In 1576 he encountered a similar spurge 'In sylva D. Joannis Coltes prope Bathoniam'. The locality mentioned is probably Collett's Wood on Claverton Down. The wood no longer exists but the plant survived on Claverton Down and in Prior Park for centuries. It was last seen in 1948 and is now assumed to be extinct. It is quite likely that this species was introduced by monks as a medicinal herb

(*left*) Hairy Spurge (*Euphorbia villosa*) specimen from the herbarium of Leonard Jenyns, and (*right*) as illustrated in Gerard's herbal, p.501. (*BRLSI collection*)

Johnson was an apothecary and practiced physic in Bath for two months in 1634. While there, he and other apothecaries visited a Mr George Gibbs, whose garden included more than 117 plants. In July of that year they left Bath for a tour of southern England.[20] The resulting plant records were listed in John Ray's *Catalogus Plantarum Angliae* (1670).[21] The Rev John Ray (1627-1705),[22] one of the first true naturalists in England, studied many aspects of natural history, not just medicinal herbs. The third edition of Ray's *Synopsis Methodica Stirpium Britannicarum* (1724)[23] was edited by Johann Jacob Dillenius (1687-1747),[24] a German botanist who became the first Professor of Botany at Oxford University (1734-47). He also made botanical excursions in the Bath area and many records are contained in his diary[25] and in his manuscript descriptions of British plants, c.1740.

Eighteenth-century Apothecaries, Agriculturalists and Historians

One of the first local authors to publish works on natural history was John Walcott (1754/6-1831).[26] Walcott was born in Ireland but lived in Bath from at least 1766 to 1783. He joined the first Bath Philosophical Society.[27] He is best known for his book on local fossils[28] but he also wrote *Flora Britannica Indigena, or plates of the indigenous plants of Great Britain* (1778-9)[29] and a *Synopsis of British Birds* (1789).[30] He unfortunately ran out of funds and was unable to complete his 'flora', the main expense being the production of numerous illustrations. He provided the original sketches for these, employing some of the best engravers available to produce the plates. These included Joseph Collyer (1748-1827)[31] who was portrait engraver to Queen Charlotte and the Bath-based William Hibbert, or Hibbart (1725-1808).[32] Their engravings were very accurately observed and would stand up to anything reproduced in a scientific journal today.

Another local author was William Sole (1741-1802).[33] He was born in Thetford, Norfolk, but moved to Bath with his relative, the poet Christopher Anstey, author of *The New Bath Guide*.[34] Sole practised as an apothecary in the city and was in partnership with a fellow apothecary, Thomas West, of whom nothing is known. Sole had a botanical garden near the River Avon at Kensington, and on the foundation of the Linnean Society in 1788, was chosen as one of its first associate members. He carried on a long correspondence with John Pitchford, a surgeon from Norwich, on the subject of mints and in 1798 wrote the monograph, *Menthae Britannicae*,[35] in which he described and figured numerous species and hybrids. Like Walcott he also employed William Hibbert and other well-known engravers to produce accurate illustrations. One mint described by Sole, the hybrid between Corn Mint and Spearmint, still bears his name, *Mentha x gracilis Sole*, and his illustration serves as the holotype (official reference specimen).[36] Sole also prepared an account of the principal English grasses and their agricultural uses, complete with 117 detailed drawings,[37] which he presented to Bath Agricultural Society in 1799. For this he was awarded a silver tankard.[38] He made some important botanical discoveries including the first British record of Fingered Sedge (*Carex digitata*), reported in the third edition of William Hudson's *Flora Anglica* (1798).[39]

Mentha x gracilis as engraved by William Hibbert for William Sole's *Menthae Britannicae*, 1798. Note the fine detail. (*BRLSI collection*)

About this time there was a great interest in publishing local and county histories which often included accounts of local natural history. Sole is reputed to have compiled a manuscript, *Flora Bathonica*, in 1782.[40] He certainly contributed a list of plants for the Rev Richard Warner's *History of Bath* (1801),[41] which is probably unique for its time in listing ten varieties of mint. Sole is also supposed to have provided a list of plants for John Collinson's *History of Somersetshire* (1791),[42] but there is little correspondence between the species and localities listed in these two publications and it is more likely that Edmund Rack, or botanist acquaintances of his, compiled the list. Although Collinson is the name associated with this impressive work, it was Rack who did most of the research.

Because of its popularity as a resort and spa town, Bath was well supplied with artists, illustrators and printers. It is not surprising, therefore, that naturalists from other parts of the west country would make use of Bath's facilities. One such was John Stackhouse (?1742-1819),[43] a Cornish naturalist with a particular interest in algae and lower plants. His most famous work was *Nereis Britannica*,[44] on seaweed, which reassessed Linnaeus' classification and described a number of new genera. It was published in Bath in three fascicles (1795-1801). He retired there in 1804.

Victorian Naturalists and the Obsession with Collecting

The nineteenth century saw a surge of interest in collecting natural history specimens, quite often just for the sake of collecting. This was usually the case with many who made large collections of stuffed birds and animals, hunting trophies, exotic shells and ferns for example. Prominent among them was Colonel John Race Godfrey (1787-1856) who, while stationed in India and Burma, shot and had stuffed a large collection of exotic birds. Australian specimens were later supplied by his son, but birds from other countries had to be purchased, often at great expense.[45] After his death his widow presented the entire collection to the city of Bath and it became a major feature of the BRLSI museum. Sadly, very few have survived to this day. Samuel Walker (c.1771-1848) was an apothecary and accoucheur (midwife). He amassed a large collection of British and exotic shells, which passed first to his daughter Sarah, and on her death to a friend, Mary Aslat, who in turn gave them to T.C.H. Walton of Clifton. On the latter's death in 1931 the collection eventually passed to his cousin John W. Walton who (noting the Bath connection and having no interest in shells) kindly offered them to the BRLSI museum together with Walker's original catalogue.[46] They now form the bulk of BRLSI's shell collection. Rev Francis Lockey (1796-1869), better known for his interest in photography,[47] was also a keen collector. His daughter Emma bequeathed his extensive museum collections to BRLSI in 1874.[48]

There were also those who wanted to know all there was to know about the natural world. They dedicated much of their free time to this and began to study plants and animals in detail. William Clark (1788-1869), a marine naturalist and shell collector, contributed papers and correspondence to the *Annals and Magazine of Natural History*. In one paper in 1849 he described two marine molluscs new to science: *Skenea cutleriae* and *Fusus branscombi*. The former was named in honour of Miss Catherine Cutler of Budleigh Salterton, an expert on marine algae. The latter was named in honour of William Branscomb who had been dredging shells for Clark for 30 years.[49] Clark's major work was *A History of British Marine Testaceous Mollusca* (1855).[50] He lived in Norfolk Crescent.

The Tugwell family had a long history in the area, their Bath residence being Crowe Hall, Widcombe. George Tugwell (c.1828/30-1910) was born in Bath, but in 1853, after receiving his MA at Oxford, took the position of curate at Ilfracombe, and at Lee nearby from 1869-71.[51] While there he became very interested in marine life and by 1856 had written *A Manual of the Sea-anemones commonly found on the English Coast*.[52] He, too, hired boats for dredging trips. In 1872 he was appointed rector of Bathwick and later Prebendary of Wells. In 1904 he gave his shell collection to BRLSI.[53]

Charles Cardale Babington (1808-1895)[54][55] was to become a professional botanist. He was born in Ludlow, Shropshire, but his family moved to Broughton Gifford when he was ten years old and, four years later, to Bath. He was responsible for the first published flora of Bath, *Flora Bathoniensis* (1834).[56] This little book was based partly on a manuscript flora of Heneage Gibbes and on records made by John Ford Davis,[57] both active members of BRLSI: most of the remaining records were supplied by Babington himself. It was followed by a supplement in 1839 with numerous additions including discoveries made by T.B. Flower and C.E. Broome. Babington had left the area for Cambridge University before either was published, but made regular visits, staying with his aunt during the summer breaks until 1853. He went on to write other regional floras including those of the Channel Isles and of Cambridgeshire. In addition to his botanical pursuits he became very interested in entomology, especially the study of beetles: this subject formed more than half his earlier scientific papers. His obsession even earned him the nickname 'Beetles'. He eventually amassed a collection of about 4,000 specimens, but after 1840, he began to concentrate on botany, as explained below.

Portrait of Charles Cardale Babington, aged 17, by Isabella Hoare just prior to his entering college at Cambridge, from his *Memoirs, Journal and Botanical Correspondence*, 1897. (*R.D. Randall collection*)

A year before Babington went up to Cambridge, John Stevens Henslow (1796-1860)[58] had been appointed Professor of Botany. Henslow introduced modern methods of lecturing using examples and illustrations, a technique then quite revolutionary at Cambridge. In time Babington became his assistant, deputising for him from 1839 when Henslow attended to the duties of his parish at Hitcham, Suffolk. He eventually took over as Professor of Botany in 1861 after Henslow's death. Babington wrote numerous books and papers on British botany: his *Manual of British Botany* (1843)[59] ran into ten editions, the last published in 1922, while *The British Rubi* (1869)[60] was the first monograph on British brambles, a most difficult and diverse group including hundreds of closely related species.

Thomas Bruges Flower (1815-1899)[61] [62] was apprenticed to a Bristol apothecary and later qualified as a surgeon. He is supposed to have practiced for a while at Seend, Wiltshire, and later at Beaufort Buildings West in Bath, but whether he did or not is unclear, for he never advertised his services in the Bath directories. He obtained William Sole's manuscript *Flora Bathonica* and as well as contributing to Babington's supplement, he provided most of the data for Swete's *Flora Bristoliensis* (1851).[63] Flower's *The Flora of Wiltshire* (1858-1874),[64] which he began in 1848, was the first account of Wiltshire plant distribution and was published in instalments in the magazine of the Wiltshire Archaeological and Natural History Society. Flower travelled widely, building up an impressive herbarium (now in Plymouth City Museum). He also provided C.E. Broome with specimens, which he incorporated into his own herbarium. Broome was one of the few botanists he allowed to access his herbarium. Flower is reputed to have been very loath to divulge details of where he collected his specimens. He was probably aware that over-collecting was having a detrimental impact on the rarer species.

So far the botanists we have encountered mainly studied flowering plants, but with the introduction of improved microscopes with achromatic lenses there was an increased interest in things microscopical. Christopher Edmund Broome (1812-1886)[65] [66] was a very industrious amateur botanist who added algae and fungi to his sphere of interest. He published numerous papers in *The Annals and Magazine of Natural History* between 1845 and 1885, mostly in conjunction with the Rev M.J. Berkeley (the most eminent mycologist of his day).[67] His first offering appears to have been the description of a new species, *Melanogaster berkeleianus*, named in honour of his friend and mentor.[68] Their collaborations resulted in the description of some 550 species new to science.

Broome's father died when he was young and he was sent to Cambridge to Dr G.B. Jermyn,[69] rector of Swaffham Prior, who was his tutor prior to entering college. Jermyn was interested in natural history and a good friend of Leonard Jenyns, an even more active naturalist, then curate of the neighbouring parish of Swaffham Bulbeck. After graduation in 1836, Broome married, went on a grand tour of Europe, and moved to Rudloe Firs near Box. After a short spell in the Bristol area (1844-1848) he moved to Elmhurst House at Batheaston. While there he did much to identify the fungi of the district, beginning with a paper *On the Fungi of Somersetshire* read by the Rev W.R. Crotch at a meeting of the Somerset Archaeological and Natural History Society and published in their proceedings in 1852. It was accompanied by a list of fungi found in the neighbourhood of Bristol, Bath and Taunton, the Bath records being supplied by Broome.[70] Broome also read papers on *Fungi of the Bath District* to members of Bath Natural History and Antiquarian Field Club between 1870 and 1885.[71] His paper of 1874 on slime moulds, then called 'Myxogasters', was one he had read to the Bath Microscopical Society the previous year.[72] He also published a list of *The Fungi of Wiltshire* in the magazine of the Wiltshire Archaeological and Natural History Society (1864).[73] This account included instructions on collecting and preserving specimens and a guide to the classification of fungi, making use of keys developed by Berkeley. In the introduction he apologised that the list was merely a catalogue of Wiltshire specimens in his own herbarium.

Nevertheless, the list was very impressive and included many that were collected at Rudlow (Rudloe), suggesting that his interest in fungi had become well established by the time he moved to the area. Among the reference works he used was James Sowerby's *Coloured Figures of English Fungi or Mushrooms* (1795-1815).[74] His own copy has many of the plates annotated to show microscopic details of the spores.

Annotated illustration in C.E. Broome's copy of Sowerby's *Coloured Figures of English Fungi or Mushrooms. (BRLSI collection)*

Broome toured Europe four times collecting plants for his herbarium and his garden at Elmhurst. He also obtained seed from botanists in Portugal and Italy. Cultivated specimens were duly pressed and preserved in his extensive herbarium along with those he had collected on his travels.[75] On his death in 1886 he bequeathed the botanical section of his library and his herbarium to BRLSI[76] and his drawings, correspondence and collection of dried fungi to the British Museum (his fungi have since been transferred to Kew). In 1887 his family arranged for the unique collection in his garden to be preserved intact and a gift of 2,000 plants was offered to the Victoria Park committee. A botanical garden had been formed there in 1839 but had not thrived. The collection was left in the care of John Milburn, formerly of Kew Gardens, until five years later Broome's collection was transferred to a newly designed botanical garden in Royal Victoria Park,[77] still known as the Broome Gardens at the outbreak of the First World War.[78]

The Rev Leonard Jenyns, later Blomefield (1800-1893),[79][80][81][82] was educated at Cambridge and lived for many years at Swaffham Bulbeck nearby. His sister Harriet married John Stevens Henslow, Professor of Geology and Mineralogy at Cambridge, later to become Professor of Botany. Jenyns was apparently first choice as naturalist to accompany Captain Robert Fitzroy on his survey of South America in the *Beagle*. He declined the position, however, as he had only recently taken the living as curate at Swaffham Bulbeck, and suggested that the young Charles Darwin might be suitable for the job. Jenyns, like Darwin, had a fascination for all aspects of natural history. While at Cambridge he was asked to write a book on British vertebrates. This required a lot of research and a comparison of earlier works. After publication of his manual he looked more closely at the smaller mammals and was able to show that British authors had misunderstood some of the European species. His papers on shrews prompted the Belgian naturalist Baron Michel Edmond de Selys-Longchamps to contact him and they carried on a correspondence on the subject of voles, shrews and bats for a number of years.

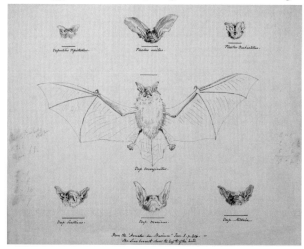

Leonard Jenyns' drawing comparing the characters of British bats. (*BRLSI collection*)

While studying mammals and other creatures he also gained an interest in the parasites found on them; his papers include observations on mites that live on slugs, and the discovery of three new insects related to the bed-bug. He built up a large collection of over 2,500 Cambridgeshire insects, which he presented to Cambridge Philosophical Society, an organisation of which Jenyns and Henslow were founder members. While at Swaffham, Jenyns also published an edition of Gilbert White's *Natural History of Selborne* and his own *Observations in Natural History*, which were intended as a sort of supplement. Although Jenyns declined the position of naturalist on board the *Beagle*, he did not escape the consequences of the voyage. He was asked to write up an account of the fishes that had been collected: these had been supposedly preserved in alcohol, but were apparently rather smelly. Despite his lack of prior knowledge of exotic fish, he managed to get the fishes volume of *The Zoology of the Voyage of the Beagle* ready for publication on time, unlike some of the unfortunate souls who had been given other accounts to write.

Jenyns was happy to stay at Swaffham Bulbeck, close to his friends at Cambridge, until his wife Jane's poor health prompted a move to the Isle of Wight where they stayed for a while. But her health was little improved so they moved to Bath in October 1850, taking up temporary accommodation at South Stoke. Most of Jenyns' library and collections remained at Swaffham until he and his wife moved into Upper Swainswick House in November 1852. Jenyns became a subscriber to BRLSI about 1858 and the same year presented the Institution with copies of his books, including *Observations in Meteorology*, which had been published that year. In 1860 he moved into the city and the following year is recorded as a proprietor (shareholder) of the Institution. In 1862 he presented the BRLSI library with a copy of his *Memoir of the Rev. John Stevens Henslow*, and his 'valuable cabinet of British shells' was deposited at the museum on loan. Jenyns had written a monograph on the small freshwater bivalves commonly known as orb mussels and pea mussels. The latter are mostly very small and are a difficult group to study. Jenyns was able to detect two species new to science and his collection contains the type specimens.

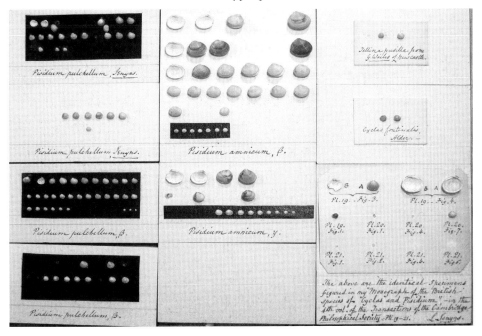

Pisidium specimens in the Jenyns' shell collection at BRLSI. (*BRLSI collection*)

Jenyns founded the Bath Natural History and Antiquarian Field Club in February 1855 and was its president until he was forced to resign due to his wife Jane's deteriorating health. Other founder members included his friend C.E. Broome, whom he had known from college days, the geologist Charles Moore and the antiquarian Rev H.M. Scarth. Although the Field Club had been organising field trips since its foundation,[83] lectures were not a regular feature, it would seem, until Jenyns resumed the presidency in 1864.[84] On 17 March 1864 he was also elected a vice-president of BRLSI, but he declined an offer to preside over the Natural History section at the British Association meeting in Bath that year. Instead he accepted the position of vice-president there also. He had regularly attended the annual meetings of the British Association since 1833 and often read papers on natural history topics. In 1864 he read a paper on the *Temperature and Rainfall in Bath* and later provided a rain gauge, a bottle and two graduated glasses for the meteorological observatory, which he set up in the BRLSI gardens the following year. He had kept meteorological records since he was a young man, but had to rely on the records of other local residents including his erstwhile neighbour Francis Lockey, Mr Mitchell, the City Engineer, the late rector of Radstock and other residents for data gathered before he moved to the area.

It was common practice then for naturalists also to have an interest in meteorology and weather patterns. Both Lockey and Jenyns kept a record in their meteorological journals of first flowering, breaking of buds, migration and nesting times of birds and other seasonal activity as an adjunct to their other observations. The study of periodic events, now known as phenology, was important then as the world moved from the 'Little Ice Age' (medieval times to mid-nineteenth century) into the current warmer period. With the acknowledgment of continued global warming during the twentieth and twenty-first centuries this science is again coming to the fore.

1868 saw Jenyns preparing to move house and beginning to tidy and distribute his scientific collections to appropriate institutions. He gave his notes on vertebrates, including those compiled when studying the fishes of the *Beagle* voyage, to Cambridge University, and on 8 April 1869 he offered his library and herbarium to BRLSI on condition that they were not amalgamated with other collections. His generous offer was accepted and the occasion reported in the *Bath Chronicle*. A new room was built to accommodate them and by January 1871 Jenyns was occupied arranging it and producing a catalogue. He contributed a further collection of works on natural history in 1873, at which time his collection of British shells was formally presented. His shell collection is still housed in its original cabinet with 30 drawers neatly labelled in Jenyns' own hand. The Jenyns herbarium consists of more than 3,000 sheets of pressed flowering plants, ferns, mosses and algae contained in 45 volumes, including one entitled *Plantae Bathonienses* which included specimens collected locally.

His library, covering most aspects of science and natural history, amounts to more than a third of the present BRLSI library. Archive items include his correspondence with 'men of science'. The Jenyns Correspondence is nationally important and has been registered with the National Register of Archives. Other items in the Jenyns archives include scientific drawings and notes, scrapbooks and the notebooks in which he recorded his meteorological observations. Jenyns' archives, correspondence, herbarium and library have been fully catalogued and a complete bibliography is listed in *Leonard Jenyns: Darwin's Lifelong Friend* (2005).[85]

Jenyns also acted as curator of the Duncan Local Museum at BRLSI until 1887, when he handed over responsibility for the herbarium to Fred Inman, a keen botanist, and the zoological collections to George Norman, a surgeon from Brock Street. Norman was a member of Bath Microscopical Society and read papers on algae and microscopic fungi. His findings were also published in the

Journal of the Postal Microscopical Society.[86] He read a paper on *The Algae of the Bath Thermal Waters* to Bath Field Club in 1885, and in 1889 or 1900, by then resident in Ireland, he communicated a short paper on fungi together with *Additions to Mr. Broome's List of Fungi of the Bath District.* The museum had been set up largely under Jenyns' guidance, and maintained with funds provided by the Duncan Memorial Fund, established in 1867. In a catalogue compiled by Jenyns, mammals were well represented, as were birds, reptiles, amphibians and fish. Among invertebrates the list of molluscs is very extensive, understandably given Jenyns' particular interest in this group. The only other conchologist he noted was Henry Bird, MD. Bird had published a *List of Mollusca found in the Neighbourhood of Bath* in volume 1 of the Field Club's proceedings.[87] These were collected within a ten-mile radius of Bath the previous year. Publication coincided with the museum's foundation and in 1868 Bird provided a cabinet of land and freshwater shells, presumably the same ones referred to in his paper. Other invertebrates were very poorly represented in the collections, comprising one horse leech and a few beetles. Many other beetle genera had been pencilled in as desiderata, but Jenyns made no attempt to estimate what other insects might be found in the area.

Aged 85.

Portrait of Leonard Jenyns,
later Leonard Blomefield, at 85 as reproduced
in the *Proceedings* of Bath Field Club.
(*BRLSI collection*)

Colonel Linley Wynter Blathwayt (1841-1919)[88] [89] was a member of the family which, until 1957, lived at Dyrham Park. He was born at Langridge Rectory where his father had the living. He retired in January 1880 after a career in the Bengal Staff Corps Army, and in 1883 moved to Eagle House, Batheaston. Blathwayt joined Bath Natural History and Antiquarian Field Club the same year and seems to have spent most of his later life studying insects. He read papers on bugs and beetles to the Field Club[90] and was later commissioned to provide accounts of all insect orders, apart from butterflies and moths, for the *Victoria County History of Somerset* (1906).[91] In it he provided most of the records for the Bath area, with a few from Henry J. Charbonnier, and many additional beetle records by Robert Gillo. In the introduction to his account of insects he states apologetically:

> with the exception of butterflies and moths, which are always favourites with collectors, the insects of Somerset have been very much neglected, and it does not appear that any local lists have ever been published. Among naturalists resident in the county collectors of the less known orders of insects are conspicuous by their absence ... , [*adding that the following lists*] are drawn up chiefly from my own collections, made for the most part in the immediate neighbourhood of my home at Batheaston and during occasional visits to the shore of the Bristol Channel.

Despite his apologies, the lists of his insect discoveries are very impressive, and for beetles he had the help of Robert Gillo (1841-1891):

> the only person, so far as I have been able to discover, who systematically collected beetles in Somerset ... but unfortunately he never published a complete list of his captures, and I do not know what became of his collection.

Luckily Gillo had published lists of beetles regularly in the entomological magazines of the time, and these were the sources used by Blathwayt.

Gillo was born in Bath and in the 1881 census registered his occupation as 'wholesale photographer'. By the 1880s he was studying closely the local insects and making some important discoveries including one beetle new to Britain. Although Blathwayt was unable to discover what happened to Gillo's collection it had, in fact, remained in the family and in 1914 his wife or son (the donor is unclear) gave his extensive collection of beetles and butterflies to BRLSI (*see Colour Plate VI*).

When Andrew Duff was gathering data for his *Beetles of Somerset* (1993) the earliest information he could obtain about beetles of the Bath area were the records of Gillo and Blathwayt published in the *Victoria County History*. Duff was unable to get access to Gillo's collection and he had doubts whether it had survived the ravages of time and other insects. Nevertheless it does appear to have survived, although it has probably been merged with other collections. Specimens have been laid out in systematic order but in most cases there is no information to identify where each species was found. A note in one of BRLSI's donations books suggests that the catalogue of his collection was at that time with the famous Rothschild family at Tring Park but it is no longer there. If the catalogue has survived it may well supply useful information on local insect distribution. Duff was unable to locate the collection of Linley Blathwayt, but if he had been able to check BRLSI's insect collection he would have discovered many specimens supporting the published records. Most are labelled with the date and place of collection.

Conclusion

To include the recent history of the study of the natural environment would require another chapter on the subject, but brief mention must be made of the continued importance of the work of amateur naturalists. Organisations like the Linnean Society, British Mammal Society, British Entomological Society, Botanical Society of the British Isles, British Mycological Society and many others are composed mainly of enthusiastic amateurs who carry out research and write scientific papers with little or no financial support. Environmental consultants regularly engage knowledgeable amateurs to carry out surveys of invertebrates and other difficult groups of plants and animals. In the last two centuries their activities have gone full circle, from Victorian collectors in many cases endangering the rarer species, to today, when the sum total of knowledge and expertise of amateurs is invaluable for the conservation of the same rare and endangered species that their predecessors at one time threatened.

Further Reading

Bath Natural History Society, Magazine of the, Bath, 1942?–present. The society promotes the study and enjoyment of natural history and records the flora and fauna within a 7-mile radius of the Guildhall, Bath.

Bristol Naturalists' Society, Proceedings of the, Bristol, 1862?–present. Includes records and papers on local natural history. The society promotes education and research into natural history, including geology, with special reference to the Bristol region (former County of Avon).

Bristol Regional Biological Records Centre: Official keeper of biological records for the Bristol region (former County of Avon). Publishes occasional monographs on local natural history: *Flora of the Bristol Region*, 2000; *Butterflies of the Bristol Region*, 2004; *Moths of the Bristol Region* (in preparation); *Dragonflies of the Bristol Region* (in preparation).

Somersetshire Archaeological and Natural History Society, Proceedings of the, Taunton, 1849–present. Includes papers on local natural history, geology, history and archaeology.

Various authors, *The Victoria County History of the County of Somerset*, London, 1906, vol.1. Includes early botanical and zoological records.

Wallace, Prof. Ian (ed.), *Leonard Jenyns: Darwin's lifelong friend*, Bath, BRLSI, 2005. Includes biographical notices of Christopher Edmund Broome, John Stevens Henslow and others.

Wiltshire Archaeological and Natural History Society, Magazine of the, Devizes, 1854–present. Includes papers on local natural history, geology, history and archaeology. The society publishes occasional monographs on local natural history: *The Wiltshire Flora*, 1993; *Butterflies of Wiltshire*, 1995.

6: Drawing with Light
Fox Talbot and Bath Photography

Peter Ford, Roger Watson and Mike Chapman

William Henry Fox Talbot (1800-1877) is a good example of an extinct breed – the gentleman scientist – a man of independent financial means able to pursue his own interests unfettered by the need to earn a living. The gentleman scientist was a feature of nineteenth-century Britain, two other good examples being Talbot's close friends Sir John Herschel and Charles Babbage. Most gentlemen scientists were polymaths, making useful contributions in several areas of research, and Talbot was no exception. He worked in mathematics, spectroscopy, botany, languages, optics and of course photography and it is for this latter that he is best remembered today.

Early Years

Henry Talbot spent much of his life living and working at Lacock Abbey in Wiltshire. The National Trust now owns the Abbey as well as a nearby museum devoted to his life and work. He was born on 11 February 1800 at Melbury House in Melbury Sampford in Dorset, the home of his maternal grandfather, the 2nd Earl of Ilchester. Talbot was the son of William Davenport Talbot, Captain in the 88th Foot Regiment, and Lady Elisabeth Theresa Fox Strangways. Captain Talbot died when Henry was only six months old leaving his baby son the estate at Lacock Abbey and, unfortunately, £30,000 of debt. Talbot and his mother lived with family members until four years later his mother remarried, this time to Captain, later Rear Admiral, Charles Feilding, who, through diligent labour and good management paid down the debt leaving his stepson solvent by the time he reached his majority. Talbot grew up in comfortable and prosperous surroundings together with two half sisters. He was part of a large family and frequently travelled with his immediate family to visit other relatives, especially his doting aunts. His visits to Penrice, his aunts' home in Wales, was also the beginning of Talbot's interest in science. Collecting shells, stones and plants with his cousins initiated a lifelong interest in the natural sciences.

Henry Talbot showed early academic promise. As a child he already appears to have had a prodigious intellect. His interest in optics, for example, was already stimulated at the age of eight, following a visit to Sir William Herschel's observatory at Slough. In his diary he recorded that although the doctor was not present on that occasion (having returned to Bath temporarily for his health), his sister Caroline Herschel was able to show Talbot his telescopes.[1] Well schooled in languages and reading by his mother, Talbot, at the age of eight, entered preparatory school in Rottingdean near Brighton in Sussex, where his teacher, the Reverend Thomas Hooker, was greatly impressed. In a letter he wrote to Talbot in 1812 he noted:

> You seem to me to set out in the World under the very fairest auspices. Most excellent & (what is not always the case) most clever Parents, brilliant & solid Talents, & a degree of improvement, if these do not hereafter, work out something different from the common run of men, I shall be most grievously deceived, & disappointed.[2]

From the age of 11 to 15, Talbot attended Harrow, living in the headmaster's house. Talbot was well liked by his peers and masters alike. With his friend Walter Calverley Trevelyan, he went in search of botanical specimens and at the age of 14 they wrote *Flora of Harrow*. The single manuscript copy of this is still held by Harrow School.

At the age of 17, Talbot entered Trinity College, Cambridge, to study mathematics and classics. His intense interest in mathematics worried his mother who thought he should be more well rounded. In a letter to him prior to his entry to Cambridge she wrote, only partially tongue-in-cheek:

> My Dear Henry
> You seem so mathematically inclined that I ought *en bonne mère* to send you to Oxford to counteract it that you may not grow into a Rhomboidal shape, walk elliptically, or go off in a tangent, all which evils are imminent if you go to Cambridge.[3]

After a distinguished undergraduate career at Cambridge, Talbot spent much of the 1820s travelling extensively within the United Kingdom as well as much of Western Europe. This decade saw the flourishing of the 'Romantic Age', which at that time dominated so much of the literature, painting, music, architecture and philosophy of western civilization. With his considerable intellect and language skills, Talbot was able fully to immerse himself in the spirit of the age.

In 1827, with his father's debts paid off and Lacock Abbey untenanted, Talbot was finally able to set himself up in the family estate at Lacock and began to take an active part within the local community. Late 1832 was a time of some consequence for Talbot who took his seat in Parliament as the Whig representative of Chippenham and also married Constance Mundy of Markeaton Hall in Derbyshire. He found the vagaries of political life incompatible with his thirst for factual knowledge and he left Parliament in 1834, refusing to stand again for his seat. His family life was also taking up more of his time with three daughters and one son born between 1835 and 1842. His friend Sir David Brewster shared this concern, especially his time taken up with politics:

> Your power of doing something original and valuable and your leisure and means of doing it should not be neglected for the infinitely less valuable occupations of a political life.[4]

For Talbot, the 1830s was his most productive decade for scientific and mathematical researches. The decade began well with his election as FRS in 1831, Michael Faraday being included among the seven signatories of the certificate of recommendation. During the 1830s Talbot began his researches into photography.

In August 1836 a meeting of the British Association for the Advancement of Science was to be held in Bristol. Talbot took the opportunity to invite a number of scientists to come to Lacock Abbey first and spend a few days in informal discussions. Accepting this invitation were Sir David Brewster, William Whewell, Charles Babbage, Charles Wheatstone, P.M. Roget and William Snow Harris. Brewster, in particular, took to Talbot and their discussions were wide ranging and according to Talbot's wife, highly animated and convivial. Talbot kept up his relationship with these and other scientists throughout his life but he and Brewster became particular friends.

The Early History of Photography

The word photography is derived from the Greek *photos*, which means 'light' and *graphos* meaning 'writing' or 'drawing'. It combines optics, which uses lenses to project the image of an object onto a surface, and photochemistry, which requires the surface to be light-sensitive. The ancestor of the photographic camera was the *camera obscura*, which in its most primitive form consists of a small, darkened room with a single, tiny hole through which light could be admitted, resulting in an inverted image forming on the wall opposite. This was first described around 1000 AD by Abu Ali Hasan Ibn Al-Haitham, usually referred to in the west as Al Hazen, a scholar from Basra in what is now Iraq. Developments through the fifteenth to eighteenth centuries, using lenses and mirrors, enabled the *camera obscura* to become much smaller and more portable, and for the image to be focused onto paper, thereby allowing an outside object to be drawn. Another important development in optical drawing aids was the *camera lucida*, invented in 1807 by the British scientist William Hyde Wollaston. It consisted of a four-sided prism mounted on a small stand placed above a sheet of paper. If the eye was placed close to the upper edge of the prism in a manner such that half the pupil of the eye is over the prism, it was possible to see both the object placed in front of the prism and the drawing paper itself. The object could then be drawn. Although it did have its uses, many people found the *camera lucida* extremely difficult to operate.

Credit for the invention of photography has been a subject of strong opinion since the beginning. Before 1802, Thomas Wedgwood, son of the potter Josiah Wedgwood, made early inroads into the development of photography. Using a solution of silver nitrate, Wedgwood was able to make pieces of paper and leather sensitive to light, but was unable to find a way to stop the further darkening of the image after an exposure had been made. Wedgwood's friend and collaborator Humphry Davy submitted a paper relating these experiments to the *Proceedings of the Royal Institution* in 1802. Although these experiments failed to produce a lasting photographic image, they were an indication of the state of science at the beginning of the nineteenth century regarding chemistry and light.

The first person successfully to obtain a primitive form of photograph using a technique involving photochemistry was a French amateur inventor, Joseph Nicéphore Niépce (1765-1833). In the early 1820s, he was able to take an engraving, which he had oiled to make it transparent, and place it on top of a material covered with a light-sensitive material. This was exposed to sunlight and after a few hours the areas under the light parts of the engraving became hardened while those under the dark areas remained soft and could then be washed away creating a plate ready for etching and printing. Using this technique he successfully obtained accurate copies of engravings onto glass, zinc and finally pewter. He also attempted to make images using the *camera obscura*, but the exposure times were too long to be considered fully successful. The earliest extant 'photograph', now at the University of Texas, is one taken by Niépce in 1826 with an eight-hour exposure of a view from his window. The actual image is difficult to see and the movement of the shadows of such a long exposure makes the image unintelligible without a lot of assistance.

Another Frenchman, Louis Jacques Mandé Daguerre (1787-1851), a Parisian artist and showman best known for his life-like paintings displayed as dioramas, worked in partnership with Niépce from 1829 until 1833 when Niépce died. In 1835 Daguerre discovered that a 'latent image' can form on a plate of iodised silver and that this can be developed by exposure to mercury vapour, whereby the mercury settled on the exposed parts of the image. This technique allowed exposure times to be reduced from several hours to about thirty minutes. By 1837 Daguerre was able to fix the image permanently by using a solution of sodium chloride [table salt] to dissolve away the unexposed silver iodide. With this technique he was able to produce pictures with a remarkably high degree of detail and clarity. He called this improved method a 'daguerreotype'. By this time Talbot had also been experimenting with obtaining photographic images and had achieved a high degree of success.

Talbot recounts the germs of the idea leading to photography in his book *The Pencil of Nature*,[5] which was published in 1844 and written using beautiful poetic English:

> One of the first days of the month of October 1833, I was amusing myself on the lovely shores of the Lake of Como in Italy, taking sketches with Wollaston's Camera Lucida ... but with the smallest amount of success. I then thought of trying again a method, which I had tried many times before. The method was to take a Camera Obscura, and to throw the image of the objects on a piece of transparent tracing paper ... On this paper the objects are distinctly seen, and can be traced on it with a pencil.

> This led me to speculate on the inimitable beauty of the pictures of nature's painting, which the glass lens of the camera throws upon the paper in its focus – fairy pictures, creations of a moment, and destined as rapidly to fade away.
>
> It was during these thoughts that the idea occurred to me ... how charming it would be if it were possible to cause these natural images to imprint themselves durably and remain fixed upon the paper! And why should it not be possible? I asked myself.

By late 1834, Talbot had developed a technique of making paper light-sensitive by soaking it in a weak solution of sodium chloride and then brushing on a solution of silver nitrate. This produced silver chloride on the fibres of the paper and when this was exposed to light, finely divided metallic silver was formed resulting in a darkening of the paper. When an object (such as a leaf or piece of lace) was placed on the sensitised paper and placed in the sun, the areas that were exposed directly to sunlight darkened but the areas covered by the leaf or lace remained unchanged. His experiments had also shown that although a weak solution of sodium chloride helped make the paper sensitive to light, a saturated solution of the same sodium chloride would make the paper almost insensitive to light. He used this saturated solution to stabilise the images he made, allowing them to be examined in light without the image rapidly disappearing.

He noticed early on that, although a detailed image was obtained using his photogenic drawing process, the tones were reversed showing things that had been light as dark and things that had been dark as light. This reversal of tones was easily corrected by putting a fresh piece of sensitised paper under the negative and exposing it to light; a positive image could then be obtained. The earliest surviving negative is that of the latticed window in the South Gallery of Lacock Abbey taken in August 1835. When it was taken Talbot recounted that it was possible to count the number of squares of glass, which numbered some 200 all told.

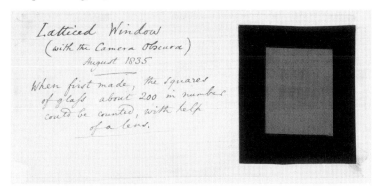

Latticed window in Lacock Abbey, August 1935, with close-up view on the right. (*National Media Museum*)

Talbot has given an interesting description of how he took his early pictures:

> Not having with me ... a camera obscura of any considerable size, I constructed one out of a large box, the image being thrown upon one end of it by a good object-glass fixed at the opposite end. The apparatus being armed with a sensitive paper, was taken out in a summer afternoon, and placed about one hundred yards from a building favourably illuminated by the sun. An hour or so afterwards I opened the box and I found depicted upon the paper a very distinct representation of the building, with the exception of those parts of it, which lay in the shade. A little experience in this branch of the art showed me that with a smaller camera obscura the effect would be produced in a smaller time. Accordingly I had several small boxes made, in which I fixed lenses of shorter focus, and with these I obtained very perfect, but extremely small pictures.[6]

The small boxes which he referred to measured some two to three inches and were affectionately named 'mousetraps' by his wife Constance because of the various places that they were found. In a letter to Talbot dated 7 September 1835, Constance asks about his plans:

> Shall you take any of your mousetraps with you into Wales? – it would be charming for you to bring home some views.[7]

Talbot experimented with various ways to fix the image and make it more permanent. In addition to the saturated solution of sodium chloride he tried various other compounds. Several were able to stabilise the print, making it much less sensitive to light, but none would remove the unexposed silver salts making the image permanent. The problem was resolved early in 1839 when his friend Sir John Herschel, recently returned from his four years' sojourn in the Cape, suggested fixing the negatives with 'hypo', sodium hyposulphite. John Herschel had a great interest in photography and it was he who first coined the words 'photography', 'positive', 'negative' and 'fixing'.[8]

Later Developments

Almost immediately after Talbot had successfully produced his first photographs he learnt about the work of Daguerre. This led Talbot rapidly to publish details of the technique behind producing what he called 'photogenic drawings' and in addition to explain it in detail to members of the Royal Society. Although there are other claimants, nowadays both Daguerre and Talbot are credited with inventing the basic techniques behind photography. In comparing their work, Daguerre produced his images onto metal whereas Talbot's were on sensitised paper. Talbot's method had the decisive advantage that it was possible to produce many copies of the original image, whereas daguerreotypes were 'one-offs'. However, the detail produced by a daguerreotype was often quite remarkable, whereas it was less so with Talbot's pictures; because of the fibrous nature of the paper the images appear slightly more diffuse.

Nevertheless, it was the detail of the photographic images which fascinated and amazed so many people when they first saw them. Talbot himself commented:

> It frequently happens, moreover – and this is one of the charms of photography – that the operator himself discovers on examination, perhaps long afterwards, that he has depicted many things he had no notion of at the time. Sometimes inscriptions and dates are found upon the buildings, or printed placards most irrelevant, are discovered upon their walls: sometimes a distant dial-plate is seen, and upon it – unconsciously recorded – the hour of the day at which the view was taken.[9]

Early Photographic Studios

Initially the daguerreotype process for obtaining images, rather than that developed by Talbot, appeared to be more successful, and from late 1839 onwards studios producing them sprung up around the world. For the first time it was possible to obtain images of some of the famous monuments in Rome, Greece, Egypt and elsewhere and these proved to be immensely popular with the general public. Great improvements to the image-making process were made using lenses and better chemicals, and these reduced the time a person had to sit in order to be photographed.

One of the earliest of these daguerreotype studios was set up in Bath by the entrepreneur Richard Beard[10] who had acquired Daguerre's patent. In March 1841 Beard opened the first photographic portrait studio in Britain in a glasshouse erected on the roof of the Royal Polytechnic Institution, London, followed quickly by a whole chain of photographic 'Institutes' throughout the country. The high cost of the daguerreotype portrait meant that a wealthy resort such as Bath was an obvious choice for one of these Institutes, and by the following November a garden plot, formerly the site of a public *camera obscura*, was acquired for the purpose in the Subscription Walk Gardens (now Victoria Park) below the Royal Crescent.

The site of this building, by the Gravel Walk at the Brock Street entrance, is now a flower garden with a large urn – a spot beloved of tourist photographers for its view across the Royal Crescent. Talbot would certainly have been aware of the Victoria Park Institute. Beard's Institute was eventually removed for the improvement of the park in 1851, but by 1850 another 'photographist', William Whaite, was already setting up two more studios, at No.1 Seymour Street and No.7A The Corridor, both of which were to remain in use by professional photographers well into the twentieth century.

Later Work of Henry Talbot

In September 1840 Talbot achieved a further important breakthrough. He found that sensitising his paper with gallic acid was highly effective in producing a latent image. The effect of this was to reduce greatly the exposure time needed, typically from about one hour down to one minute. The consequence of this was to revolutionise photography using paper, and Talbot patented the process in 1841. He called it the calotype process (from the Greek word *kalos* meaning beautiful). During the next two to three years he continued to work on improving the technique and in 1842 the Royal Society awarded him its prestigious biennial Rumford Medal for 'many important discoveries made in photography'. The following year he took out a further patent on photography, which was quite wide ranging in nature and in it he described a system for the production of photographic plates suitable for publication.

'The Ladder', c.1845. Salted paper print by William Henry Fox Talbot. (*National Media Museum*)

Nelson's Column under construction, Trafalgar Square, London, first week of April 1844.
Salt paper print from a calotype negative by William Henry Fox Talbot. (*National Media Museum*)

By this time photographs produced using the calotype technique had greatly caught the public imagination and there was a high demand for such pictures. To try and satisfy this demand Talbot set up a workshop facility for the commercial production of photographs at a house in Reading in Berkshire, which had formerly been a school. Today a plaque at No.55 Baker Street, Reading marks the original site. From this workshop came *The Pencil of Nature*, the first published book in the world containing photographs.

The Great Exhibition of 1851 did much to highlight the considerable progress taking place at that time in science, engineering and technology and this included photography. In 1851 Talbot took out a further wide-ranging patent in photography. However, by far and away the most important event for photography in 1851 was the invention of the collodion process for making glass negatives by an English sculptor, Frederick Scott Archer. The technique involved coating glass plates with a mixture of potassium iodide and collodion, which is a solution of nitrocellulose dissolved in ether. The plates had to be sensitised immediately before use by dipping them into a solution of silver nitrate.

Talbot maintained Archer's invention was merely an extension of his calotype patent and challenged photographers who used the collodion process without a licence from him. This insistence on his patent rights for the calotype process led Talbot to become embroiled in recriminations in the press and legal battles in court. There was a particularly acrimonious case, which reached the High Court in 1854, where Talbot, claiming that the collodion process came under his original patent, brought a suit against a Mr Laroche who had set up a studio making portraits. The Court ruled that this newer process was outside his patent and the resulting furore put something of a stain on his character. It should be appreciated that at that time there was great controversy over the ethics and necessity for patents. They were also very expensive to obtain, partly to discourage unimportant or trivial applications, and this tended to make them rather wide-ranging.

Talbot had ceased to make photographs after 1846, but he did make one further important contribution to photography. In 1851 he became the first person to obtain a photograph of an object illuminated by an electric flash. At the time there was great interest in how objects moving at high speed could be studied. Talbot had discussed this much earlier in 1833 with his friend John Herschel. Charles Wheatstone, one of the great scientists of the nineteenth century, had employed electrical discharges to study high-speed events. In June 1851, at the Royal

MOFFAT,   103, Princes St. Edin?

A studio portrait of William Henry Fox Talbot by J. Moffat, Edinburgh, 1864. (*Fox Talbot Museum*)

Institution in London, Talbot fastened part of a newspaper to a disc, which was then allowed to revolve rapidly. When it was illuminated by an electric discharge and a photograph taken, the letters on the newspaper appeared as sharp as if they had been stationary. He reported this jubilantly to Michael Faraday, the Director of the Royal Institution.

Although most closely connected to Lacock because of his invention of photography there, Talbot and his family frequently took houses in London, Edinburgh and other cities for extended periods of time to take in the advantages of urban life, and from 1871 to 1876, the family took the lease on No.4 The Circus in Bath.

By the early 1850s many people were involved in photography. One local enthusiast was the Reverend Francis Lockey (1796-1869), who lived at Swainswick just outside Bath. Lockey was typical of many clergymen in the nineteenth century who managed to combine their pastoral activities with a great interest in natural science. Lockey kept a series of notebooks from 1834 to his death in 1869 in which he recorded details of the daily temperature, barometric pressure, rainfall activity and air humidity as well as noting cloud formations, wind direction, insect emergence and flowering patterns. In addition, he kept details of his various pursuits in photography such as the subject and different techniques that he employed. Some of Lockey's pictures showing buildings in the Bath area are remarkable for their sharpness and composition.[11]

Bath Abbey, with the Literary & Scientific Institution (on the left) and the Institution gardens in the foreground. From a paper calotype negative by Francis Lockey dated 11 April 1854. *(BRLSI collection; image processing by Matt Williams)*

Cinematography and Photographic Studios in Bath

The logical extension to the still photograph is to produce a moving image. Once again there is an interesting Bath connection. At No.1 New Bond Street Place, close to the unusually named *Volunteer Rifleman's Arms* public house, are two plaques commemorating the work of John Rudge and William Friese-Greene. One of the plaques says that the latter was 'The inventor of commercial kinematography being the first man to apply celluloid ribbon for this purpose'. More recent research indicates that this is a rather optimistic statement and nowadays the invention of cinematography is generally attributed to that great American inventor, Thomas Edison, and also to the Lumière brothers from France.

William Friese-Greene comes across as a rather tragic figure. He was born William Edward Green at College Street, Bristol, on 7 September 1855 and was the youngest of seven children. In 1869, aged 14, he became apprenticed to a photographer in Bristol named Maurice Gutenberg. At that time being a photographer was still a comparatively unusual occupation. In 1875 he ceased working for Gutenberg as a result of a quarrel and then set up his own studios in Bristol and Bath, later expanding his business to include further studios in London and Brighton. He married Helena Friese in 1874 and changed his surname to Friese-Greene, which he felt better reflected the image of a rising photographer.

By this time there were 24 professional photographers working in Bath, mostly located in or near the wealthy shopping area of Milsom Street. The earliest of these, set up in about 1852, was William Whaite's premises in The Corridor shopping arcade, mentioned above, which consisted of a timber 'penthouse' extension built above the 'Corridor Rooms' (originally a Masonic Hall) which the architect Henry Edmund Goodridge had added at the back of the shops. Later known as No.7A The Corridor, this extension appears to have been the first purpose-built photographic studio in Bath after Beard's Institute.[12]

When the Corridor properties were sold in 1877, the Rooms and photographic studio were purchased by Frederick Charles Bird, himself a well-known photographer in Bath and neighbouring towns. However, in the deed of sale the actual occupier of the studio is shown as (Friese)-Greene, who appears to have been expanding his business in Bath at about that time. Mrs. Friese-Greene

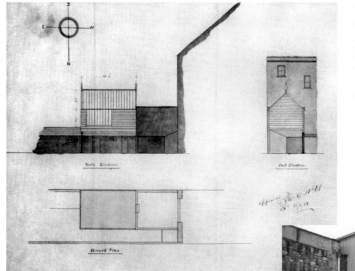

(*left*) Friese-Greene's studio at the rear of 34 Gay Street, as shown on the Building Control Plan of 1882. (*Bath Record Office, Bath & North East Somerset Council*)

(*below*) As the studio appears today (*Photograph by Mike Chapman*).

is temporarily recorded as 'photographic artist' at No.3 Old Bond Street, and Friese-Greene himself at No.9 Lorne Terrace (now Lorne Road) in East Twerton. His main centre of operation, however, was his house at No.34 Gay Street, acquired in 1882, at the back of which he built a studio extension similar to the timber penthouse in The Corridor. This structure still exists, although it ceased to be used as a studio in 1925 and now serves as a kitchen. With his wife and sisters, Friese-Greene successfully ran these two studios in Bath and throughout the 1880s in other towns.

In Bath he met John Arthur Roebuck Rudge, the son of a wood-turner and antique dealer, who was born there. Rudge, a scientific instrument maker, began to specialise in making magic lanterns at his premises at New Bond Street Place, only a few yards from The Corridor. He acquired quite a reputation through the many shows he gave to the public using magic lanterns. Rudge invented the 'Phantascope' or 'Biophantic Lantern', an ingenious device able to display seven slides in rapid succession, thereby creating the illusion of movement. Friese-Greene was fascinated by this and the two men began to collaborate. To be able to see a moving image depends on persistence of vision, which is a physiological effect whereby the retina of the eye is able to record an impression for a brief moment after the image itself has disappeared. Friese-Greene quickly appreciated that glass plates were totally impractical for obtaining the rapid changes necessary to produce a moving image. Instead he began to experiment initially with oiled paper, then later obtained more success using celluloid.

In 1889 Friese-Greene took out patent No.10131, which was for a 'Chronophotographic' camera said to be capable of taking up to ten photographs per second on a roll of perforated celluloid film moving intermittently behind a shutter. This is indeed the principle behind a motion picture camera. He demonstrated this to members of the Bath Photographic Society in 1890 but it failed to make the hoped-for impact because the rate at which the pictures were being produced was insufficient to give rise to the illusion of animation.

It is quite likely that some of these experiments were carried out in the Corridor premises, but in 1889 Friese-Greene gave up this studio in order to further his career in London, although he retained the Gay Street premises until 1893. The Corridor studio, taken over by his nephew Tom Leaman and remaining in use until 1999, still exists, although the interior has been completely modernised since Friese-Greene's time. It was probably during the 1880s that Friese-Greene met William Harbutt, inventor of Plasticene and keen amateur photographer, who at that time was headmaster of a 'Government Art Night Class' and School of Art in the Victoria Rooms adjoining the studio. Both Harbutt and Friese-Greene were members of the Bath Photographic Society (the latter serving on the committee between 1890 and 1893 and probably a founder member), and Harbutt would almost certainly have been a witness at Friese-Greene's demonstration to the Society in 1890.[13]

From then on Friese-Greene's career seems to have taken a turn for the worse. The cost of developing his moving images took a considerable toll on his finances and in 1891 he was declared bankrupt and spent a short time in prison. He was forced to sell his patent rights for the 'Chronophotographic' camera for £500. Since he was unable to afford the patent renewal fee, it lapsed in 1894. In the following year the brothers Louis and Auguste Lumière in France patented their invention of 'Le Cinematographe', which marks the real beginning of motion pictures.

Friese-Greene appears to have had a very fertile and creative mind, and all told between 1889 and his death in 1921 registered over 70 patents, many but by no means all in the area of photography. His tragedy, however, was that he lacked the scientific and technical expertise to bring any of them to fruition as the basis for a successful industry. His death occurred while he was attending a meeting in London of members of the Cinematography Exhibitors Association. This proved to be a stormy occasion and while he was making a speech pleading for unity in the profession he collapsed and died. He was found to be almost penniless at the time. Friese-Greene is buried in Highgate cemetery in North London and Sir Edwin Lutyens, the famous architect, designed his gravestone. On it is inscribed that he was 'The Inventor of Kinematography'.

Conclusion

Bath's place in the history of photography is undoubtedly assured by its nearness to Lacock, where the pioneer and inventor Henry Talbot lived. Its further connections with William Friese-Greene and his early work in cinematography adds to the importance of Bath in the founding of the imaging arts. Bath was also home for two decades of the Royal Photographic Society's collections, the finest privately owned collection of photographs in Britain, which resided in the Octagon in Milsom Street. This collection covered the depth and breadth of photography as an art and as a science from its birth in the 1830s through its development and maturity throughout the nineteenth and early twentieth centuries and finally into the digital age at the turn of the twenty-first century.

Photography as a medium is ubiquitous, appearing in all of its guises on a daily basis. It is a tool used by scientists and artists to expand our knowledge and understanding of our world, and as a common tool used by all of us to record momentous occasions in our family's lives or the mundane 'snaps' of events of passing interest. Bath itself must have been the subject of millions of photographs over the years from visitors from around the world.

Further Reading

Arnold, H.J.P., *William Henry Fox Talbot; Pioneer of Photography and Man of Science*, London, Hutchinson, 1977.

Schaaf, Larry J, *Out of the Shadows: Herschel, Talbot & the Invention of Photography*, London, Yale University Press, 1992.

Schaaf, Larry J, *The Photographic Art of William Henry Fox Talbot*, Princeton NJ, Princeton University Press, 2000.

Schaaf, Larry J, *Records of the Dawn of Photography: Talbot's Notebooks P & Q*, Cambridge, Cambridge University Press, 1996.

7: City and Landscape
The Mapping of Bath

Mike Chapman

Maps have been an essential element in the progress of Bath as a premier health resort and centre of cultural change. Land surveys were necessary before any of the classic architectural developments could take place, and published maps were always needed by the visitors as guides to the city and its hinterland. Bath was therefore a fertile ground for enterprising and innovative mapmakers and provided its own individual contribution to British cartography.

The Early Surveys and the Bristol Connection

At the time when the great county maps and atlases were being produced in the late sixteenth century by Christopher Saxton, John Norden and John Speed, large-scale surveys of towns and land estates were also starting to appear. Norden, for example, carried out surveys of the Kingswood and Fillwood 'forest' and other crown property in this region including, in 1612, the manor of Englishcombe; and a sketch plan (author unknown) of Bathford was made about 1605 for a legal case. William Harrison, writing in Holinshed's *Chronicle*, published in 1577, stated that map engravings of 26 English cathedral cities, including Bath, were then in preparation, perhaps a reference to the compilation of manuscripts by the herald and topographer William Smith (not the geologist) entitled *The Particuler Description of England with the portratures of certaine of the cheiffest citties & townes*, 1588. However, Smith's perspective 'portrature' of Bath was little more than a sketch and was not published until later,[1] so it is possible that Harrison was referring to another survey of the city which is known to have been made at about that time.

Our knowledge of this survey comes from engraved copies, particularly from John Speed's county maps in his *Theatre of the Empire of Great Britaine* (1611), in which a map of Bath is included, together with inset plans of the baths and a site key, in the corner of the Somerset sheet. Speed explains that some of the town maps in his *Theatre* were derived from the work of others, distinguished from his own by the omission of a 'Scale of Pases'. Since the Bath map does not include a scale, it can be assumed that Speed used a pre-existing survey,

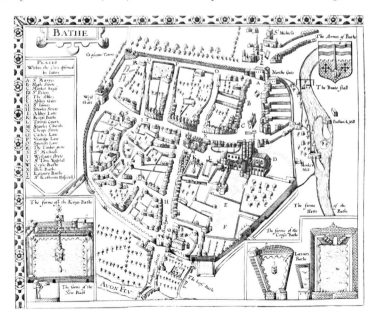

John Speed's map of Bath in his *Theatre of the Empire of Great Britaine* (1611). (*Bath Record Office, Bath & North East Somerset Council*)

93

though much reduced in size from the original and with the suburbs outside the walls compressed and simplified to fit into the available space. Nevertheless, as shown by a comparison with a written survey of the city some 30 years later, the detail shown appears essentially correct. Quite recently another printed map came to light showing the same features but at larger scale and in more elaborate style, engraved with the author's name 'H.Savile desc[ripsit]'. Whilst its provenance is unknown,[2] this too appears to be derived from the same source. Whatever the motives for undertaking this survey, it came at a key moment when Bath was in transition from a medieval monastic and industrial town to a national health resort. The popularity and usefulness of Speed's print is testified by the many copies and reprints of it that continued to be published until the eighteenth century.

In common with the national trend, no new surveys of Bath were made until the late seventeenth century. This time the initiative came locally, from a Bristol mercer Jacob Millerd, who published in 1671 *An Exact Delineation of the Famous Cittie of Bristol and Suburbs Thereof*, which he himself had surveyed and engraved. No doubt Millerd, like Speed, was aware of the contribution maps could make to the mercantile prosperity of this country.[3] Millerd's map proved so successful that in 1673 a greatly enlarged and more detailed version was produced on four plates at one inch to 250 feet scale (1:3,000), surrounded in the border with twenty local views, mostly of public buildings. Interestingly, one of these is a sketch of 'The south prospect of Bathe' – one of the earliest pictorial views of the city. Clearly there was an interest in the growing commercial potential of Bath among Bristolians, as illustrated by the timber merchant John Hobbs who later became a leading investor in the Avon Navigation and early Georgian building developments. Also, the mathematical skills involved in navigation and global trade could readily be applied to mapmaking, and it was presumably the success of Millerd's map which inspired Joseph Gilmore, 'Teacher of the Mathematicks in the City of Bristol', to publish a similar map, *The City of Bath*, in 1694. Engraved by John Savage on four plates at two chains to the inch (1:1,584, almost twice Millerd's scale) and orientated to the west, it too has a border filled with 36 views of public buildings, except that 29 of these are Lodging Houses – complete with an accompanying list of 23 principal Inns! This map, evidently aimed at the wealthy visitor, appears to have been popular, as a further six editions, printed and sold by Thomas Bakewell, Fleet Street, London, were reissued with few alterations up to 1731.

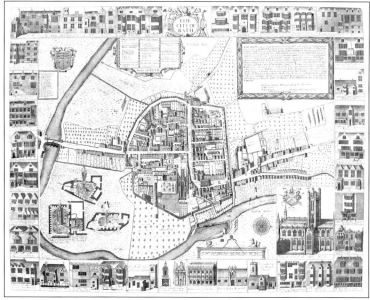

Joseph Gilmore's map, *The City of Bath*, published in 1694. (*Bath Record Office, Bath & North East Somerset Council*)

The Early Eighteenth Century: John Wood and Thomas Thorpe

Until the early eighteenth century the topography of Bath had changed little since Elizabethan times, but as the Georgian development gathered pace, Gilmore was soon overtaken by a new generation of mapmakers operating in Bath itself – the most famous and influential being the architect John Wood. While working for Lord Bingley in the mid 1720s Wood had already produced a map of Bramham Park Estate in Yorkshire depicting a classically-inspired geometrical landscape which he was to translate into an urban context. After returning to Bath, in 1735 he produced *A Plan of Bath in Somerset* 'after the Manner of the celebrated Plan of Paris', at a scale of 1:3,000, copied by the noted London engraver John Pine and published by James Leake, the well-known Bath bookseller in Terrace Walk. Like Gilmore's map, it is orientated to the west, and though surrounded in a highly ornamental oval cartouche decorated with surveying instruments and emblems of health (hence sometimes known as 'Wood's Coffee-table map'), the city is shown in block plan instead of the perspective views of Gilmore and his predecessors. Maps of Bath in plan had already been published by the antiquarians William Stukeley (in his *Itinerarium Curiosum*, 1724) and his colleague John Strachey (inset in his map of Somerset, 1736), but these were merely revised versions of a copy of Speed's map, published with minor alterations in 1634 by Dr Thomas Johnson in his *Thermae Bathonicae*. Wood, too, used Johnson's map for his own antiquarian purposes, in his *Essay towards a Description of Bath* in 1742, to draw attention to the T-shape of the street pattern in which he saw the outlines of the *ankh*, the ancient Egyptian symbol of health.

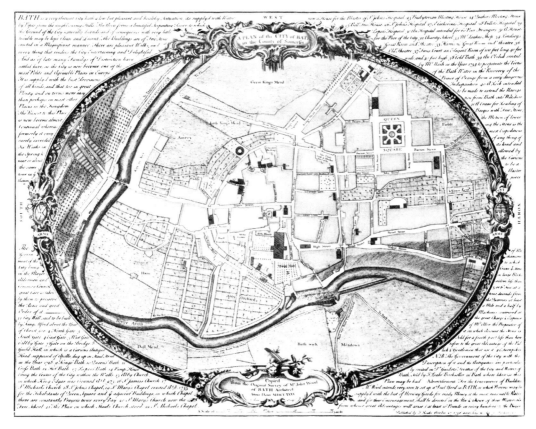

John Wood's map of 1735, *A Plan of Bath in Somerset*. (Bath Record Office, Bath & North East Somerset Council)

More importantly, Wood's map was the first of an English area outside London to be produced with a view to urban planning,[4] and Wood's own Queen Square development appears in strong contrast against the medieval outlines of the old city. An advertisement is even included in the margin announcing his intention to set up a deal yard for the sale of Norway timber 'for the Convenience of Builders' who 'for their Encouragement, shall be directed in their Use and Choice of their Materials from whence great Advantages will arise ...' Also included are several proposals by Wood which were never carried out as depicted on the map. One, 'An Hospital intended for 60 Poor Strangers', no.30 in the key, was later built elsewhere in the city (the 'General Hospital'). Another, no.40, 'A Lock intended to be made to extend the Navigation from Bath into Wiltshire' was part of a scheme for by-passing the town weir which Wood, with his business connections in Bristol, promoted himself. It was not until 70 years later that locks were built further downstream when the city was connected to the Kennet & Avon Canal. Nevertheless, from this survey Wood was able to produce new development plans for any part of the city as the opportunity arose, with the added advantage of providing, in his *Essay*, exact descriptions and distances to different parts of the town as a guide to visitors. It was still being advertised ('There being a few Prints now remaining') in his 1765 edition of the *Essay*, for sale at Leake's bookshop and Hitch's in Paternoster Row.

However, several landowners in the neighbourhood, aware of the potential increase in land values, had already commissioned surveys of their own estates. In 1725 *A Map of the Scite of the Dissolved Priory of Bath called ye Bath Abby with the several Lands & Tenements within ye Liberty and Precincts thereof adjoyning to the City of Bath (see Colour Plate XI)* was produced for the Duke of Kingston who owned the south-eastern sector of the city.[5] This large-scale manuscript map (one chain to the inch, 1:792), surveyed according to Wood by a 'Mr. Reynolds', shows the whole city within the walls in block plan and may well have provided much information for Wood's map ten years later. Indeed, the outline of John Wood's 1739 building proposals for his 'Royal Forum' on the Ham Meadow (the area lying in the bend of the river between the railway station and the city centre) are also shown superimposed. Individual properties belonging to the Duke are outlined in more detail, probably compiled from deed plans which began to appear in legal documents from this time onward, and a second version of the map was made in 1750 to include a table of reserved rents. On the opposite side of the river several surveys of the manor of Bathwick were similarly commissioned: first in 1727 by William Sutton for the Hon William Pulteney, with another around 1770 for William Johnstone Pulteney prior to the development of the Pulteney estate.

The most influential of the land surveyors attracted to Bath was the somewhat shadowy figure of Thomas Thorpe. Thorpe's first survey, in 1740, was of the parish of Walcot on the north and west side of the city (where most of the Georgian development was eventually built) for Robert Gay, the principal landowner. In 1741 a smaller survey of Lilliput Farm on Lansdown was completed for the Bath surgeon, Dr Jerry Peirce, but in 1742 Thorpe moved on to the larger task of surveying Ralph Allen's estates south of the river in the parishes of Widcombe and (Monkton) Combe, and in 1743, the manor of (Bath)Hampton further east which Allen had just acquired from his brother-in-law, Charles Holder. On the latter occasion Thorpe was assisted by John Overton, presumably from the family of well-known mapsellers and publishers in London. Allen later had these surveys, together with another of the manor of Claverton (date and surveyor unknown), proudly combined into one enormous manuscript map about six feet square entitled *A Survey of the Manours of Hampton, Claverton with Widcombe belonging to Ralph Allen Esqr.* Drawn at a scale of 1:3,168 (four chains to the inch, there is no scale line) it is beautifully detailed, but orientated south to show Allen's Prior Park mansion at the top and Bath at the bottom.[6] Details of the city itself appear to have been taken from John Wood's plans of the 1740s, brought up-to-date to include his most recent work, the King's Circus, completed about 1767.

In the meantime Thorpe had already prepared his own survey of Bath and its neighbourhood, which he published himself in 1742 under the title *An Actual Survey of the City of Bath, in the County of Somerset, and of Five Miles Round*, engraved by James Cole in Hatton Garden, and printed by Mr Thomas Boddely of Kingsmead Street. This large sheet, nearly 3ft 6ins square at 1:16,000 scale (about four inches to the mile), consists of a circular map overlaid with concentric rings with radii at one-mile increments centred on the 'Bear Corner' at the top of Stall Street. Distances from Bath can be seen at a glance, and the river and all roads leading from the city are marked every half-mile from the centre. At this scale, details of the city (taken from Wood) are still visible, though field boundaries are only roughly sketched in. It is evident that this map – subsequently described as 'a very useful airing companion and director' – was designed to be folded and used as a visitors' guide for walks or rides in the surrounding rural landscape. Published by subscription, it was well-supported, as indicated by the number of eminent and influential names among the subscribers.

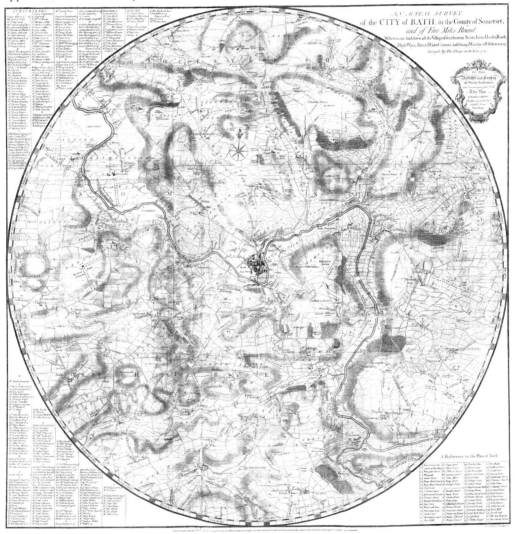

Thomas Thorpe's 1742 map, *An Actual Survey of the City of Bath, in the County of Somerset, and of Five Miles Round.* (*Bath Record Office, Bath & North East Somerset Council*)

Like Wood's map, this too was sold by the well-known Bath booksellers James Leake and William Frederick as well as Mr Hitch, Bookseller in Paternoster Row, and the printselling shops in London. Thorpe seems to have left Bath soon after this, as nothing further is heard about him except for a survey carried out in 1752 for the Earl of Powys of his lands in and around Caerleon in Wales.

After Wood, no new surveys of the city seem to have been required for many years, although the rapidity of building development meant that, in detail, subsequent versions of his map had to be constantly revised, the first being *A New and Correct Plan of the City of Bath and places adjacent*, published in 1750. Redrawn at the same scale and including Wood's place key, this map was instead orientated to the north and featured a compass rose, table of postage times and 'Rules of the Pump Room', but omitting a scale line or any imprint details. In the same year a reduced version appeared inset in Emanuel Bowen's Somerset map, and in 1764 was included in John Rocque's *Collection of Plans of the Principal Cities of Great Britain and Ireland* at a scale of 1 inch to 100 yards (1:3,600). An interesting use of this map by visitors is recorded in 1765 by Rev John Penrose, who sent a copy home to be pinned on the wall so that his family could follow his progress in his letters during his stay by means of the numbered key.[7] During the next 20 years it was reissued several times, but in 1770 was suddenly eclipsed by the appearance of a whole rash of new revisions. These included *A New and Correct Plan of the City of Bath with the New Additional Buildings*, published at 1:3,444 scale by the booksellers H. Leake, W. Frederick and W. Taylor (presumably the publishers of the previous map), *A Plan of the City and Suburbs of Bath according to the latest improvements*, published at the same scale

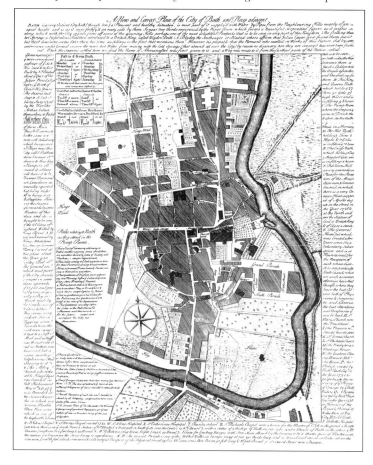

by the Milsom Street bookseller John Basnett and engraved by R. Coffin of Bristol, and another by the booksellers William Bally and A. Tennent of Milsom Street at a smaller scale, optimistically entitled *A New and Accurate Plan of the City of Bath much preferable to any other extant*. In the following year this small format, at one inch to the furlong (1:7,920), was adopted by Leake and his partners for the *New and Correct Plan* – for insertion into their booklet *A New Bath Guide; or useful pocket companion*, first published in the early 1760s.

A New and Correct Plan of the City of Bath and places adjacent, published in 1750, probably by H. Leake, W. Frederick and W. Taylor. (*Bath Record Office, Bath & North East Somerset Council*)

From hereon a pattern emerges of revised versions of previous maps being published almost on a yearly basis by a new generation of Bath booksellers[8] such as J. Sheldon, William Meyler & Son, Samuel Hazard, J. Savage and others, well into the nineteenth century.[9] One of the reasons why this was possible was the appearance of artist-engravers running family businesses in Bath, the most prominent being William Hibbert (who first set up in the Market Place in 1755), his sons John and Charles (the latter unfortunately hanged in 1819 for forging banknotes), and William Gingell of Marchant's Court and his son.

It was also in 1771 that Thorpe's *Five Mile* map was reissued by Frederick and Taylor, 'from a survey of Thos. Thorpe with alterations and improvements', at a reduced scale of 1.5 inches to the mile (1:42,240) but with indication of latitude and longitude. Similar copies by Bally & Tennent soon followed, and many editions (excluding Thorpe's name) continued to be produced in the guide-books well into the nineteenth century. In 1769 Thorpe's idea of a circular map was also taken up by mapmaker and 'Master of Mechanics to His Majesty' Benjamin Donn,[10] then running a mathematical academy in Bristol, when he published his *Map of the Country 11 Miles round the City of Bristol*, engraved by R. Coffin at the same scale. His nephew, also Benjamin, followed this up in 1790 with *A Map of the Country Eleven Miles round the City of Bath from Actual Surveys* 'by Several Hands' and engraved by 'B.Donne iuvenis'. However, at a scale of 1:88,000, it mainly functioned as a road map to neighbouring towns, and although Donne junior went on to produce *A New and Correct Plan of the City of Bath* from a recent survey in 1810 at 1:4,693, he seems to have preferred the smaller scale, eventually producing a 'Fifteen Mile' map in 1814.[11]

The Early Nineteenth Century: Charles Harcourt Masters

At the end of the eighteenth century the city was at the zenith of its prosperity and still expanding. Surveys of the adjoining estates continued to be produced for development purposes, such as that of the manor of Lyncombe & Widcombe on the south side in 1799 produced by Joseph Charlton[12] for the owners, Bruton Hospital, or on the east side the parish of Bathwick by the architect John Pinch and his son John in the early 1800s. Previous maps of the whole city had also been brought up-to-date by local surveyor Thomas Chantrey for publication in Taylor and Meyler's *New and Accurate Plan of the City of Bath to the present year 1793*, engraved by R. Hancock at a scale of 2.5 inches to 100 feet (1:480). Though revised by Lawrence Hill of Bristol and regularly reissued up to 1813, the time was ripe for a wider and more detailed survey, and Chantrey's map was immediately overshadowed by the work of Charles Harcourt Masters, son of Bath goldsmith Benedict Masters.

Better known today as an architect, Masters was initially trained as a land surveyor by William Day of Pitminster, near Taunton, whom he assisted during Day's survey of the county of Somerset. Masters showed such great promise that his name was included as joint author when their prize-winning[13] *County of Somerset* map at one inch to the mile was published in 1782, thereby instantly establishing his reputation.[14] Moving back to Bath, he was immediately employed by the Bath Turnpike Trust to make a series of beautiful large-scale manuscript maps of all their roads and adjoining lands which he completed in 1786. By 1787 he had become City Architect and Surveyor of the city of Bath, and had produced plans of Bath Common (for the Corporation) and of the city centre (for the Improvement Commissioners). During this period he also completed maps of the Manor of Priston (c.1793) for William Davies Esq, and of Dyrham Park (c.1799) for William Blathwayt. In the meantime, Masters was also preparing his own survey of the whole of Bath – partly for the construction of a model of the city, at a scale of one inch to 30 feet (1:360), which he eventually exhibited in 1789/90 at his house in Orchard Street and later, after receiving royal approval, in London. There appears to have been something of a competition here, as a rival model was immediately produced by Joseph Sheldon, a drawing master and portrait painter possibly associated with J. Sheldon, the Bath firm of booksellers and map-publishers mentioned above.

In 1795 Masters' magnificent *Plan of the City of Bath* was published – engraved in great detail at one inch to four chains (1:3,168) by S.I. Neele of the Strand, London (later engraver of Greenwood's map of Somerset, 1822) and showing intended developments in the city centre and Bathwick. In traditional fashion, it was orientated to the west and ornamented with the usual allegorical figures of health, but included a magnetic meridian – a new feature introduced by Masters on all his maps. A reduced version (about a third of the scale) was produced at the same time, later to appear inset in Day & Masters' 1803 re-issue of their *Somerset* map, and in Rev Richard Warner's *History of Bath*, 1801. It is worth noting that Warner also included in his book a facsimile of Gilmore's 1694 *City of Bath* map, a specimen of early English lithography printed by John Hibbert. Though Bath was certainly one of the earliest centres where lithography was practised in Britain, there is no other indication that it had any impact on the printing of maps here.[15]

In 1806 a revised edition was published, showing the newly-built Kennet & Avon Canal, followed in 1808 by a much-simplified *Plan of the Liberties of the City of Bath* at a scale of 1:3,243, engraved by Masters himself, but drawn by George P. Manners. Manners, whom Masters had taken on as a protégé in about 1804, also proved to be a proficient mapmaker, producing a fine large-scale (1:840) map of St.Michael's Parish in Bath in 1818. By this time however Masters had moved away from mapmaking towards architecture. He appears to have taken Manners as a partner for a while, but by 1820 Manners, too, had set up on his own as an architect, and in 1823 was appointed City Architect and Surveyor of Works.[16] During his subsequent career Manners continued to make many surveys, particularly of the city water-supply systems and, like his mentor, of Bath Turnpike Trust roads, and in 1839 (presumably after Masters' death, c.1818) published *A New and Correct Plan of the City of Bath, from Masters's original and elegant and accurate Plan, with all the additions and improvements to the present time.*

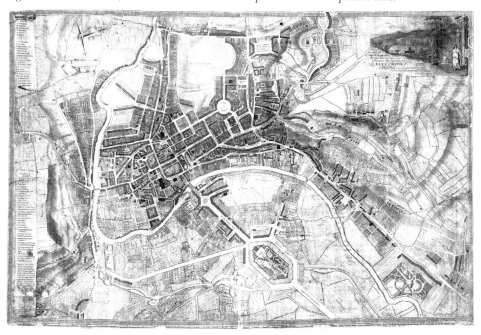

The 1806 revised edition of Charles Harcourt Masters' *Plan of the City of Bath*, showing the Pulteney Estate and the newly-built Kennet & Avon Canal on the lower half. (*Bath Record Office, Bath & North East Somerset Council*)

William Smith and the First Geological Map

As can be seen from Manners' career, the skills of surveying not only applied to mapmaking and architecture but increasingly to engineering. It was also at this time, and in Bath, that a new application was created by William Smith – later known as the 'Father of English Geology'. Smith, born in 1769 in Churchill, Oxfordshire, was trained as a land surveyor, and in 1791 was sent to map the estates of Lady Jones in Stowey and High Littleton and to make underground surveys of her High Littleton coal-works. Since he had acquired an interest in landscape geology from his experience as a surveyor, the geologically diverse area around Bath provided an ideal opportunity to develop his ideas. Here also he came into contact with the work on the stratigraphy of the North Somerset Coalfield by Lady Jones' uncle, John Strachey (mentioned above), whose own philosophical interests probably originated with his father's friend and neighbour in Pensford, John Locke. Smith's abilities soon attracted the attention of other colliery proprietors in the area, and in 1793 he was appointed to assist the engineer John Rennie in surveying the route of the proposed Somersetshire Coal Canal south of Bath and to carry out a country-wide fact-finding tour. Having prepared plans of deposit for the canal, published by the London mapmaker John Cary in 1795,[17] he was then engaged as Surveyor and Sub-engineer to the works under the Chief Engineer, William Bennet. It was from his observations during the cutting of the canal that Smith was able to establish the succession of strata, identified by the classification of fossils, and seek ways of recording them on a geological map.

However the opportunity to promote these discoveries did not come until the termination of Smith's engagement with the Canal Company in 1799, when he produced two geological maps of the vicinity of Bath; one (now lost) being drawn onto the northern section of Day & Masters' 1782 map of Somerset, the second drawn at a slightly larger scale onto a 1799 edition of Taylor & Meyler's *Map of Five Miles round the City of Bath*, derived from Thomas Thorpe's circular map.[18] Both were exhibited that year to the Bath and West of England Society, and by 1801 he had also completed a draft of the geology of the whole country on one of Cary's small-scale maps of England. Though his intention to publish a full geological map of England and Wales did not initially meet with great enthusiasm, in 1815

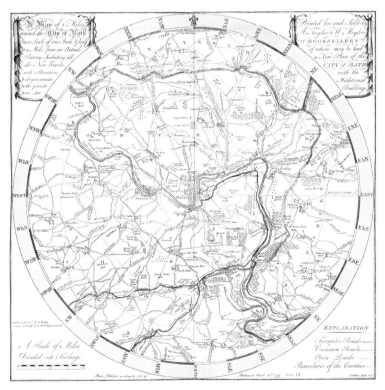

An 1800 edition of Taylor & Meyler's Map of *5 Miles round the City of Bath*, used by William Smith as the base for his first geological map of the vicinity of Bath. (*Bath Record Office, Bath & North East Somerset Council*)

his *Delineation of Strata of England and Wales with Part of Scotland* was eventually published by John Cary (*see Colour Plate VI*) on a specially prepared base map at five miles to the inch (1:316,800). A curious spin-off from Smith's work was a unique 'Fossilogical Map of the Country five miles around Bath' published in 1811 by his acquaintance Rev Richard Warner in his book *A New Guide through Bath and its Environs*. This, too, is based on one of Taylor and Meyler's *Five Mile* maps, but re-engraved by Gingell to show deposits in the area of the different classes of fossils identified by Smith.

From 1802 to 1804 Smith was in partnership with a fellow land surveyor, Jeremiah Cruse, taking premises in Bath at No.3 Trim Bridge to exhibit his fossils and, presumably, his maps. Cruse was employed as Clerk and Surveyor to the Marquess of Bath's estates, as well as producing local parish maps, such as those of Twerton (1807, now part of Bath), Hallatrow and Rode, but some of his work seems to have been derived from his association with Smith. He is credited, for example, with the large wall plan of the Somersetshire Coal Canal produced for the Company, c.1810, and in 1813 produced a map of the Cold Bath Farm Estate in Batheaston (site of Smith's unsuccessful exploration for coal there the previous year). It is interesting to note that Smith also worked with Masters, in 1811, when they and the Somersetshire Coal Canal engineer William Bennet were commissioned by Bath Corporation to survey the line of the proposed Bath to Bristol Canal (never built) to assess its impact on the city and environs. However, Smith's association with Bath came to an end in 1819, when, as a result of financial difficulties, he was forced to continue his career elsewhere as a mineralogist and hydraulic engineer.

Conclusion

By the mid-nineteenth century, a growing number of local surveyors like Thomas Chantrey and Jeremiah Cruse had established family firms in and around Bath, often working in partnership. In 1841 six land-surveying firms are listed in the directories, not to mention five building surveyors, three road surveyors and three 'street' surveyors. Most prominent of these 'dynasties' was the firm of Cotterell, apparently founded by Henry Fowler Cotterell in the 1820s. Cotterell started as an engineer, his most notable work being the horse-drawn Avon & Gloucestershire Railway known as the 'Dramway', completed in 1832, which carried coal from the Coalpit Heath to the River Avon near Keynsham. However, in the late 1830s, when large-scale maps of every parish were required by the Tithe Apportionment Survey, most of the parishes in the Bath area were surveyed by the Cotterell family,[19] usually in partnership with Thomas Cooper junior, operating from No.35 St James's Parade. In about 1849 Jacob Henry Cotterell, Henry Fowler's son, took over the firm and moved into new premises at No.6 Terrace Walk. Perhaps his most impressive work is a fine series of large-scale 1:480 manuscript map sheets of the city produced with Henry Spackman in 1852 for the Corporation, showing the water supply system (*see Colour Plate XII*). In the same year however he produced a *Plan of the City and Borough of Bath and its Suburbs* at eight chains to the inch (1:6,336), engraved by Hollway & Son of Union Street, and published by S. Hayward, bookseller in the Abbey Church Yard. Much of the information on this map was evidently acquired during the tithe surveys; administrative boundaries are accurately depicted, as are the field boundaries in the surrounding countryside. Although still orientated in traditional manner to the west, it was the first published map of Bath to show spot heights.

Soon after this, Cotterell went into partnership with Henry Spackman (apparently related to Charles Spackman, the eighteenth-century Bath property developer and patron of the painter Thomas Barker), and from hereon the firm became involved with architecture rather than mapmaking. Indeed, though the firm of Spackman continued as surveyors and land agents at Terrace

Jacob Henry Cotterell's 1852 *Plan of the City and Borough of Bath and its Suburbs.*
(*Bath Record Office, Bath & North East Somerset Council*)

Walk up to the 1950s, Jacob Henry's 1852 map turned out to be the last significant independent publication before the arrival in the early 1880s of the Ordnance Survey large-scale surveys at 1:2,500 and (in the city centre) at 1:500. Since then many interesting town guides have been published and local surveyors are still required, but technological advances in cartography and in the production of maps ensures that serious mapmaking is now the affair of the large organisation rather than the talented individual.

Further Reading
Anon., 'Old Plans and Views of Bristol', *Bristol and Gloucester Archaeological Society Journal*, vol.48, 1926.
Mowl, Tim & Earnshaw, Brian, *John Wood: Architect of Obsession*, Bath, Millstream Books, 1988.
Skelton, R.A., *Decorative Printed Maps of the 15th to 18th Centuries*, 2nd edition, London, Spring Books, 1965.
Smith, David, *Maps and Plans for the Local Historian and Collector*, London, Batsford, 1988.
Tyacke, Sarah & Huddy, John, *Christopher Saxton and Tudor Map-making*, London, British Library, 1980.

8: Trenches and Tunnels
Discovering Roman Bath

Marek Lewcun

Bath in the nineteenth century went through many changes in character and in prosperity, beginning with a time during which the country was at war with France and the local economy was dependent on its wide range of shops and industries surrounding a declining spa. Many builders and tradesmen were trying to recover from bankruptcies brought on by the collapse of the banks and other lenders after the outbreak of war in January 1793. The property boom of the preceding decade began with further expansion on the slopes of Lansdown, and accelerated with the laying out of the Pulteney Estate in Bathwick and John Eveleigh's London Road developments in the early 1790s. Together, large tracts of land had been developed, no doubt wiping away numerous archaeological sites in the process. What nobody could have predicted was the profound effect which the archaeological discoveries of the ensuing years would have on the city and its economic future, taking it into the twentieth century as not just one of the most important archaeological sites in Great Britain but one to which the nations of the world would come to marvel. However Bath is not just the Roman Baths. The Roman landscape was far greater, and this chapter seeks to explore the chronology of its nineteenth-century discovery in its wider context, beyond the centre of the town to which attention is normally concentrated. To do this requires a consideration of what was known at the turn of the new century but in the context of what is known today.

The Century Opens

From the writings of John Leland in the sixteenth century, and occasional finds made during the eighteenth-century rebuilding and expansion of the city, it was clear that much more awaited discovery. The finding of the bronze head of Sulis Minerva during the construction of a drain at the foot of Stall Street in 1727 pointed to the cult nature of the centre, and the discovery of what are now known as the East Baths in 1755[1] hinted at the nature of things to come. The present-day Pump Room opened soon after the start of the new century, during the construction of which the first tantalising glimpses of the temple of Sulis Minerva were seen. At the time it appeared that 'it will of course be for a long time covered from future excavation'[2] (it would in fact be nearly 200 years before it would again be seen). One of most important finds at the time was the magnificent gorgon's head centrepiece of the temple pediment, which has more recently been described[3] as one of the finest and most important in the Roman empire. Such was the interest in what had been found that the remains were to feature prominently in Samuel Lysons' *Reliquiae Britannico-Romanae*.[4] However, the amount which must have been destroyed and gone without record during much of the second half of the eighteenth century, during which John Wood the younger did not share his father's enthusiasm for the past, should not be underestimated. But from 1800 this was to change, with new attitudes to the buried history of the city and the advent of a new breed of antiquarians conscious of the importance of presenting their findings to a wider audience.

The Early Years: Discoveries in the Suburbs

The first half of the nineteenth century was dominated by scattered finds from the areas away from the city centre. Beyond the North Gate there was a history of finds before 1800. As early as 1803 the re-use of Roman stonework was observed during building work at the North Gate,[5] and in 1808 stone coffins were being discovered when trenches were dug for the foundations of a new house at St. Catherine's Hermitage, just behind Lansdown Crescent.[6] Not far away, Roman coffins were also found during the construction of St Stephen's church in 1840.[7] When extensions were being made to buildings in Russell Street in 1818 more stone coffins were found,[8] and when a sewer was being enlarged at the top of the street some years later at least eight further burials and the remains of what may have been a funerary monument were discovered.[9] What must have been found when the houses and basements of Russell Street and Rivers Street were first built between 1770 and 1773, let alone the other eighteenth-century buildings in that neighbourhood, can only be imagined.

To the west of the centre, burials were found during construction work for the gas works on the Upper Bristol Road in 1815,[10] and a large number of burials as well as structural remains during the building of Partis College in Newbridge between 1824 and 1827.[11] Closer in, the construction work between Norfolk Crescent and Norfolk Buildings in 1818 also led to remains being uncovered,[12] including a tessellated pavement or mosaic. In that year, Thomas Moore, the Irish poet and songwriter who lived in Bromham, near Devizes, recorded in his journal that 'a sort of Pompeii has been discovered at Bath – a great part of a Roman street or streets, and some remains of the houses.'[13] To the north-east of the centre in 1815, many finds, including not just burials but another tessellated pavement and further remains, were found at Walcot Methodist Chapel on London Street.[14] In the same year similar finds were made at the nearby Walcot Brewery.[15] Even as far out as Lambridge, burials were being recorded alongside the Fosse Way and the London Road in 1824.[16] On the Bathwick side of the river, finds have also been numerous, including a lead pig in 1809, and numerous burials – one in a lead coffin – were found between 1819 and 1823 on Bathwick Hill and at Sydney Buildings.[17] To the south of the centre, similar finds can be added.

Together, the finds in the first half of the nineteenth century paint a picture of an intensely utilised landscape, showing that not only had much been lost in the eighteenth century but that the back gardens and a few open spaces were ripe for further investigation. We are fortunate in having had the Rev H.M. Scarth to thank for drawing together many of these earlier discoveries, some of them through making enquiries with friends and colleagues. Scarth was an early member of the Somerset Archaeological and Natural History Society and, publishing between 1852 and 1886, his *Aquae Solis* of 1869 remains a useful gazetteer. More would be added to the suburban collection of finds in the second half of the century.

It is impossible to calculate the population of Bath at any one time during the Roman period, but over 350 years as a cult centre, tourist resort and the thriving town that supported it would have kept the funerary trade busy. Some of the more burials closer to the city centre probably date to the early period when the expansion of the built area had not been foreseen, whilst others clearly belong to a later period. Difficult to determine is whether or not any of the burials found slightly further afield, such as those along the Upper Bristol Road, belong to cemeteries set aside for the general populace. The problem lies with the fact that those reporting at the time tended to report the 'more interesting' finds such as the discovery of skeletons and coins. Unless a mosaic was found, old walls tended to go unreported, and consequently it is possible that the nineteenth century may well have seen more evidence of Roman development.

The Discovery of the Bathing Establishment

The existence of a bathing establishment at the heart of the city was known to the academic world at the beginning of the nineteenth century. It was in 1755, during the demolition of Abbey House to make way for the Duke of Kingston's Baths, that the area today known as the East Baths was found,[18] comprising a suite of warm and hot baths which had seen numerous transformations to meet the changing needs of the baths and their frequenters. Further details of these baths, plus small parts of three apses which would later be recognised as belonging to the Great Bath, were discovered below Abbey Passage and York Street between 1799 and 1803.[19] Nothing could prepare the city, however, for what would gradually emerge over the course of the ensuing decades. During building work in 1825 part of a hypocaust in what are now the West Baths was found,[20] but it was not realised at the time that together these belonged to a single, sprawling establishment. Bath was heading towards a low point in its economic history in the middle of the century, and anything that could improve things would be welcomed.

The first serious excavation undertaken in the baths, approached in a scientific and methodical manner, did not take place until 1867, when James Irvine, clerk of works for Sir George Gilbert Scott's restoration of Bath Abbey, found himself distracted to carrying out small excavations not only below the derelict *White Hart Hotel* in Stall Street but also at the south end of the East Baths.[21] Although the results of this early work were not published, here began the compilation of a superb archive of plans, cross-sections and notes which he made in successive years.[22] It was Major Charles Davis, the City Surveyor, however, who was to move things forward. Having discovered a little more of the West Baths in 1869,[23] it was in 1871[24] that in finding the steps and part of its lead-lined base he became the first person to expose the Great Bath at its north-west corner. This no doubt fired even further his desire to learn more of what existed there, but also widened the eyes of the Corporation to an opportunity to turn around the fortunes of the city. Sadly, with complaints about falling water levels in the Kingston Baths, he was forced to abandon any further work, but not without the foresight to first arch over the remains rather than fill them back in again.

It was not until 1878, after the acquisition of the Kingston Baths by the Corporation, that anything more was done. Great interest in the remains was aroused amongst the public, and subscriptions were made to enable the purchase of the various properties which covered the remainder of the bath and thus to permit a more open excavation.[25] Davis had not wasted any of his time, meanwhile, and had instead put builder Richard Mann to work, tunnelling around the east and north sides of the building which housed the Sacred Spring, which he was to investigate the following year. Numerous objects offered to the goddess were found during the process. By 1881 most of the Great Bath had been exposed, and for the first time the world could see what Bath had

Looking south down the more recently expanded tunnel (left) dug by Richard Mann in 1878 under the direction of Major Davis. The east wall of the temple precinct is on the far left, and the large masonry dominating the view is the buttress against the north wall of the vaulted building which housed the sacred spring. With this making further excavation problematic, a shaft (top right) was dug below the pump room in order to reach the other side before Mann proceeded to 'chase' the north wall to its west end, where a similar buttress was encountered. The original tunnels were dug in cramped, claustrophobic, steamy and poorly lit conditions. (*Photograph by the author*)

(*above*) A digger emerges from a trench excavated below the sixteenth-century Queen's Bath during its demolition in the early 1880s. It was here that the circular bath south of the sacred spring was found. (*Reproduced by courtesy of the Roman Baths Museum*)

(*right*) An unusual view of the Great Bath in the early 1880s viewed from behind the diving stone at the north-west corner, with buildings believed to be the offices of the Bath Poor Law Union still standing prior to their removal during excavations. (*Reproduced by courtesy of the Roman Baths Museum*)

to offer the archaeological world. Speaking at the evening meeting of the Somerset Archaeological and Natural History Society in August 1881, Jerom Murch, seven times mayor of Bath, summed up the year's achievements:

> Mr. Jerom Murch said he thought the meeting ought to be made aware how much, not only the city of Bath, but the archaeologists of Somerset, owed to Mr. Davis for these interesting dis-coveries. They had not been made in consequence of any precise commission given to him by the Corporation, but were the result of untiring energy and hard work, pursued in the face of many discouragements. The large baths which had been discovered occupied a space four times the size of the Abbey Church, and that would give them some idea of the extent of them, and also some idea of the grandeur of the buildings which the Romans constructed for bathing purposes.[26]

Another prominent local figure was also at the meeting:

> The Rev. Prebendary Scarth said he considered this was one of the most remarkable dis-coveries that had yet been made. This, he believed, was the finest system of baths that had been discovered in Britain, or perhaps, on the continent. There was nothing on this side of the Alps that had yet come up to it, with the exception of those found in Paris.[27]

Between 1883 and 1887 further investigations were carried out to the west, in the process uncovering the Circular Bath and the heated rooms to its west.[28] With what had been found earlier

A presentation by Major Davis, possibly to the Society of Antiquaries, in an empty Great Bath, which had been fully excavated and cleared by 1886. Davis is standing on the pillar to the left of the two ladies holding parasols, whilst a large crowd looks down from behind a fence on York Street. (*Reproduced by courtesy of the Roman Baths Museum*)

it was now realised that together, the Great Bath and the suites of hot and cold baths to its east and west, formed a single great bathing establishment attached to the sacred spring and Temple of Sulis Minerva. Much of Davis's later work went without the recording he was responsible for in earlier years, and it was in 1900, when Davis was absorbed in the construction of his lifetime's dream, the *Empire Hotel*, that Mann, with whom he had fallen out, was commissioned by the Society of Antiquaries to put together a record of the remains.[29]

Elsewhere within the City Walls

The walls as we know them were probably erected sometime in the third century. Here, however, their function would have been to protect not the working town but rather the temple, bathing establishment, public buildings and in particular the immense civil engineering work that had gone into containing the springs and the associated water supply and drainage works. If damaged in any great way, the repair of the latter would have faced a considerable amount of difficulty in an incessant flow of hot water. The Sacred Spring alone produces 250,000 gallons per day. Only piecemeal evidence of what lay beyond the baths in this walled area was found in the nineteenth century, leaving, just as today, large areas relatively unknown. That is not to say, however, that what was found was insignificant.

Early finds included an altar to Sulis Minerva from the Cross Bath in 1809[30] and a mosaic in Abbey Green in 1813.[31] The following year the first of a number of mosaics was found in the north-west part of the walled area, in the corner between Westgate Street and Bridewell Lane.[32]

Further mosaics were found at the top of Bridewell Lane in 1859 when the Blue Coat School was rebuilt and in the same year when the west end of the Mineral Water Hospital was extended.[33] Two mosaics were found here earlier, on the west side of the lane, in 1738.[34] Excavations on the east side of the lane in the 1990s[35] found no trace of structures, and may have gone down into the courtyards or gardens of a number of wealthy, high-status buildings that clearly exist here.

Amongst the best-recorded remains found within the walls during the nineteenth century are those made by Irvine when extensions to the Royal United Hospital were under construction between 1864 and 1866. Here, a number of buildings were recorded in some detail, and included a suite of heated baths.[36] In the following two years, Irvine was again busy below the *White Hart*

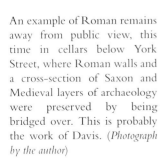

An example of Roman remains away from public view, this time in cellars below York Street, where Roman walls and a cross-section of Saxon and Medieval layers of archaeology were preserved by being bridged over. This is probably the work of Davis. (*Photograph by the author*)

Hotel where the ground was being cleared for the *Grand Pump Room Hotel*. Here, he was responsible for establishing the position of the rear edge of the temple podium as well as the colonnaded ambulatory surrounding its paved precinct, around which an early road had been diverted after its construction. Fragments of stone relating to a building of monumental proportions in the vicinity of the junction of Stall Street and Westgate Street were also found at this time.[37] Another building of some size, perhaps a theatre or other such public building, was found by Irvine below the Abbey during the restoration of 1867.[38] One of the last finds within the walls, besides those at the baths, was made on the site of the Weymouth House School in 1897, when yet another mosaic was uncovered.[39]

Beside the better known stretch of the City Wall itself, visible opposite the Mineral Water Hospital, a more significant stretch could be found in Lot Lane, just outside the East Gate. Scarth said of this site that the gate was medieval, 'but in the piece of wall running towards the Institution the older work could be perfectly traced'.[40] Sadly, and unusually for him, Davis destroyed without record in 1899 almost all but the smallest trace of what part of this lay in the way of his *Empire Hotel*. The only visible surviving is a short stretch below the front terrace, but investigations in the 1990s found that to the south much of the wall survives below the surface.[41]

More Discoveries in the Roman Suburbs: St Andrew's Church

This was one of the few suburban sites of which there are many records in the second half of the century, and again we have James Irvine to thank. The new church here on Julian Road, towering above the Royal Crescent, was destroyed in the blitz of 1942. During the excavations for its construction between 1870 and 1873 a large number of quite significant finds were made. These included, below the tower, a gravelled road heading towards the rear of Royal Crescent and, below the south porch and heading onto Crescent Lane, what he took to be the remains of a villa. At the north-east side of the church, more buildings were found to have encroached onto an earlier burial ground.[42]

The Surrounding Countryside

No work on the history of archaeology in Bath is complete without mention of the Rev John Skinner (1772-1839). He was an important figure in the study of local archaeology during the first quarter of the nineteenth century. Skinner was born in Claverton, where an abundance of well-preserved Bronze Age and Iron Age remains on his doorstep on the Claverton and Bathampton Downs must have been just one inspiration to his later study of all matters antiquarian. After graduating in Oxford, his Somerset birthplace became his first, albeit brief, curacy. After an even shorter stay in Brent Knoll he returned east and settled at Camerton, where he is best known as the keeper of his journal.[43] When he needed to retreat from the troublesome times of parish life he turned to archaeology, where an obsession with the possible origins of Tacitus's Roman Camolodunum at Camerton led to the creation of 98 volumes of manuscripts, filling three chests.[44] He was, however, to look at his childhood surroundings of Bathampton in some detail. Overlooking the city, the landscape here possessed a wealth of opportunity for study, and his early plans of this area,[45] the extent of which cannot be appreciated without a visit, were an immense achievement, despite the fact that so much more was left to survey. A later resident of Claverton, Colonel H.D. Skrine, succeeded his work and extended research onto the adjoining Claverton Down.[46] Skinner's interest did not stop on the skyline visible from the city below, but spread to the numerous villas and settlements that were set in the rolling hills of north Somerset, and thus he set up the contextual framework within which the city could be placed.

The Legacy

The emergence of scientific archaeology in Bath during the nineteenth century has provided an inspiring and invaluable legacy to the archaeologists of today, and will continue to do so for future generations. Gone, with one or two exceptions, are the days of merely chasing walls, and instead we find the likes of Skinner, Irvine, Davis and Mann making detailed records of what they found, with measured plans, elevations and detailed cross-sections of which many modern archaeologists would be proud. The legacy that they left twentieth-century Bath is perhaps unrivalled. The drawings by Mann are of superior quality, whilst the superb Irvine Papers, now preserved in Bath Central Library, bear testimony to the diligence of James Irvine, who recognised the value of both the written and drawn record and left the modern world an exceptional legacy. More than 100 years after his death they still provide an invaluable reference for modern archaeologists. Even at the time of writing, the archive is being used to prepare for investigative work below the former Royal United Hospital site on Beau Street, which is proposed for conversion to an hotel. It is now known that much of the archaeology here is preserved, contrary to earlier beliefs.

Albeit in a piecemeal way, determined partly by what building work was being undertaken, the excavators and recorders of the nineteenth-century city and its surroundings had demonstrated the true size of Roman Bath, and it was only at the end of the twentieth century that we found ourselves drawn back to some of those places excavated up to more than a hundred years ago. From the beginning of the new century we see the likes of the Bath Field Club investigating on the surrounding downlands.[47] In 1923 the East Baths were once more uncovered.[48] The 1950s saw the

The re-excavation of the East Baths by W.H. Knowles in 1923, with a sign pointing to their original discovery in the 1750s. This area of the baths was found when the range of the Abbey cloisters was demolished to make way for a new bathing establishment set up by the Duke of Kingston. The discoveries were recorded by Dr Charles Lucas and the architect John Wood the elder before the remains were once more covered over. The baths were finally incorporated into the museum after a full survey and additional minor excavation trenches by Sir Ian Richmond in 1954 (*Reproduced by courtesy of the Roman Baths Museum*)

Bath & Camerton Archaeological Society looking at sites such as London Road, where evidence of structures alongside the Fosse Way were found as far out from the city centre as below Snow Hill.[49] The 1950s saw Sir Ian Richmond digging at the Baths[50] and in the 1960s the Bath Excavation Committee and Sir Barry Cunliffe widening and extending the investigations of the baths and temple.[51] In 1979, exactly 100 years after Davis first descended into the Sacred Spring, we found ourselves going once again into its steamy depths, removing the deposits which he left untouched, and gaining a more complete understanding of the structures containing them.[52] Moreover, on Julian Road in 2002 and under the spotlight of national television, Bath Archaeological Trust returned to where, 130 years earlier, James Irvine had been working on the site of St Andrew's church.[53] It emerged that Irvine had inadvertently stumbled not upon an isolated villa but ribbon development not just along the Roman forerunner of Julian Road but along a spur of the Fosse Way which rises from a river crossing up to the plateau here. The Norfolk Crescent 'villa' might now be seen as just one of a number of more fashionable suburban buildings on that side of the town, and the recent discovery of another hypocaust below a house in New King Street lends weight to such a theory.

In the countryside, the pioneering work of Skinner on Bathampton Down continues to attract interest and attention. He was the first to recognise the importance of what is one of the best-preserved Iron Age and Roman landscapes in southern Britain. Today, his plans and those of his successors provide a useful springboard from which to examine the downs in closer detail, and in the early twenty-first century the curator of much of that landscape, The National Trust, commissioned a report that would add to Skinner's work.[54] Further barrows have been discovered and added to those in which he found such fascination. More farmsteads and villas have since been found within sight of the temple, and reveal an intensely managed landscape surrounding a bustling town of some size at the heart of which were hot springs which created a vibrant economy drawing not only from the remainder of Roman Britain but indeed the wider empire. On entering from any angle, especially the London direction, the Roman visitor would have taken some time to traverse the town or city. It is a greater distance across the site of Roman Bath than it is across many other 'small' or even larger towns of Roman Britain, or even the likes of Pompeii.

Sir (Charles) Leonard Woolley (1880–1960)

In any account of Bath's archaeological heritage, the Bath connections of the distinguished twentieth-century archaeologist Leonard Woolley[55] should be mentioned. Around 1920 he purchased *Uplands* on Bathwick Hill, sold in 1929/30 after his father's death. Best known for the excavations he directed at the Mesopotamian city of Ur[56] in 1922-34, he presented an exquisite pot from Ur to the Roman Baths Museum.

With his strong sense of public relations Woolley turned Ur into something of a tourist attraction, claiming it as the birthplace of the patriarch Abraham. He gave English names to the newly-excavated streets of the city, some of them such as Gay Street and Quiet Street perhaps derived from his familiarity with Bath.

The pot from Ur, about 25cm high, presented to the Roman Baths Museum by Sir Leonard Woolley. (*Photograph by David Mitchell*)

Conclusion

As this chapter shows, the nineteenth-century discoveries relating to Roman Bath stimulated some outstanding archaeological work at the time and provided a secure foundation for the worldwide reputation that the city now enjoys. Roman Bath also contributes substantially to the economic life of the city following construction of the Roman Baths Museum towards the end of the nineteenth century.

Further Reading

Cunliffe, B., *Roman Bath Discovered*, 2nd edition, London, Routledge & Kegan Paul, 1984

Cunliffe, B., 'Major Charles Davis, Architect & Antiquarian', *Bath History*, vol.i, Gloucester, Alan Sutton, pp.27-60

Davenport P., 'Archaeology in Bath. Excavations 1984-1989', *British Archaeological Reports*, no.284, Oxford, Bath Archaeological Trust, 1999

Scarth, H.M., *Aquae Solis, or Notices of Roman Bath*, London, Simpkin Marshall; Bath, R.E. Peach, 1864

Skinner, J., *Journal of a Somerset Rector, 1803-1834*, ed. H. & P. Coombs, Bath, Kingsmead Press, 1971

9: Providing Infrastructure
Bath and Civil Engineering

Angus Buchanan

Engineering, in the sense of the ability to design and build large and complex artefacts, is an ancient skill, being at least as old as human civilisations. But for most of its history there has not been sufficient continuity of work or security of employment in the skills of engineering to sustain a permanent body of practitioners and thus to provide the basis for a profession. Such conditions only emerged with the rapid spread of industrialisation in Britain in the eighteenth century, when the demand for mills, factories, and other industrial buildings, together with the infrastructure of transport systems and urban services, became sufficiently strong to call into existence a body of men who declared themselves to be 'civil engineers'. They chose this title to distinguish themselves from the military engineers, who had already acquired a role, albeit a fairly spasmodic one depending upon the duration of wars, in providing fortifications and supply services for the armed forces. The 'civil' type, however, concentrated on the engineering requirements of the new industrial society, and the most able amongst them quickly found it possible to develop a practice in which they undertook commissions for a variety of clients. In this chapter we will be considering the activities of civil engineers in Bath in the eighteenth and nineteenth centuries, excluding for treatment elsewhere local mechanical and electrical engineers such as Stotherts and Horstmanns.

John Smeaton (1724-1792)

John Smeaton, the son of a Leeds attorney, was amongst the first men in Britain to adopt the title of 'civil engineer'. He rose to fame with his successful construction of the third lighthouse on the Eddystone Rock in 1759, and went on to build many fine masonry arch bridges. He also improved the performance of water mills and steam engines, and undertook the construction of canals. He was elected FRS, and in 1771 established the 'Society of Civil Engineers', which later changed its name, in his honour, to the 'Smeatonian Society of Civil Engineers'. This body, which survives today as a select dining club of senior engineers, was not strictly a professional organisation, but it was the first gathering of engineers for social and convivial purposes. Inevitably, as its members met together and discussed matters of common professional interest, the Society came to have an influence on the way in which the new profession developed. It would be nice to be able to claim that Smeaton had made an engineering contribution to Bath, but his only visit to the city appears to have been in 1783, when he brought his sick wife in the hope that she would revive with the help of the spa facilities. He seems to have found the period of enforced idleness a strain, and was anxious to leave. But it is remarkable that, as an accomplished amateur astronomer, he might have enjoyed the company of William Herschel, who had made the observations that led to the discovery of the planet Uranus two years before. However, Herschel had already moved to Slough, and there is no record of the two men having met, so any such opportunity was missed.[1]

John Rennie (1761-1821)

Amongst the generation of young civil engineers who came to maturity immediately after Smeaton were two men who became giants of the new profession, John Rennie and Thomas

Telford, both of whom made their mark on Bath. Rennie came from a prosperous farming family in East Lothian and, having learnt the craft of a millwright, he assisted James Watt (1736-1819) in the construction of the Albion Mill, the first large steam-powered mill in London. He went on to become pre-eminent as a canal builder, and it was his work on the Kennet & Avon Canal (K&A) that brought him to Bath. This was one of the first cross-country canals, linking London with the Severn estuary, and was substantially larger than the narrow canals that had hitherto been built in Britain. It was 75 miles long from Reading to Bath, with 99 locks, including the seven originally built in the Widcombe flight. The canal was brilliantly engineered and had two dramatic masonry aqueducts at the western end where it twice crossed the River Avon, at Dundas and at Avoncliff. Rennie designed an ingenious pumping station at Claverton, moreover, with a broad-breast water wheel (still in working condition) providing power to two beam pumps to replenish the long level reach in the canal between Bradford-on-Avon and Bath. The approach to Bath was made in a cutting through Sydney Gardens, and the canal then descended to the River Avon at Widcombe.[2]

Claverton Pumping Station. Designed by John Rennie to provide water for the last long reach of the Kennet & Avon Canal, between Bradford-on-Avon and Bath, this was driven by a broad, low-breast wheel drawing water from the River Avon, in the low building on the right, with two beam-pumps in the main building raising water up to the canal, running along the top of the picture. (*Photograph by the author, 1965*)

This was not the first waterway improvement in Bath, as the River Avon had already been made navigable up to the city by the Avon Navigation, completed in 1727, with six locks in the 15 miles between Hanham and Bath, the last of which was in a short 'cut' at Weston to avoid the weirs in the river serving the local textile mills. The engineer for the Bath end of this scheme was John Padmore (fl.1710-1739), a clever but elusive figure who had also designed a 'Great Crane' in the port of Bristol, and the gravity-powered tramway from Ralph Allen's stone mines on Combe Down to Widcombe which has some claim to be regarded as the first railway in the world. Padmore was typical of many talented engineers in these years before the profession had taken shape, who picked up jobs erratically and rarely had the chance to share knowledge and experience with other operators.[3] Another such was William Smith (1769-1839), a land surveyor from Churchill in Gloucestershire, who went on to become a mining engineer and a canal engineer, designing the Somersetshire Coal Canal that joined the K&A at Dundas Aqueduct. He became famous as a pioneering geologist, the first person to understand that the succession of rock strata can be 'dated' by the fossils they contain. In this capacity he created the first geological map – it was a map of the Bath region, with the range of rocks in different colours.[4]

Rennie completed the K&A in 1810, and the link with the Avon Navigation meant that a busy traffic developed between London and the West Country, with Bath providing wharves for the barges in what became, for a time, a thriving inland port. He went on to build other canals and bridges, including the new London Bridge, replacing the ancient structure which had been the only river crossing in the capital for many centuries. He died before it was finished, and the work was completed by his sons in 1830. Rennie also served his profession well by nourishing the Smeatonian Society.[5] It remained a very select group of senior engineers, but it demonstrated effectively to others the benefits of such collegiate activity, so that a handful of junior engineers took the momentous step in 1818 of founding the Institution of Civil Engineers, welcoming into their membership anybody who could produce the credentials of a civil engineer. Two years later, they invited Thomas Telford to become their first President, and he accepted.

Thomas Telford (1757-1834)

Telford was four years older than Rennie, but it took him longer to establish his career. Like Rennie, he was another Scotsman, being the son of a Dumfriesshire shepherd who died soon after the child had been born. His mother struggled for many years to bring him up, but he benefited from the 'kirk school' that was a feature of every Lowland parish in Scotland and was able to gain an apprenticeship as a stone mason. Moving south to London in search of work, he made useful connections and was appointed a surveyor and architect in Shropshire. Then he moved into road and canal building and became a civil engineer, pioneering the use of cast iron in bridges and aqueducts. Despite the similarities of age and background, Rennie and Telford do not appear to have got on well, and it is possible that Rennie used his influence to keep Telford out of the Smeatonians.[6] If he did so, it had the unexpected result of turning Telford's interests towards the Institution of Civil Engineers, into which he poured an enormous amount of energy. Thanks to his efforts, the Institution received its Royal Charter in 1828, and he presented the 'Civils' with his library and other benefactions which ensured its rise in prestige to become the acknowledged mouthpiece of the profession. When Telford died in 1834, he was the doyen of his profession and he was honoured with a funeral in Westminster Abbey, where he was buried.[7]

Telford's best-known contribution to engineering history in the West Country is probably his participation in the competition for the Clifton Bridge in 1828-31, first as adjudicator and then, when he had criticised all the submissions, as a designer. His design, however, was deemed to be inappropriate and too expensive by the Bristol Merchant Venturers who had promoted the competition. They politely put it on one side, appointed new adjudicators, and re-examined some of the original submissions. From this complicated procedure, the young I.K. Brunel emerged as the winner in 1831, and he went on to design the bridge although it was not completed until after his death. As far as Telford was concerned, with only three years of life left to him, it was bound to be something of a snub, but it does not seem to have bothered him unduly. His reputation was already secure. What is not so well known is that he had another West Country venture in 1823 when the city of Bath invited him to advise them on flood prevention in the city.

Bath wrestled with the problem of recurrent flooding for many years until a thorough and determined effort to resolve it was made in the 1960s. The problem derived from the position of the city, in a narrow valley alongside a large river with a widely varied seasonal flow, but it was accentuated by the growth of the suburbs in closest proximity to the river, and by the increased run-off of rainwater as the buildings and roads spread out. Periodic attempts were made to relieve the problem, but they threatened to be expensive and the city fathers were reluctant to find the resources. This was the situation when Telford's advice was sought. He accordingly visited the city and submitted a report, saying that the masonry of the five-arch Old Bridge to the south of the city appeared to be sound but he recognised that its shape made it a potential obstruction and helped to cause the flooding. Further severe flooding caused him to be consulted again, and this time he proposed 'that a new cast-iron bridge, of one hundred and ten feet width of span, should be thrown across the Avon instead of the present stone bridge'. Nothing came of this proposal because the Corporation could not face the costs, estimated at £47,900, and Telford wrote stiffly withdrawing from the commission: 'I must therefore beg leave to decline proceeding further in this matter'.[8]

Bath Bridges

Whether or not they were stimulated by Telford's suggestion, there were a variety of schemes for iron bridges over the Avon in the following decade. Cleveland Bridge, in Bathwick, was built as a single-span cast-iron bridge in 1827, the span consisting of seven parallel segmented arches with lattice-work in the spandrels. It was designed by H.E. Goodridge (c.1800-1863), a local architect, and remains in heavy use, although it has been modified and strengthened on several occasions.

Cleveland Bridge. The first cast-iron bridge over the River Avon in Bath, built by H.E. Goodridge and opened in 1827. (Author's collection)

A very similar bridge was built over the Avon at North Parade in 1835, designed by William Tierney Clarke (1783-1852), a London engineer with impeccable credentials as a bridge builder. Like Cleveland Bridge it remains in use, but in 1936 the ironwork was completely encased in masonry so that it looks like a stone bridge. Then, in 1836, a competition to replace the Old Bridge that had been inspected by Telford, produced two remarkable designs: one by James Dredge, a local brewer, who devised an ingenious suspension pattern whereby all superfluous weight was removed from the bridge chains and platform; and the other by Thomas Motley, a Bristol engineer, which was strikingly innovative because it anticipated the 'cable-stay' design that has become so popular in modern bridges. Both were built, but neither of them replaced the Old Bridge, which continued undisturbed until it was replaced by the modern Churchill Bridge in 1966. Dredge's bridge, with a span of 139 feet and a width of 18 feet, was built as a footbridge close to Norfolk Crescent and survives as Victoria Bridge. Motley's bridge was built, also as a footbridge, at Twerton, with a span of 120 feet. It was demolished in 1894.[9]

(*above*) Twerton Bridge. Thomas Motley designed this bridge, which was built in 1837 and demolished in 1894. Its main novelty was the use of wrought-iron bars to carry the weight of the platform, as clearly shown in this contemporary print. (*Author's collection*)

(*left*) This remarkable archive photograph from the 1890s shows that Motley's design was faithfully carried out, although the detail is hard to see. It anticipates the 'cable-stay' type of suspension bridge that became very popular in the second half of the twentieth century. (*Bath in Time, Bath & North East Somerset Council*)

Victoria Bridge. This is the bridge designed by James Dredge in 1836. It survives as a footbridge near Norfolk Crescent, although the factory buildings behind it have now been demolished. (*Photograph by the author, 1968*)

Bath Roads

The roads of the nation were traditionally the responsibility of the local parishes, but municipal corporations like Bath took on this task within their boundaries. In the eighteenth century, however, many of the roads leading out of the city were leased out to Turnpike Trusts, which were empowered to raise capital for road improvement by imposing tolls on traffic using them. These Trusts developed in a rather haphazard manner, in Bath as elsewhere, undertaking their responsibilities unevenly. But they were an effective way of getting road improvement started, after many centuries of neglect. There was little professional guidance in techniques of road construction in the early days of the Trusts, but by the beginning of the nineteenth century, expertise had grown and a number of professional road-builders had emerged, amongst whom the family of John Loudon MacAdam (1756-1836) was outstanding. MacAdam made no pretensions to being a civil engineer, preferring to regard himself as a road surveyor, but he performed all the functions of an engineer in stipulating the design of his roads and supervising their construction. In 1815 he was appointed Surveyor General of the Bristol Roads, and ten years later he took on a similar role with the Bath Turnpike Trust. He and his sons were responsible for the significant improvements in the approaches to Bath on the London Road and elsewhere.[10]

I.K. Brunel (1806–1859)

The boom in road construction came to a sudden end in the 1830s with the advent of railways. By a curious coincidence, in the week after Isambard Kingdom Brunel[11] was appointed as engineer to the enterprise that became the Great Western Railway he was also called upon to adjudicate a dispute between a local Turnpike Trust, the Black Dog Trust, responsible for the new road up the Limpley Stoke valley, and the Kennet & Avon Canal. He recorded in his diary that he called 'at McAdams' on the morning of Monday 11 March and walked along the canal with 'Mc & Son', which probably meant William, the son of John Loudon, and his son, also called William, as they were acting on behalf of the Black Dog Trust. At Claverton they met John Blackwell (c.1775-1840), the canal engineer, described by Brunel as 'a bigotted obstinate practical man', and lawyers and surveyors representing various interested parties. The dispute concerned the proximity of the proposed road to the canal in a narrow stretch of the valley notorious for land-slipping difficulties. The precise nature of Brunel's judgment is not known, but the road went ahead and the canal was obliged to recognise its presence. It seems likely that he might have been influenced by this experience to avoid the Limpley Stoke valley in deciding to take his new railway through the Box Tunnel and the Vale of the White Horse rather than following the route chosen by Rennie for the canal along the Kennet valley to Reading. The latter link was indeed made within a few years, but by that time the canal was already struggling in competition with the railway, and was soon taken over by the GWR. It is curious, however, to find the representatives of road, canal and rail meeting in this cameo discussion at the dawn of the railway era.[12]

A week before this episode, on 4 March 1833, Brunel had been appointed as engineer to the projected railway from London to Bristol. He was not yet 27 and had no previous experience of railway building. But he was a hugely talented young man, and had already established himself as an engineering leader of some flair as assistant to his father, Marc Isambard Brunel (1769-1849), on the Thames Tunnel project. Work on the tunnel, however, had been suspended in 1828 when the River Thames had broken in and the Company had run out of resources, and the young Brunel had looked around for other enterprises. This is how he had come to be involved in the Clifton Bridge competition, in which he had successfully challenged the judgment of Telford and been given the commission to build the bridge. This had brought him into contact with a lively group of Bristol businessmen and entrepreneurs, who turned to Brunel first to improve their port facilities, and then to build their trunk railway and their steamships.

Brunel thus established close relationships with the West Country, which endured for the rest of his life. He came to know Bath well, canvassing William Beckford, the fabulously rich eccentric antiquarian of Lansdown Crescent, for support for his Clifton Bridge submission in 1830, and staying frequently at Bath inns in the course of his railway engagements. His mother had relatives in Chilcompton, ten miles south of Bath, where she and Marc Brunel spent a holiday in 1843, when I.K. Brunel was busy with the launch of the *S.S. Great Britain* in Bristol.[13] But by far his most important connection with Bath was the fact that he made it a major stop on his railway from London to Bristol. The line entered the Avon valley at Bathford and swept into the city through Bathampton, where it came alongside the Kennet & Avon Canal, although some 40 feet lower. Like Rennie with the canal, Brunel cut a slice through Sydney Gardens, although unlike Rennie he capitalised on this by taking the opportunity to display the railway to visitors in the park. To this day, the trains can be watched as they glide across the 'stage' set up by the engineer against a handsome 'back-drop' of masonry. The line then swings westwards in a pronounced curve on a viaduct over the River Avon and into Bath Spa station (*see Colour Plate X*).

The site chosen for the station placed it discreetly outside the ancient city of Bath, from which it maintained a respectful but comfortable distance. The station was in the southward bend of the river, so that having crossed it to reach the 'down London' platform the line then re-crossed the river as it made its exit towards Bristol. A long viaduct, castellated and faced with Bath stone towards the city led out to Oldfield and then, after a short cutting, another viaduct passed through the once separate village of Twerton, now in the course of being fully absorbed as the industrial suburb of Bath. In the middle of the nineteenth century, Twerton was dominated by Carr's textile factory, a multi-storeyed mill drawing water-power from the Avon. The proprietors of this mill, the Carrs, lived in a large house in woodland adjacent to the village, appropriately called 'Wood House', and in driving his line through their garden Brunel buried it in a short 'cut and cover' tunnel before plunging into the Twerton Tunnel under the wood itself, and so on its way down the Avon valley to Bristol. He did not show similar deference to the other citizens of Twerton, whose access to the river was disrupted and whose main road was realigned.[14]

The passage of the Great Western Railway through Bath was only a short section of the whole route from London to Bristol, but it demonstrated Brunel's confident mastery of the engineering problems in placing the line well above the flood level of the river while making the most of the opportunities for some architectural flamboyance in the presentation of the stations, the viaducts,

Skew Railway Bridge, Bath. The Great Western Railway entered Bath Spa Station from Bristol by a skew-bridge over the River Avon, which I.K. Brunel designed in composite arches of laminated timber, faithfully drawn in this lithograph of J.C. Bourne from the 1840s. (*Author's collection*)

the tunnels, and the bridges, as well as the display in Sydney Gardens. Every detail of the railway bore the print of the master, from the broad gauge of seven feet which he persuaded his directors to adopt in the interests of maintaining consistently high speeds, even though it was not in harmony with the national standard gauge, to the splendid broad gauge locomotives, the distinctive rolling stock, the unique signalling system, and the decorative flourishes on the stations and their furniture. Nothing escaped Brunel's attention, and he insisted on supervising every aspect of the railway system for which he took full responsibility. The line was opened throughout in 1841, and there can be no doubt that Bath received an outstanding railway service in the GWR that made a strong but unobtrusive contribution to the urban landscape.

Other Railways
Other railways subsequently reached Bath, the Midland Railway and the Somerset & Dorset Railway sharing for a time a second railway station. These lines have now closed, but the building remains as Green Park Station, its glazed arched roof sheltering a useful range of functions. The GWR itself acquired important additions, with the line continuing beyond Bristol to Exeter, to Plymouth, and eventually to Penzance. Subsidiary lines were developed, such as the link through the Limpley Stoke valley with Westbury and the 'direct' route from Reading to Exeter, and on to the seaside at Weymouth. After Brunel, many other engineers contributed to the extension and maintenance of the system, but few of them made much impact on Bath. Amongst those who did were Daniel Gooch (1816-1889, baronet 1866) who designed the broad-gauge locomotives for the GWR; and T.E.M. Marsh (1818-1907), the assistant who carried out the excavation of the Roman villa at

Newton St Loe for Brunel, when it was encountered on the main line of the GWR. Marsh remained in the district and developed his own practice as an engineer, being consulted about the replacement of the Widcombe footbridge behind Bath Spa station, the original having collapsed into the river in 1877. Large metal plates commemorate Marsh's contribution to this wrought-iron girder bridge, still in regular use.[15]

The death of Brunel in 1859, coinciding as it did within a year with the deaths of Robert Stephenson (1803-1859) and Joseph Locke (1805-1860), marked an abrupt change in the character of British civil engineering. With the 'Railway Triumvirate' removed from the scene, it seemed that the 'Heroic Age' of British engineering had come to an end. It was not that the profession became less important: on the contrary, many more engineers were trained and came into practice. But they became more specialised, so that instead of ranging like Brunel over railway, tunnel, bridge and ship building – or like Robert Stephenson over railway, bridge and locomotive building – the engineers became increasingly limited to one or other of several distinct specialisms. The first of these was mechanical engineering, which had existed happily as part of civil engineering until 1847, but then the growth of the railway systems encouraged the creation of a new Institution of Mechanical Engineers to cater for these specialist interests. This was followed in the second half of the nineteenth century by an impressive range of specialist Institutions, catering for electrical engineers, gas engineers, naval engineers, marine engineers, mining engineers, metal-working engineers, municipal engineers, water engineers, structural engineers and so on. Many of these new professional groups, who continued to regard themselves as 'civil' engineers as distinct from 'military', had an impact on Bath.[16]

Another aspect of the comparative anonymity of engineers since 1860 is the fact that increasing specialisation has been accompanied by greater emphasis on a scientific understanding of the problems involved, which has meant more theoretical or academic instruction. It is no longer possible, as it was in the Heroic days of British engineering, to learn one's practice on the job by a form of apprenticeship. Instead, it became necessary to acquire academic qualifications before one could expect to be considered for a post. So while the profession of engineering has grown and flourished, the impact of individual engineers has diminished. The Second World War brought large numbers of Naval and Ministry of Defence personnel to Bath, including some leading members of the Royal Corps of Naval Constructors. When the city acquired a University in 1966, it brought with it from Bristol able teams of senior mechanical, electrical and aeronautical engineers, but not initially civil engineers. These were eventually accommodated in the School of Architectural Studies and, in the person of Sir Edmund ('Ted') Happold (1930-1996) produced at least one structural engineer of international distinction.[17]

Water Control and Public Services

Civil engineers played an important role in providing public services for the city. Bath had traditionally relied upon the abundant local springs for its supply of fresh water, but as the city grew it became necessary to provide water works, with catchment reservoirs north of Batheaston and cisterns for distributing the water on Claverton Down and elsewhere, with many miles of water mains supplying it to homes in the city and its expanding suburbs. Concurrently, foul water was removed through a network of sewers, originally discharging into the river but then channelled to the sewage works established in Saltford.[18] A gas works to supply coal gas was built at Locksbrook in 1818, and gas mains quickly extended to carry this service throughout the city. Writing his *Historic Guide to Bath* in 1864, Rev G.N. Wright observed: 'The works are near to Brook's Lock, a judicious site, both for the discharge of foul water, and evaporation of effluvia, at a sufficient distance from the city'.[19] The growth of the city around the gas works made the choice of site seem less 'judicious', but it flourished and continued to send a barge full of coal tar down the Avon to Butlers in Bristol every week until coal gas production ended in the 1970s. An electricity supply was installed in 1890, when H.G. Massingham, an entrepreneur and electrical engineer, acquired the site between Old Bridge and the GWR station to build his boiler room and generators. This remained in operation until 1966, the site now being cleared to make space for the new bus station.[20]

The River Avon continued to present engineering problems, and after suffering recurrent flooding of the River Avon into the middle of the twentieth century, the problem was tackled systematically by Frank Greenhalgh when he became Engineer to the River Avon (Bristol) Catchment Board in 1953, although it took another disastrous flood in 1960 finally to focus attention on the need to do this. Work started in 1963 and was completed ten years later, when it won a Civic Trust Award in 1973 for its success with dredging, sheet-piling, and renovation of the weirs and sluice gates.[21]

Conclusion

Posterity has recognised the importance of the contribution made to society by all these modern civil engineers, but it has been less kind towards individuals. Engineers have come to be so useful to the community that, paradoxically, they have been taken for granted. Their work is all around us in the fabric of the city and its infrastructure of transport and other services, but they no longer astonish us in the way that James Watt, Thomas Telford or I.K. Brunel dazzled their contemporaries with their great works. The Heroic Age of Engineering may be over, but the need for good engineers is greater than ever.

Further Reading

Buchanan, R. Angus, *The Engineers: A History of the Engineering Profession in Britain 1750-1914*, London, Jessica Kingsley, 1989

Buchanan, R. Angus, *Brunel, The Life and Times of I.K. Brunel*, London, Hambledon, London, 2002

Buchanan, R. Angus, 'The Bridges of Bath', *Bath History*, vol.iii, Gloucester, Alan Sutton, 1990

Buchanan, R. Angus, 'Brunel in Bath', *Bath History*, vol.x, Bath, Millstream Books, 2005

Buchanan, R. Angus, 'The Floods of Bath', *Bath History*, vol.vii, Bath, MillstreamBooks, 1998

10: Machines and Industry
Engineering and Invention in Bath

Stuart Burroughs

While Bath's commercial development has traditionally been associated with the service industries, particularly those concerned with the city's function as a tourist resort, these business concerns have often obscured a thriving manufacturing sector. Over the centuries this sector has, at times, been more visible and obvious, for example during the Middle Ages when the production of fine quality woollen cloth made Bath internationally famous, or during the nineteenth and twentieth centuries when printing and engineering employed thousands.

It was the acceleration of commercial activity in manufacturing, transport and other sectors nationwide in the eighteenth century that virtually invented the new skill of engineering. While this process of business development was countrywide, a particular combination of local conditions in Bath created new opportunities for engineers and inventors.

Between 1700 and 1765 Bath had become a fashionable resort during this period and had grown at an astonishing speed. Its resident population tripled and during the rest of the century nearly tripled again. By 1800 it was larger than Leicester, Nottingham and Coventry, and welcoming 40,000 visitors each year. The exploitation of these visitors ensured a boom in service sector employment such as retailing and domestic service and, whether resident or tourist, all needed accommodation, stimulating a building boom.

The transport of building materials, whether from near or far, would need to be efficient and effective if the supply was to keep up with the insatiable demand of the construction industry. Such material included bricks, floorboards, and most importantly building stone. In this regard Bath was doubly blessed. An easily worked limestone, Bath stone, was not only close by, extracted from the hillsides to the south of the city, but its use had been officially sanctioned by architectural fashion. Improvements to the transport infrastructure followed in the wake of the city's growth including work to roads, river, the construction of an artificial river – the Kennet & Avon Canal – and John Padmore's stone-carrying carriageway.

In addition there was a need for other materials from which a Bath townhouse, whether grand or humble, might be manufactured. These included metal goods for railings or fire grates, cooking stoves or drainpipes. In addition to 'fitting out' a house there was the subsequent need for the furniture to make a house a home. As a result, during the second half of the eighteenth century the cabinet-making industry and the metal-working and metal-supplying trades flourished. Many businesses established during the city's 'economic miracle' – from the early 1700s to the 1790s – would grow to become the manufacturing giants of the nineteenth and twentieth centuries. Invention would follow close behind the business of serial and mass production.

The existence of a thriving manufacturing sector in engineering in turn created a trained workforce, many of whom left their employers after apprenticeship to try to make their own way in the world by establishing their own businesses. This 'chain reaction' was a characteristic of Bath as much as any other commercially vibrant city in the nineteenth and twentieth centuries. Whilst some would fail, others such as Joseph Day who had been apprenticed at Stothert & Pitt, would have qualified success. The precision engineering firm established by Roland Cross, apprenticed at the Bristol Aeroplane Company, is still flourishing.

The combination of those commercial characteristics particular to Bath with those affecting the entire country from the eighteenth century onwards are the backdrop against which the following accounts of invention and innovation are played.

John Harington and the Water Closet

To start, however, we must consider the case of an aristocratic inventor. His invention was never commercially exploited, not that there was a market, and was pursued more as a gentleman's hobby than as a business. Nevertheless the originality of the device and the ubiquity of its descendants make it worthy of inclusion.

John Harington (1561-1612) is credited with the development of what we would now consider an essential device for healthy living – the flushing water closet. Harington was born in 1561 at Kelston Manor, a few miles west of Bath, and was Queen Elizabeth I's godson. In 1596 his publication *A New Discourse of a Stale Subject, called the Metamorphosis of Ajax* appeared, in which he suggested the design of a simple water closet, or as he called it, 'a privy of perfection'. Resembling, in many respects, the design of a modern flushing lavatory, a high-level water tank was emptied to flush an open pan below. The pan was flushed into a vault at a much lower level. 'Privies' placed over running water had been used since Roman times, but the principle of a device that could be installed away from running water, in the home and operated through a refillable water tank, was a new idea. No detailed description is given as to how the tank might be refilled but it must be assumed that it was done manually.[1]

There was one drawback to any widespread installation of Harington's privy and that was the lack of any sewerage system which could remove what was euphemistically referred to as 'flow' from the lower vault. Harington suggested to anyone adventurous enough to adopt his device to 'always remember that at noon and at night empty it [the vault] and leave it half a foot deep of fair water'. Despite this drawback this simple device made Harington quite famous though he himself said that 'but to conclude this is, in a few words, but a close stool easily emptied'.

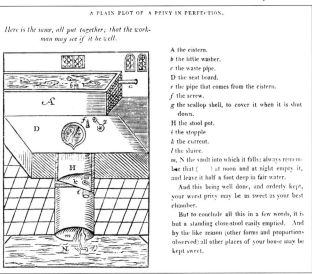

John Harington's water closet assembled. (*from* A New Discourse of a Stale Subject, called the Metamorphosis of Ajax, *published in 1596*)

Aside from this invention, Harington's military career and time as a member of the royal court were chequered and he died in 1612 aged 51. Whether he ever proposed his water closet to be widely adopted is unlikely; more probably he intended that the aristocracy might install one, such as Harington had himself at Kelston, as an interesting novelty. Certainly flushing water closets were neither widely installed nor Harington's design improved upon until the eighteenth century and the name 'water closet' does not appear until 1755. Few Bathonians (or for that matter inhabitants of Kelston) would have used or even seen a flushing water closet until mass production of ceramic sanitary ware in the nineteenth century.

Allen and Padmore

Ralph Allen, whose business interests included stone mines and quarries on Combe Down, south of Bath, had invested heavily in improvements to the River Avon during the 1720s. The Avon Navigation Company had undertaken structural works along the river between Bath and Bristol, bypassing the river weirs which greatly reduced the time taken to ship goods in or out. After its completion in 1727, Allen used the 'navigable' river to send his stone to Bristol for distribution onwards by coastal traffic around the country. The problem was how to transport the stone from his hilltop quarries and mines to his riverside wharves, a distance of 1½ miles with a fall of 500 feet.

John Padmore's tramway as built for Ralph Allen.
(*Bath Record Office, Bath & North East Somerset Council*)

John Padmore (fl.1710-1739), a celebrated Bristol engineer, was engaged by Allen to build a tramway to carry the stone on iron-wheeled waggons which would descend to the river by gravity and would then be hauled back empty to the mines by horse. Allen and Padmore would have been aware of the use of horse-hauled tramways in the Newcastle coalfields. Allen's gravity tramway, however, which opened in 1731, was the first of its kind in the country. It greatly reduced the cost of transporting the stone and was of considerable interest to visitors to the city. Padmore also devised two 'rat tail' cranes, considered advanced for the time in using cast-iron components, at Allen's Widcombe wharf where the stone was loaded aboard barges. Within a few years 1,800 tons of Bath stone a year were being transported.

In 1734 the tramway was described by a visiting science lecturer:

> There is a fine contrivance of an inclined waggon way made of timber to bring down stone in waggons which come down the declivity on the artificial way by their own gravity as the coal carriages do at Newcastel (*sic*). But this being much altered for the better and the carriages themselves contrived to carry much more weight without danger.[2]

Unfortunately Padmore's tramway was dismantled after Allen's death in 1764 although the route can still be traced as it followed the line of the present Ralph Allen's Drive in Widcombe.

Bath's Ironmasters

To find the historic roots of one of the city's most accomplished engineering firms in the elegance of Georgian Bath may seem surprising, yet the rapid growth of the city, and its construction industry, had created a great demand for all manner of structural and decorative metalwork. In such circumstances an ambitious and practical ironmonger could flourish.

George Stothert (1755-1815) had taken control of an ironmonger's business in 1785 in Horse Street (now part of Southgate Street) and as well as selling materials to contractors he employed his own craftsmen. For example, in 1786 he employed smiths, braziers, tinmen and plane makers. Stothert was sole agent in the Bath area for the goods of Abraham Darby's Coalbrookdale Company.[3]

As early as 1785 Stothert was also dabbling in invention. He had developed a ventilator which was fitted to the 'perpetual stoves' (those in which a fire was kept burning continuously) and ovens he was supplying to local homes. In particular his ventilator was advertised as being fitted to 'Register Stoves with air pipes for warming rooms on the same principle as the late Sharp's'.[4]

During the building of the Kennet & Avon Canal through Bath in the 1790s Stothert supplied iron castings to the value of over £1,000 – a sizeable sum at the time. Two iron footbridges, supplied from Coalbrookdale but erected by Stothert, were installed in Sydney Gardens. By 1815 the business was not only supplying iron goods but making them as well, at a foundry in Horse Street, including two further bridges for the canal. By 1827 the firm of Messrs Stothert was advertising itself as 'Furnishing ironmongers to his Majesty'.[5]

By the 1840s the firm's business in supplying the civil engineering and transport industries was eclipsing its domestic market. Providing contractors' and cargo-handling equipment, at home and abroad, would sustain the firm for 150 years, right up to the 1980s. Products from this period include water pumps and building and lifting equipment. The market for these goods expanded enormously with the railway building boom, the improvement to roads, and the upgrading or rebuilding of canals, bridges and ports.

In 1844 Robert Pitt (1818–1886) became a partner and the firm became Stothert & Pitt. When the Great Western Railway was built through Bath in the 1840s Stotherts probably supplied contractors' equipment, and in 1851 exhibited a hand-operated crane at the Great Exhibition in London.

By the 1890s the company was operating from two large sites along the Lower Bristol Road and manufacturing large cargo-handling and construction cranes. One type of crane, the Titan, was used in the building of artificial harbours and could lift loads of up to 50 tons whilst 'block setting'. Another type, the Goliath, was made in sizes capable of lifting up to 220 tons!

An early steam crane built by Stothert & Pitt in 1867. (*Museum of Bath at Work*)

A Stothert & Pitt steam crane aboard a steam lorry in 1905. (*Museum of Bath at Work*)

As well as supplying cranes for dock, deck or building sites, the company also manufactured cement mixers and in 1928 supplied two enormous mixing and distributing towers used in building the Metur Dam in India. Each tower weighed 1,400 tons and each could deliver 2,000 tons at a time.[6]

Cranes remained the most important part of the company's output. In 1912 Claude Toplis, chief designer at the firm, suggested an improvement that was widely adopted by other crane manufacturers. Toplis's invention was an improvement for the 'level luffing' of cargo cranes at docks.[7] This allowed the height of the load being transferred from ship to shore (or vice versa) to remain absolutely level, regardless of the angle of the crane jib. This required an intricate system of compensating cables but the installation of such a system greatly reduced the time taken in moving goods. The principle could also be used to ensure that lifeboats remained level while being lowered. After the war a host of developments

Deck crane as supplied by Stothert & Pitt to Harland & Woolf for loading holds aboard their 'Titanic' class steam liners, showing Toplis's levelling mechanism. Two such cranes went down on the *RMS Titanic* in April 1912. (*Museum of Bath at Work*)

to cranes, including the tubular steel DD2 design, won various awards for the firm's design department.

In 1920 Ernest Feuerheerd's highly effective rotary displacement pump went into production with Stothert & Pitt as sole licensees.[8] This pump became the standard design in the company and was still in production when the firm closed in 1989. In the late 1940s the Vibroll road roller was the company's response to the great post-war road and motorway building boom.

Although the company flourished throughout the twentieth century supplying docks and building sites across the world, it closed in 1989.

Internal Combustion

While the steam engine was being developed and improved throughout the late eighteenth and nineteenth centuries it had long been thought that an engine might be driven by the burning of high-energy fuel inside a closed cylinder. It was not until 1876 however that a reliable motor was developed by a German merchant Nicholas Otto. Otto had devised what is now known as the 'four-stroke cycle' of operation in which an engine burning a gas/air mixture admits a charge of fuel, compresses it, burns it and expels the burnt gas. After these four operations, or strokes, the cycle begins again.

Until 1890, when the patent expired in the UK, inventors attempted with varying degrees of success to evade Otto's monopoly by proposing alternatives.[9] In 1883 Bath engineer Samuel Griffin proposed a radical alternative design to that of Otto. In addition to the four strokes of the Otto cycle, Griffin suggested two extra operations drawing in a 'charge' of fresh air and then expelling it. The idea, claimed Griffin, was to cool and completely clear the cylinder, though in practice this was a clear attempt to circumvent the Otto patent.[10] However, with only one working stroke (the ignition operation) in every six, Griffin's engine was less efficient than Otto's, which had a power stroke in every four. Griffin was nevertheless ahead of his critics. His engine was conceived to be 'double-acting', that is to say fuel would be burnt at both ends of the cylinder working on a shared piston alternately. While common practice in steam engines, this was

The maker's plate for Samuel Griffin, dated 1881.
(*Museum of Bath at Work*)

little used in gas fuel engines at the time. Although Griffin's six-stroke engines were prone to overheating they ran steadily and were ideal for water pumping or driving electrical dynamos. In 1886 Griffin sold the rights to his invention to Dick, Kerr & Co of Kilmarnock who marketed the engines as 'Griffin' or 'Kilmarnock' engines until the early 1900s.[11]

Griffin established the Griffin Engineering Company with the proceeds of the sale of his invention and from a new factory in Oldfield Park manufactured a range of patented oil and petrol engines for both stationary and marine use. He died in 1929.[12]

Another innovator, Joseph Day (1855-1946), after an apprenticeship at Stothert & Pitt, patented his simplified two-stroke engine in 1892 from his engineering works at Bathwick.[13] In Day's engine a gas/air charge was burnt in every revolution of the crank of the engine – i.e. two strokes rather than every four.[14] The engine was designed to be simple and easy to use. Fuel was compressed at one side of a piston moving in a vertical cylinder; it was then directed to the other side where the fuel was burnt. The movement of the piston ejected the exhaust after burning, while drawing in fuel at the same time for the next cycle. This highly simplified engine used only one valve to admit the fuel, and with one ignition every revolution of the crank, the engine gave a very steady and regular output. But despite the obvious advantages Day had difficulty in marketing the engine. This, together with his involvement in other, less certain financial schemes resulted in his bankruptcy in 1894 and the closure of his Victoria Iron Works in the same year. With no choice but to raise funds to clear his debts, Day sold the rights to manufacture the engine to a number of licensees and eventually retired to Weston-super-Mare, where he died in 1946.

Roland Cross (1895-1970) had been part of the design team for the Bristol Fighter at the British & Colonial Aeroplane Company in Bristol. After the First World War, Cross invented a rotary

A Cross motorcycle engine fitted with a rotary valve and patent Cross cylinder. (*Museum of Bath at Work*)

valve petrol engine which could be adapted for motor car, motorcycle or even aero engines. In a conventional internal combustion engine the admission of fuel and the exhaust of burnt gas are achieved by using lifting valves. In Cross's rotary valve engine, such valves were replaced by a single revolving cylinder that admitted fuel and expelled the exhaust in a single movement.[15] Cross set up a company to develop and market his invention in 1938, but as there was little money for development Cross undertook consultancy work on the pasteurisation of milk using ultra-violet light, the transport of awkward loads by ship, and a novel design of lavatory cistern!

By the mid-1930s his experimental rotary valve engines had been refined and tests on motorcycles and motorcars were going well. The engines ran faster, and at higher temperatures and pressures, than conventional engines which consequently made them more efficient under test. However, conventional cast-iron piston rings (used to seal the engine cylinder from the moving piston) were brittle and broke. Cross then devised a method of making high-performance piston rings from steel wire and this process of manufacture is still used at Cross Manufacturing Company to this day. Although the company company no longer makes rotary valve engines, at least two companies make high-performance model aircraft that use the Cross type of rotary valve. The piston ring-making process Roland Cross devised could be employed to make rings in other metals such as the 'super alloys' used in gas and steam turbines. Today many jet engines powering civil and military aircraft all over the world have parts designed and manufactured by the company at factories in Bath and in Devizes.[16]

Time and the Horstmanns

In many ways clock and watch makers were the ancestors of the modern precision engineer. From the Middle Ages these craftsmen refined the skills of working with complex mechanisms, in different metals, in varying environmental conditions, to keep good time.

Gustav Horstmann (1828-1893), an experienced and medal-winning watchmaker had left his native Westphalia in 1854 and by 1856 was trading in Bath from premises in Bennett Street.[17] By the 1860s he had established a flourishing business, and in 1866 patented a heat-driven motor, later known as the Horstmann Thermo-Auto Motor, designed to power domestic clocks.[18]

The design involved the use of a system of sealed pipes and a cylinder containing a volatile liquid such as alcohol. As the ambient temperature changed, so too the pressure in the cylinder would fluctuate as the liquid within was affected. The changing pressure, whether rising or falling, was intended to drive a system of gears which in turn could be used to wind the clock. Sadly, the device proved a failure as the movements of the piston were not sufficiently powerful to drive the clock winder.

When Gustav Horstmann died in 1893 his sons inherited a successful business, but although they continued to repair and make timepieces it was in the field of industrial clocks and motorcars that the family business would prosper in the future. In 1902 Sidney Horstmann (1881-1968), Gustav's youngest son, devised an automatic gearbox for motorcars which so impressed his brothers that a company, the Horstmann Gear Company, was established to market it. Unfortunately the gearbox could not be made to work. However, three of the older brothers had devised an industrial clock and, rather than winding the gearbox company up, they utilised the name to market this completely new product.

Portrait of Gustav Horstmann, c.1890.
(*Museum of Bath at Work*)

The patented clock, which first appeared in 1905 advertised as the Horstmann Auto-Equation clock, had been devised originally for the accurate control of the lighting and extinguishing of gas street lamps.[19] Previously street lighting could be controlled either by employing lamplighters who manually lit or extinguished the lamps at predetermined times, or by the use of a simple clock that supplied or interrupted a supply of gas rather in the way an alarm clock tells the time and rings a bell. As the time of sunset and sunrise varies according to the time of year, these early clocks (or the lamplighters!) had to be reset at regular intervals, sometimes daily, to avoid the lamps being lit at the wrong time. The Auto-Equation clock automatically reset itself during the course of a year through a series of compensating gears and allowed the 'self setting' of the mechanism controlling the supply of gas. An extra feature allowed the clock to extinguish the lights at sunrise, which of course also varies. Over succeeding decades the company developed a range of precise timekeeping and controlling devices, but it was this first clock which ensured the company's international success. By 1907 the clock was being marketed as the Solar Dial Compensator and until the expiry of the first patent the company dominated the international trade in automatic street-lighting control.

The Improved Horstmann Solar Dial Compensator. (*Museum of Bath at Work*)

In 1915 a new factory was opened at Newbridge. By the 1920s an electrically driven time control had been developed, removing the need for anything other than routine maintenance. Through two world wars the company diversified into the domestic market. Household time controls were produced for central heating, cooking equipment or domestic lighting. In 2002, the company, now much reduced in size, moved from Newbridge to Bristol as Horstmann Timers.[20]

Although Sidney Horstmann had failed with his gearbox invention he opened a motor garage in 1907 and in 1913 established Horstmann Cars Ltd at James Street West in Bath, for the manufacture of a two-seater car. The 1913 production model of the car featured a novel foot-starting mechanism (allowing the car to be started from the driver's seat), as well as an aluminium chassis. Sidney Horstmann was one of the first car manufactures to use cellulose spray paint. This and other novel features made the car relatively expensive and the company folded in 1929. Sidney nevertheless continued to develop inventions for cars and vehicles and with his chief engineer, George Carwardine (1887-1947), worked on as Horstmann Limited, consultant engineers, into the 1930s.

Two spring-based inventions came from this fruitful business partnership. First, Horstmann patented his 'Slow Motion' suspension system in 1932.[21] Although it proved far too sensitive (and gave a very bouncy ride) for motorcars, it proved ideal for heavier vehicles such as tanks. A refinement of this system is still supplied by Horstman Defence Systems (which Horstman Limited became in the 1970s) from a factory in Bath.

Secondly, George Carwardine, through his suspension system research with Horstmann developed the 'poise suspension' that he successfully marketed to Terry & Son of Birmingham as 'Anglepoise'. A range of such lamps is still in production.

Bell and the Telephone

Whilst many inventors in Bath have pursued their developments and succeeded or failed through its exploitation in the city, one famous inventor went elsewhere before he changed the world. Alexander Graham Bell, inventor of the telephone, spent the 1866-67 academic year in Bath as a young man teaching elocution at the Somerset College. He lodged first at No.22 Charles Street, moving early in 1867 to No.21 Bennett Street.[22] Bell had become interested in the creation of synthetic sound by electrical means. A German physicist, Hermann von Helmholtz, had used tuning forks

maintained in vibration by electrical means to create pure synthetic tones. In 1867, in an attempt to investigate for himself the possibility of transmitting such synthetic sound over a distance, Bell suspended wire between Nos.18 and 21 Bennett Street and used Wheatstone needle instruments to transmit and receive telegraph messages. The knowledge and experience that Bell gained was evidently put to good use after he left Bath – in February 1876 Bell made his patent application for the telephone.[23]

Nos. 18-21 Bennett Street.
(*Photograph by David Mitchell*)

The Tradition Continues

Those industries which have survived into the twenty-first century continue to invest in high technology and development.

Rotork, established in Bath in 1957 by Jeremy Fry, manufactures distance-operated valve controls. These actuators are used all over the world for the control of valves in the oil, chemical and water industries, operated remotely over great distances. Rotork has expanded beyond Bath to manufacture in USA, Italy, Malaysia and India.

The Admiralty moved to Bath in 1939 and a number of companies have flourished supplying design services including Stothert & Pitt who also manufactured for the Royal Navy. British Marine Technology (BMT) was formed in 1985 and has become a world force in naval architecture. Operating from the Lower Bristol Road the firm has (in 2008) a workforce of over 200; recent work has included the design of an aircraft carrier for the Royal Navy and the development of the Astute class of nuclear-powered submarine.

Conclusion

Bath is widely regarded as simply a holiday destination with its major employment confined to the service sector. However, as has been described in this chapter, the city has flourished with manufacturing, engineering and innovation for centuries.

Further Reading

Andrews, Ken & Burroughs, Stuart, *Stothert & Pitt: Cranemakers to the World*, Stroud, Tempus Publishing, 2003

Cummins, L, *Internal Fire*, Lake Oswego OR, Carnot Press, 1976

Davis, Graham & Bonsall, Penny, *The History of Bath: Image and Reality*, Lancaster, Carnegie Press, 2006

Derry, T.K. & Williams, T.I., *A Short History of Technology*, Oxford, Clarendon Press, 1960

Donkin, S.B., *A Textbook on Gas, Oil and Air Engines*, 2nd edition, London, Charles Griffin, 1896

Harper, Duncan, *Bath at Work*, Bath, Millstream Books, 1989

Neale, R.S., *Bath: A Social History 1650-1850*, London, Boston & Henley, Routledge & Kegan Paul, 1981

Torrens, Hugh, *The Evolution of a Family Firm: Stothert and Pitt of Bath*, Bath, Hugh Torrens, 1978

Torrens, Hugh, *Joseph Day 1855-1946*, Bath, Bath Industrial Heritage Trust, 1991

Perkins, J.W., Brooks, A.T. & Pearce, A.E.McR., *Bath Stone: A Quarry History*, Cardiff, Department of Extra-mural Studies, University College, Cardiff, 1979

Williams, W.J. & Stoddart, D.M., *Bath – Some Encounters with Science*, Bath, Kingsmead Press, 1978

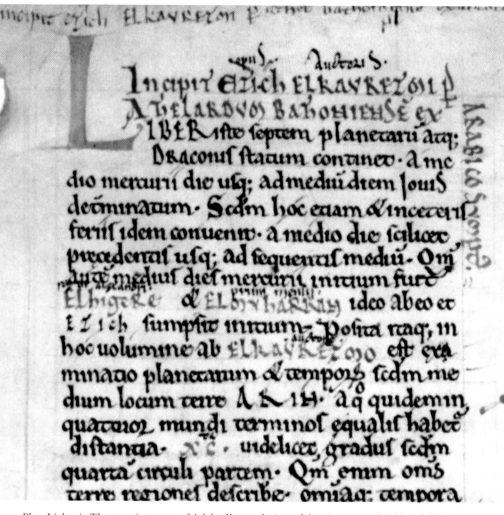

Plate I (*above*). The opening page of Adelard's translation of the *Astronomical Tables of al-Khwarizmi* showing, on the second line, his reference to himself as Adelard of Bath.
(*Bodleian Library, Oxford, Auct. F.1.9, fol.99v.2*)

Plate II (*right*). A further page from the same translation, showing the course of the moon.
(*Bodleian Library, Oxford, Auct. F.1.9, fol.103v*)

OO E DIALITAS LVNE · ET ARGVMENTVM E INSDE H

	OO E DIALITAS LVNE in mensib9			Argumentum LVNE in mensibus			Numerus diebus	Argumen VA LVNE IN DIEBVS			ARGVMENTVM LVNE IN DIEBVS		
	S	G	oo	S	S	G	oo	S	S	G	oo	S	S	G	oo	S
El ovii	I	V	xvii	xxxi	I	I	lvi	lix	I	V	xiii	x	xxxi	V	xviii	III	lvii
										V	xxvi	xxi	xxx	V	V	xxxi	vii
Taf	I	I	xxxvi	xlvi	xvii	I	xv	I	V	III	I	ix	xxxi	xli	I	ix	xi	xlii
										I	xxvi	xli	xx	I	xxxii	xv	vi
Saber	III	II	xli	xlii	II	xxi	xliii	III	V	II	V	lii	liii	II	V	xxi	xxx
										II	xxx	III	xxii	II	xvii	xxi	xxx
Sat sen	III	xvii	xlv	xxxv	III	xi	xl	x	VII	III	II	xiiii	iiii	III	I	xxviii	xx
										III	xx	xxvii	xii	III	xiiii	xv	xxxi
Gu s.	V	V	VI	II	III	xii	xxx	ix		III	xiii	xxx	xiii	III	xxvii	xxxix	xxx
										IIII	xi	xlv	xliiii	IIII	x	xx	V
Guar	V	xxvii	xii	liii	V	II	xxx	xx	xii	IIII	xxii	lvi	xxiii	IIII	xxiii	xli	liii
											viii	vi	lx	V	VI	xliii	xvii
Re s.	VI	xxviiii	xxx	xx	V	iiii	xxv	xiii	xiii	V	xxi	xvii	xxii	V	xix	l	xli
										VI	iiii	xxvi	viii	VI	II	liii	xv
Sea bm	VII	xxx	xxx	xlii	VI	xx	xv	xx	xv	VI	xxvi	xxxv	xlii	VI	xv	lviii	xxx
										VII	V	xlvi	xviii	VI	xxviii	II	viii
Otti ti	VIII	xxii	liii	xxx	VII	xxvii	xxii	xxxv	xviii	VII	xiii	lix	liii	VII	xii	VI	xxxii
										VII	xxvi	x	xxvi	VII	xxv	xxx	vi
Sea wel	ix	xxii	l	xxx	VIII	xiii	x	xx	xxx	VIII	x	xxi	III	VIII	VIII	xxii	vi
										VIII	xxiii	xxv	xlii	VIII	xxi	xlvi	V
Ovl k	x	xxii	xvii	lvi	ix	xxi	vii	xx	xxi	ix	VI	xliii	vii	ix	iiii	xxxi	lix
										ix	xix	lii	xlvi	ix	xvii	lx	xxx
Ball br la	ix	xiiii	xxx	xlvii	x	V	V	xxx	xxiii	x	III	III	xxii	x	V	xxx	xli
										x	xvi	xiii	lvii	x	xiii	xxx	xxx
									xxx	x	xx	xxiii	xx	x	xxxi	xlv	xxx
									xxxi	xi	xii	xxx	vii	xi	ix	xli	xiiii
									xxxii	xi	xxx	xlix	xlii	xi	xxvi	xlv	xlii
									xxxiii	V	viii	lvi	xvii	V	V	xlix	ii
									xxxv	V	xxvii	VI	lii	V	xviii	liii	V
									xxxvi	I	V	xvii	xxvi	I	I	lvi	lix

Secundi Emerbum cu fuere mino. argumeta Sacru Lunaras ꝯ sole. qnei adeqs contra duo · c · ꝯ xx · ꝯꝯ · erant ipsi instatione pus scorsie, cu fuere mg contra ere ꝯ solem alu. ext. opuet ipsi instatione solis · Scendi ena q uen a Sole ñ alter Alteri · Correptiusu nou ultra · vii · recedit ·

Plate III. Dr Rice Charleton in the portrait painted by Thomas Gainsborough.
(*Holburne Museum, Bath*)

Plate IV. William Herschel in 1781, the year he discovered Uranus.
(*The Herschel Museum of Astronomy, Bath*)

Plate V. William Smith's famous map of 1815, *A Delineation of the Strata of England and Wales with part of Scotland.*
(© *Natural History Museum, London*)

Plate VI. Specimens from Robert Gillo's beetle collection.
(*BRLSI collection*)

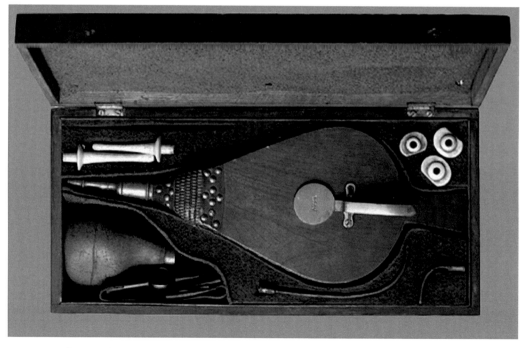

Plate VII. Resuscitation set with bellows and tobacco smoke enema apparatus, c.1805,
formerly belonging to the Bath Humane Society. (*BRLSI collection*)

Plate VIII. Dr. Edward Barlow who proposed the formation of Bath (Royal) Literary and Scientific Institution. (*BRLSI collection, Victoria Art Gallery, Bath & North East Somerset Council*)

Plate IX. An artist's impression of the Lower Assembly Rooms burning down in 1820.
(*Victoria Art Gallery, Bath & North East Somerset Council*)

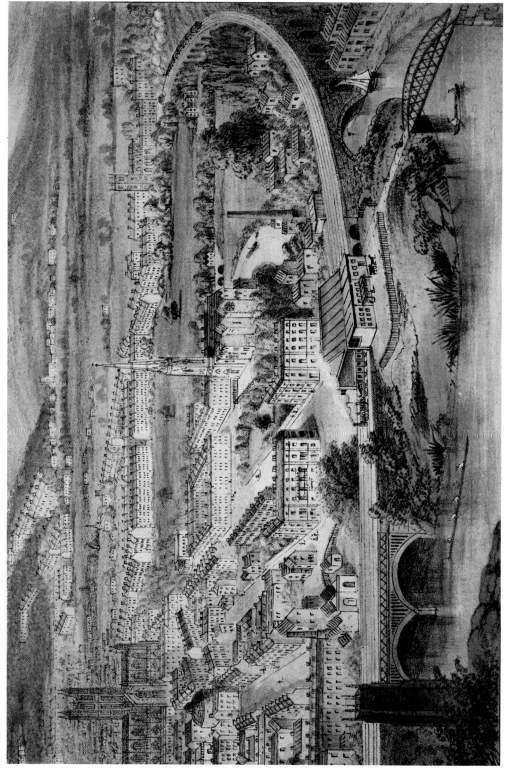

Plate X. The Railway in Bath. A painting, probably from the 1850s, showing the sweep of the Great Western Railway through the southern part of Bath, with the Skew Bridge on the left, the station in the middle, and St Jame's Bridge on the right. In the bottom right-hand corner is the timber-framed pedestrian bow-bridge to Widcombe which collapsed in 1877. (*Bath in Time, Bath Central Library*)

Plate XI. A Map of the Scite of the dissolved Priory of Bath called ye Bath Abby with the several Lands & Tenements within ye Liberty and Precincts thereof adjoyning to the City of Bath, surveyed by 'Mr. Reynolds' for the Duke of Kingston (1750 version). (*Bath Record Office, Bath & North East Somerset Council*)

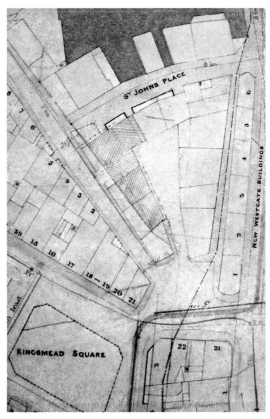

Plate XII. An extract from one of Jacob Henry Cotterell's map sheets of Bath produced with Henry Spackman in 1852 for the City Corporation, showing the water supply system. (*Bath Record Office, Bath & North East Somerset Council*)

Part II
Organisations

11: Science Lecturing in Georgian Bath

Trevor Fawcett

Bath, still a small, rather unsophisticated spa in the 1720s, was nevertheless one of the first venues outside London to hear a commercial public lecture on any aspect of 'natural philosophy' or Newtonian science.[1] The occasion was a total eclipse of the sun in May 1724 when Dr J.T. Desaguliers, FRS, the most influential of all the early lecturers, explained the phenomenon to an audience of 30-40 three-guinea subscribers.[2] Among them may have been fellow freemasons, since Desaguliers, in his other capacity as deputy grandmaster of the Grand Union Lodge, used his visit to receive into Bath's fledgling Queen's Head Lodge several new members, including the spa's flamboyant master-of-ceremonies, Richard 'Beau' Nash. This conjunction apart, enlightened freemasonry played no further obvious role in Bath science, though Desaguliers continued to pay occasional lecturing visits, sometimes on wider West Country tours.

1729-1755

Desaguliers was certainly back in 1729 and 1730:

> Bath, Septem.3 [1730]. This Day Dr. Desaguliers came here in order to have Courses of Experimental Philosophy during the Season: He has brought down, besides the common Apparatus usual in his Courses of Experiments, several new Machines for the Entertainment of his Subscribers. He will have his Lectures at Mr. Harrisons Room, where he was last Year, at the same Price of three Guineas, one Guinea at Subscribing, and the other two the first Day of the Course. Subscriptions are taken in by Mr. Leake, Bookseller in Bath.[3]

References to the 'Season' and Harrison's Assembly Room suggest that Desaguliers was directing his publicity mainly at well-heeled visitors, and we know that Viscount Percival was among the subscribers to this typically expensive series. Yet the encouraging reference to 'Entertainment' did not imply any lack of didactic rigour. While not taxing his listeners (women among them) with difficult mathematics, Desaguliers did expect their close attention as he launched into proving a chain of axioms through experiments and demonstrations.[4] A disciple of Newton, he was also a convinced Baconian, believing in the application of scientific knowledge to bettering the world. Hence his apparatus for demonstrations included not only measuring and optical instruments, prisms to split light, an air pump, a device to simulate the motions of heavenly bodies, and other laboratory equipment, but also levers, model engines and machines, the visible evidence of natural philosophy in action. Much engaged himself in practical projects, from curing smoky chimneys to improving water supplies, Desaguliers was impressed at Bath by Ralph Allen's horse-cranes and innovatory tramway for transporting stone, and he subsequently published accounts of both.[5] Documentation of his lecture courses in the 1730s remains patchy, but he undoubtedly performed at the spa in 1731 and 1737-8 as well as adding Bristol and Worcester to his West Country circuit. In 1737, in addition to his standard demonstrations of the principles of mechanics, hydrostatics and optics, he expounded the phenomenon of tides with a brand-new piece of clockwork, and illustrated the solar system on an improved planetarium – probably the costly 4-foot apparatus he devised with the instrument-maker George Graham.[6]

Others besides Desaguliers had by now embarked on the uncertain career of itinerant lecturer, among them Benjamin Martin, a former Chichester schoolmaster turned instrument maker. By 1743, when he arrived in Bath, Martin's touring equipment included an orrery (for explaining the solar system), a cometarium, celestial globe, reflecting telescope, air pump, a 'very precise' baroscope, various other measuring devices, and models of a forcing pump and marine depth-gauge. His lecturing syllabus had a serious ring. It was far from being 'a Shew, for Amusement only; but is intended as a Science to exhibit a just Idea of the true Nature, Reason, and State of Things, as far as they can be known'.[7] Apparently satisfied by his reception, Martin made Bath his base for the next nine years or so, eventually living just off Orange Grove and giving courses of lectures at his 'Experimental Room' there. His time at Bath coincided with the public excitement over the phenomenon of electricity inspired by the recent discovery of the capacitor (Leyden jar) which could discharge to order. Travelling showmen quickly seized on the entertainment potential of administering electric shocks and producing showers of sparks, but Martin remained wary about introducing the topic into his lectures, preferring instead to concentrate on traditional useful science. In private, however, he tried out his own electrical machine and in October 1746 published a book describing 42 'capital' experiments.[8] Almost at once he came under attack from a London surgeon and religious Pietist, John Freke, who called him a 'mercenary showman' sacrilegiously prying into

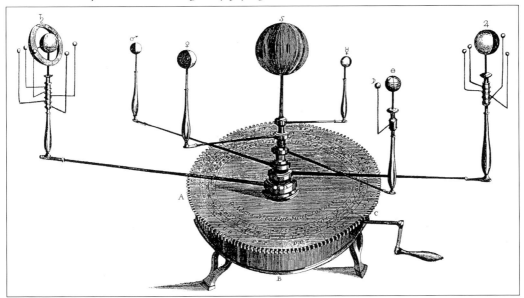

AN

ESSAY

ON

ELECTRICITY:

Being an ENQUIRY into the

NATURE, CAUSE and PROPERTIES thereof,

On the PRINCIPLES of

Sir *Isaac Newton*'s THEORY

OF

VIBRATING MOTION, LIGHT and FIRE;

And the various *Phænomena* of Forty-two

CAPITAL EXPERIMENTS;

With some

OBSERVATIONS relative to the USES

That may be made of this Wonderful

POWER of NATURE.

By BENJ. MARTIN.

We Mortals have not yet learn'd all Things of Jove; many Things hitherto remain hidden; of which some, when it shall please him, he will give us in Futurity to know.

Arat. Solenf. Phænom,

BATH,

Printed for the AUTHOR; and Mr. LEAKE, and Mr. FREDERICK, Booksellers: Mr. RAIKES, Printer, at *Gloucester;* Mr. COLLINS, Printer, at *Salisbury;* and Mr. NEWBURY, Bookseller, at the *Bible and Sun* in St. *Paul's Church-Yard,* London. M.DCC.XLVI.

[Price *Six-Pence.*]

(*above*) Title-page from Benjamin Martin's *An Essay on Electricity* (1746). (*Bath Central Library, Bath & North East Somerset Council*)

Example of an orrery constructed by George Adams the younger, from his *Astronomical and General Essays* (1781).

145

the mysterious life spirit of electricity. Though Martin answered his critic with some vigour,[9] Enlightenment science of any sort always ran the risk of being charged with irreligion. Even Desaguliers, who unlike Martin had Royal Society credentials and rich backers, had met hostility and misrepresentation on occasion. The standard defence of course, used well into the nineteenth century, was that scientific investigation, far from undermining faith, actually heightened the sense of religious awe and led the mind, in Pope's often-quoted phrase, 'through Nature up to Nature's God'.

Unable to survive on his Bath teaching alone, nor by the sale of scientific instruments, Martin undertook extensive lecturing tours – such as his summer sweep through East Anglia in 1750. Meanwhile his wife ran a haberdashery business in Wade's Passage, where in November 1751 she had on sale James Ferguson's 'Portable CARD-DIALS' and 'LUMINARIUM', an almanac device.[10]

James Ferguson, in an engraving of 1776. (*Bath Central Library, Bath & North East Somerset Council*)

Since Ferguson likewise lectured for a living, it must be assumed that Martin did not regard him as a rival. In fact Martin soon removed to London and established an instrument shop there. Ferguson, a self-taught Scot, had already lectured at Bath, his forte being astronomy – which for Martin had been only one component within a much broader curriculum. Ferguson's five-lecture, five-shilling courses at Wiltshire's Assembly Rooms in the autumns of 1750 and 1751 featured an elaborate orrery of his own making which could represent the movement of Sun, Moon and planets, explaining the calendar and the causes of eclipses and tides. He kept this and other apparatus on daily view at his lodgings, where during his stay he also gave private lessons and made ink portrait drawings on vellum, perhaps a more lucrative activity than lecturing.[11] Whatever his immediate success at Bath, Ferguson did not return until the 1760s, leaving the field mainly to another itinerant philosopher, William Griffiss, who included the spa in his lecturing tours of 1752 and 1755-6. Griffiss is a less familiar figure than many other itinerant natural philosophers, yet he travelled assiduously, covered all the physical sciences except electricity, and owned a considerable quantity of apparatus. His first Bath series opened at *The Pineapple*, Orchard Street, in April 1752 with at least 30 subscribers attracted by a prospectus describing his demonstration equipment as the 'compleatest ... in Britain'. Returning in December 1755 for Bath's winter season, Griffiss more ambitiously hired Wiltshire's Assembly Rooms and now required at least 40 subscribers. In ten sessions he would then cover natural philosophy in general ('to illustrate and confirm Sir Isaac Newton's Principles'), mechanics, hydrostatics and hydraulics, pneumatics, chemistry, the useful applications of science, optics, military architecture ('illustrated by a large Model of a fortified Town'), geography, and astronomy. Other models would show how engines worked and their uses, and the whole course would provide a succinct but entertaining overview of 'the more rational and sublime Parts of Knowledge'.[12] In this and a repeat course Griffiss was targeting not merely the gentry (of both sexes), but 'all Sorts of Persons, especially those well read or employed in Mechanicks, &c.', suggesting that the audience for science lectures was now broadening to include the professional and commercial middle class.

1756–1779

In spring 1756 Griffiss gave a final series at Bath on the eve of the Seven Years' War – a conflict that for a time depressed the market for science lectures. A possible lecturing visit by James Ferguson in 1763 has not been substantiated, but he did come at Christmas 1766 on a trip arranged by his bookseller to promote a reissue of his popular *Lectures in Mechanics and Astronomy Explained*. Ferguson, now a FRS, had extended his range and probably brought with him many working models of cranes, wheel-carriages, mills, pumps, and other mechanical devices besides his faithful orrery. At the start of his second 12-lecture course he offered an evening course to suit people with daytime occupations. Astronomy was still Ferguson's strongest suit with the public, and two months later a proposed course of a dozen lectures deploying his full battery of machinery models had to be abandoned in favour of a further short course on the solar system.[13] Only once more was he recorded at Bath, when in April 1774 at the age of 64 he delivered a double series of 12 lectures. It was these that enthused William Herschel in his own voyage of astronomical discovery.

A new generation of lecturers dominated the last third of the century at Bath, notably John Arden, Benjamin Donn (or Donne) of Bristol, John Warltire, Henry Moyes, Adam Walker junior, and John Lloyd. Expounding science was now a reputable activity and took place against a surge of fresh discoveries and interest in astronomy, electricity, the chemistry of gases, geology and botany. British skills in inventions and instrument-making – which had already produced Knight's artificial magnets, Dollond's achromatic lens, Ramsden's scale-divider and Harrison's chronometer – remained unsurpassed, and before 1780 Bath had acquired its own specialist 'optical, philosophical and mathematical' instrument-makers in Ribright & Smith. The scientific public was expanding.

In a growing market for popular instruction, even children were addressed in publications such as *The Newtonian System of Philosophy adapted to the Capacities of Young Gentlemen and Ladies* (1761). At Bath, public lectures now ranged beyond natural philosophy and treated literature, elocution, the visual arts, medicine, and veterinary science.

John Arden and Benjamin Donn both sought a Bath audience from the late 1760s. Arden, with much experience of teaching and lecturing in the North and Midlands, first tried his luck in winter 1768-9 with two long courses on physics, astronomy and geography, in which he promised to make the experiments 'as plain and intelligible as possible, even to those who have not applied Time or study this Way'. For 20 lectures he charged one guinea, where Desaguliers had once asked three, but he exploited his stay by giving private lessons to young people on elementary astronomy and geography. His subsequent visits in 1769-70 kept to the same pattern.[14]

Title-page from John Arden's book giving the prospectus for his lecture course delivered at Bath, probably c.1768. (*reproduced from Turner, A.J.(ed.)*, Science and Music in Eighteenth Century Bath: An Exhibition in the Holburne of Menstrie Museum, Bath, 22 September 1977-29 December 1977, *illustration 151*)

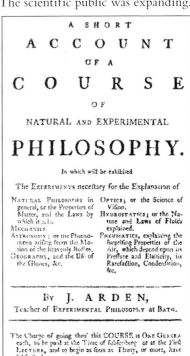

Meanwhile Donn, too, had started to lecture. Coming from a gifted family of Bideford mathematics teachers, he moved to Bristol about 1759-60 and eventually opened a mathematical academy. At Bath he advertised a first course in December 1769 together with details of his academy and his various publications (including the important *Navigation Scale Improved* and excellent maps of Devon and the Bristol area). Next spring he offered another 'whereby any one with only common Sense and a moderate Degree of Attention' could easily grasp the principles involved. Further courses followed that December and again in spring 1773 when he seems to have lectured at both *The Queen's Head*, Cheap Street, and at the Ladies' Coffee House by the Pump Room, sometimes twice a day.[15] In an ambitious 16-lecture series at the Upper Assembly Rooms in 1776 Donn dealt with electricity but said nothing yet on the new topic of gases – which it aptly fell to John Warltire to introduce at Bath. 'Aptly' because Warltire was in the forefront of recent discoveries in this area, being not only in close touch with the industrial Midlands but a collaborator with Joseph Priestley at Bowood.[16] As soon as he reached Bath in summer 1776 Warltire announced courses of 'New Experiments upon Air' at the Lower Rooms, each of three meetings. These he had to repeat at least four times, such was the interest, with sessions at 11.00am and 7.00pm to suit different audiences. Systematically he spoke of atmospheric gases, artificial gases, and the actions of gases in organic life and industrial processes. As usual the discourse was illustrated with experiments.

> Mr.WARLTIRE flatters himself these Experiments claim attention the most of any discoveries since the introduction of Experimental Philosophy; because they are highly interesting to the ladies as well as gentlemen, and are the most entertaining, and the easiest understood of any in the circle of Philosophy – besides, they are quite new discoveries, and the chief part of them never yet published ...[17]

There can be little doubt the topic must also have appealed to medical practitioners, some of whom would in the 1790s try out carbon dioxide and nitrous oxide in treatments. More immediately the discoveries were relevant to the spa's literal source of wealth, the sparkling hot waters whose potency had always been agreed to be greatest when drunk straight from the pump before their vital gases had evaporated. Deploying their limited knowledge of chemistry, local and visiting physicians and apothecaries had often – and controversially – analysed the springs, but Priestley's discovery of dissolved carbon dioxide ('fixible air') in the waters made it possible not merely to reconstitute Bath water gone flat but, more threateningly, to produce artificial waters from scratch.[18]

Warltire's success at Bath drew him back in October 1777 to give another state-of-the-art series, this time with four lecture-demonstrations in which he undertook to manufacture each gas as his audience watched (with an entire session on nitrous oxide and another partly devoted to acid compounds). Nodding invitingly towards the recently formed Bath and West Agricultural Society he proposed further lectures that would treat the still embryonic science of agricultural chemistry. It is likely that John Arden sat in on Warltire's lectures. After some years' absence Arden had settled at Bath, and in late 1776 resumed lecturing to select audiences at his own house in St James's Street. Next April he was already into his third course when he first ventured onto Warltire's ground by discoursing on the properties of air. Later in the year that advance was more definite as he offered sixteen lectures 'in the course of which will be exhibited Dr. Priestley's new experiments upon different kinds of air'.[19]

Early in 1778 competition was keen. Arden's third winter series clashed directly with Donn's six lectures 'on the most entertaining Parts of NATURAL PHILOSOPHY' (astronomy, pneumatics and electricity) – lectures he repeated in a separate evening course to 'accommodate People in

Business'. That April, facing a rival course on the genius of Milton and another – in French – on the humanities and sciences, Warltire seasoned his five lectures at a room on George Street with several novelties. Besides experiments, he would reveal 'an application to the doctrine of fossils, minerals, &c' and display a new kind of opaque solar microscope capable of explaining many recent discoveries.[20] The somewhat cryptic reference to fossils and minerals is noteworthy in view of the specific Bath interest in geology and its rising significance as a science. Ancient shells, corals, sea urchins, belemnites ('thunderbolts') and spectacular ammonites ('snakestones') abounded in the nearby lias and oolite quarries, and several Bath residents made collections – including Edmund Rack, secretary of the new Bath Philosophical Society whose formation in late 1779 may well have been precipitated by John Arden's simultaneous course of lectures. Only a week earlier Rack recorded that he had begun attending

John Arden, from a pastel by J.G. Huquier.
(*Bath Record Office,*
Bath & North East Somerset Council)

a Course of Philosophical Lectures on Electricity – the Air, Chemistry, Astronomy, Hydrostatics, & the Globes – these Lectures are given by Wm [*actually John*] Arden of this City, a very Ingenious Man, & who has a Noble Apparatus of the best Instruments. Entertainments of this kind are the most truly Rational & instructive of any that can Employ the Human mind. And a few Lectures explaind by experiments convey more lasting instruction than many volumes of theory. We have them read here all winter. At these Lectures were many Men of great scientific Knowledge ...[21]

Arden joined the Society himself, but abandoned lecturing at Bath not long after – except, that is, for one return visit in 1786-7 when he gave three courses while seeking a buyer for his scientific library and apparatus.

1780–1820

The 1780s and 1790s resembled earlier decades in the unpredictability of offerings on scientific topics. Benjamin Smith, who ran a shop selling optical and scientific instruments, delivered a few self-promotional lectures on electrical machines (and their use in medical treatments), solar microscopes, and other devices. Donn came over intermittently from Bristol until as late as 1796 with wide-ranging courses. A demonstration he gave in December 1783, at the height of the Montgolfier balloon craze, was partly devoted to making 'inflammable air' (i.e. hydrogen) 'wherewith AIR BALLOONS are filled'. Warltire's tours brought him back to the spa in 1786 and 1788, and on the second occasion he focused on the useful applications of modern chemistry.[22] Chemistry was also the theme of the blind lecturer Henry Moyes when he proposed an extraordinarily long course of 28 one-hour lectures (four per week) for a mere guinea in 1781. This was still early in his career, but the amiable Moyes was already an impressive performer. Priestley in 1783 even considered him superior to most sighted lecturers – 'and tho' he cannot himself make many experiments, he gets them made for him by an assistant, so that none of his hearers ever complain on that account'.[23] Priestley also thought well of the London lecturer, Adam Walker, who had purchased William Griffiss' famous equipment in 1766 and made full use of the 'Eidouranion', a huge transparent orrery that permitted almost theatrical demonstrations of astronomical phenomena. For example when Walker's son William lectured at Bath in 1783, one scene showed

> every planet and satellite in annual and diurnal motion at once; a comet descends in the para-
> bolic curve from the top of the machine, and turning round the sun, ascends in like manner;
> its motions being accelerated and retarded according to the laws of planetary motion.

Moreover, he gratifyingly told the Bath public, all Herschel's recent discoveries would be woven into the exposition, not forgetting the new planet Uranus.[24]

Walker's Eidouranion set a fashion. With Benjamin Smith's technical assistance, Abraham Didier, a former actor at Bath, constructed a small, glass 'Lilliputian orrery' or 'Aetheroides'. Claiming the mechanism created an unparalleled illusion of 'suspended Orbs' and had an 'inconceivably smooth' movement, he employed it – and two similar glass globes, the 'Tellurium' and 'Cometarium' – in lectures to small groups in 1788 and late 1789. Didier's show was challenged, though, in autumn 1788, by the visiting John Lloyd, a well-known metropolitan lecturer, who likewise explained the solar system by means of a model, much larger than Didier's, the so-called 'New Eidouranion'.[25]

There was, however, a constant risk of confusing science with mere showmanship. What, for instance, was the status of Mr Bradberry's travelling exhibition of Newton's philosophical experiments – 'with a variety of deceptions' – in 1787? And how did the curious react to the expensive tuition offered by John Holloway and his local disciple John Giles in 1790-1 on the contentious subject of 'animal magnetism' or Mesmerism, in which its mysteries and medical effectiveness would be divulged, in the strictest secrecy, in costly five-guinea lectures? Even such established lecturers as Henry Moyes grew more cautious in the 1790s as political paranoia about radical subversion intensified and the whole Enlightenment project of disinterested science was at times called into question for introducing dangerous Illuminist doctrines and undermining Christian faith. Assisted by his nephew, and always giving generous value of around 20 lectures for a guinea, the blind Moyes was now the most constant of the visiting lecturers at Bath. Several times at the Lower Assembly Rooms in 1793, 1796 and February 1798 he repeated his wide-ranging series on the relatively safe theme of 'natural history', in which he discussed celestial bodies, the Earth's geography, the plant and animal kingdoms, and the natural economy and health of humans. But in February and December 1797, switching to chemistry, he must have felt it prudent to cover himself with a pre-emptive defence in the local press, signed 'B', pointing out that he avoided all 'cabbalistic jargon' and any hint of 'modern scepticism'.[26]

Astronomy was the subject most capable of evoking feelings of religious awe and (next to electricity) the one most suitable to dramatic presentation. Both John Lloyd, from the Lyceum and Royalty Theatre in London, and William Walker, from the Haymarket Theatre Royal, paid return visits to Bath as the century closed. In 1799 and 1800 Lloyd displayed his *pièce de résistance*, the 'Dioastrodoxon', a huge transparent orrery 21 feet in diameter and 'richly decorated with appropriate scenery', by which to demonstrate 'the sublime Economy of the SOLAR SYSTEM' and send the spectator's mind soaring 'through Nature up to NATURE's GOD!' The whole complex apparatus, which by 1800 permitted over 40 scene changes, was expensive to transport and set up. That year Lloyd hired Potter's large auction room in Monmouth Street, dubbed it the 'Theatre of Astronomy', and delivered four three-day courses, morning and evening, probably to a hundred or more subscribers a time. Later in the year Walker, whose current Eidouranion measured a mere 15 feet across, went one better by hiring the Theatre Royal itself, which besides admitting a bigger audience, enabled him to heighten his effects with staging, curtains, and the aetherial strains of a celestina. This was science lecturing turned into polished, mannered, self-conscious performance.[27]

Yet a more everyday style was also represented at Bath in 1800, when Dr Raphael Gillum, a physician from Bath Dispensary, provided the first public botanical course at the spa, a month-long series on the Linnaean system and its applications, illustrated with specimens from a local botanic garden, and held at the Bath Agricultural Society's rooms.[28] He no doubt drew a fashionable audience, though there was no guarantee with fashionable lectures that every listener would be thoroughly receptive. In 1806 after attending a series by Dr Clement Archer, chemist to the Agricultural Society, the ageing Mrs Thrale/Piozzi confessed she had learned nothing

> except that where the Sphere of Attraction ceases, the Sphere of Repulsion begins ... We had much Talk ... concerning Oxygen, & much Talk concerning the Analogy between our Animal & Vegetable Kingdoms ... A Lady at ye Lecture ask'd me if ye 3 Kingdoms Dr Archer talked so of were England Scotland & Ireland.[29]

Mary Shelley, by contrast, must have hung on the lips of the independent Bath lecturer, Dr C.H. Wilkinson, especially alert to his account of the new galvanic chemistry, when she subscribed to his lectures in autumn 1816, for she was then still working on her novel *Frankenstein*. Indeed her character Professor Waldman, with his vital message concerning chemistry's miraculous powers, may be a partial portrait of Wilkinson – a colourful character in his own right discussed in the next chapter in connection with the scientific society he established at his lecture room beside the Kingston Baths.[30]

Gillum, Archer and Wilkinson all had an institutional base at Bath, and this would tend increasingly to be the case with nineteenth-century lecturing. Outside lecturers still turned up of course. Thus in 1820 both Robert Addams of the Royal Institution and D.F. Walker (third of the lecturing Walker clan) performed at the Lower Assembly Rooms. Armed with a huge array of engines, working models, and other apparatus (including a transparent orrery) Addams went through the entire gamut of the sciences from electricity to astronomy. Walker confined himself to astronomy, but had the advantage of displaying a more spectacular orrery, his improved Eidouraneion. His final lecture took place on 20 December; the precious orrery was stored in the Lower Assembly Rooms vaults overnight and removed next morning. That night the Rooms burned down, possibly the result of smouldering from a previous fire in one of Walker's packing cases (*see Colour Plate IX*). A devastating event in itself, this nonetheless opened a new horizon for Bath science, as the next chapter tells.[31]

Further reading

Fawcett, Trevor, 'Science Lecturing at Bath, 1724-1800', *Bath History*, vol.vii, Bath, Millstream Books, 1998, pp.55-77, offers additional information and references.

12: Bath Scientific Societies and Institutions

Trevor Fawcett

At first sight Edmund Rack may seem an unlikely founder of the Bath and West of England Society.[1] A retired Essex shopkeeper, and a Quaker to boot, he was not among the West Country land-owning gentry who could most expect to benefit from an organisation of this kind. All the same he was socially ambitious, had an inquiring mind and progressive ideals, and was already well known in Bath literary circles by summer 1777 when he proposed forming a society 'for the encouragement of Agriculture, Planting, Manufactures, Commerce and the Fine Arts'. The idea was hardly novel except in a Bath context. Societies for economic improvement, especially for promoting agriculture, trade and industry, abounded in eighteenth-century Europe, some of them state-sponsored. Typically their aim was to stimulate productivity and promote good practice by disseminating tested new methods, materials and technology. Some of these bodies adopted a strict experimental approach to problems, conducting trials and rigorously assessing the evidence in a more-or-less 'scientific' manner.

The Bath and West, 1777-1825

In Britain possible models for the Bath and West already existed in a handful of provincial agri-

Edmund Rack, after a portrait by Lewis Vaslet. (*Bath Central Library, Bath & North East Somerset Council*)

cultural societies as well as in two more prestigious institutions, the Royal Dublin Society (1731) and the London-based Royal Society of Arts (1754). The meeting Rack called at the *York House* hotel on 8 September 1777 to launch the Bath project attracted just 22 town gentry, businessmen and doctors – though by then 40 other names were on the list of would-be subscribers, including Joseph Priestley, then living at Calne.[2] A second public meeting approved the plan and, with Rack as Secretary and the Earl of Ilchester as President, the Society quickly got under way. It was not wholly modelled on the Royal Society of Arts, since this body, as Rack pointed out, was 'more directed to commerce, mechanics, and the fine arts' than to agricultural improvement, his own chief concern. Both Rack and his Quaker colleague William Matthews seem to have been struck by the relative backwardness of farming in the West Country compared with the region they best knew, East Anglia, and this was the issue they most wanted to tackle. So the Bath and West focussed on rural matters from the start, taking all Somerset, Wiltshire, Gloucestershire and Dorset for its constituency.

An Account of the progressive Improvement in Weight, *and* Value, *of a FLOCK of SHEEP, of different kinds, kept together* and folded *for Thre Years,*
By the MARQUIS of BATH, at LONGLEAT, WILTS,
In Order to ascertain their respective Merits for Wiltshire Husbandry; and afterward fatted and killed together.

Sorts of Sheep, ALL BEING LAMBS of 1791, And put to Flock in July 1792.	Average Weight July 1792, when put to Flock.	Average Value July 1792, after being shorn.		THREE YEARS' WOOL, 1793, 1794, and 1795. WEIGHT.		VALUE.		Weight per Sheep July 1795, after being folded three Years.	Increase in weight per sheep.	WEIGHT OF MUTTON, and VALUE. When killed fat, Dec. 1795. Average WEIGHT.	Average VALUE			IMPROVEMENT on the Original Value, including three Years Wool.		
	lbs.	*s.*	*d.*	*lbs.*	*oz.*	*s.*	*d.*	*lbs.*	*lbs.*	*lbs.*	£.	*s.*	*d.*	£.	*s.*	*d.*
LEICESTER.	105	19	$8\frac{1}{4}$	14	$11\frac{1}{4}$	11	0	125	20	$79\frac{1}{2}$	1	19	9	1	11	$0\frac{1}{4}$
COTSWOLD.	95	17	$9\frac{3}{4}$	15	12	11	$9\frac{3}{4}$	$108\frac{1}{2}$	$13\frac{1}{2}$	76	1	18	0	1	12	0
DORSETSHIRE.	119	22	$3\frac{3}{4}$	10	$0\frac{1}{2}$	10	$0\frac{3}{4}$	141	22	$83\frac{1}{2}$	2	1	9	1	9	$5\frac{1}{2}$
WILTSHIRE.	$98\frac{3}{4}$	18	6	8	$9\frac{1}{4}$	8	11	140	$41\frac{1}{4}$	$82\frac{1}{2}$	2	1	3	1	11	8
MENDIP.	$95\frac{3}{4}$	17	$11\frac{1}{4}$	10	$6\frac{1}{2}$	11	$2\frac{3}{4}$	$136\frac{1}{2}$	$40\frac{1}{4}$	82	2	1	0	1	14	$3\frac{1}{2}$
SOUTH-DOWN.	$82\frac{1}{2}$	15	$5\frac{1}{2}$	7	15	10	$4\frac{1}{2}$	$129\frac{1}{4}$	$46\frac{1}{4}$	$84\frac{1}{2}$	2	2	3	1	17	2

In this Experiment, Regard must be had not only to the comparative Improvement of each Kind of Sheep, but to the comparative Quantity of Food consumed by each. It being a well-ascertained Fact, that during the Time they are kept in a working (or *folding*) State, their Food is nearly in proportion to their Weight. So that not only eight South-Down Sheep have improved equal to ten Dorsets, but the Food that maintained ten Dorsets, would have maintained fifteen South-Downs.

The Object of this Experiment was, to determine what Kind of Sheep would best bear hard Keeping and constant Folding.

The above Sheep were kept on a Tract of very poor heathy Land, not worth 3s. per Acre, and from thence driven to Fold *every Night*, (chiefly on Arable Land) from one to two Miles distant from their Food.—The Result seems to prove that the *smaller* Kinds of Sheep are the *hardiest*. The small Increase in Weight in the Leicestershire and the Cotswold during the time they were folded, seems to shew that long-woolled Sheep are not fit for that purpose. And as the three Kinds of horned Sheep, (the Dorsets, Wilts, and Mendip) have increased in Value nearly an inverse Ratio with their original Size, it seems that increasing the Size of the Animal has made them less hardy. This experiment also proves decidedly, that the South-Down Sheep are full as profitable to the *Grazier*, as to the Farmer.

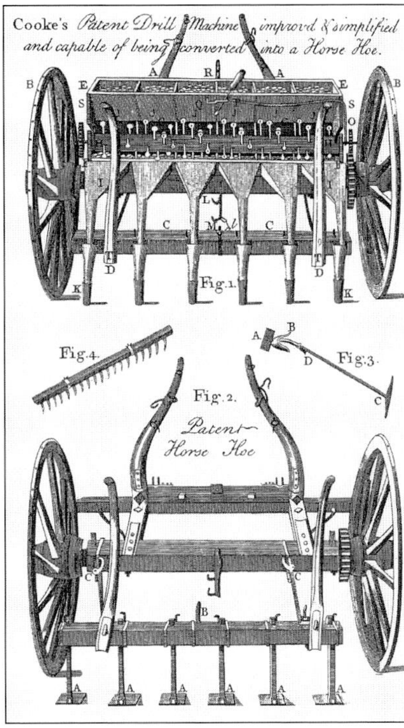
Cooke's Patent Drill Machine improved & simplified and capable of being converted into a Horse Hoe.
Fig.1.
Fig.2.
Fig.3.
Fig.4.
Patent Horse Hoe

(*above*) Table of sheep yields at Longleat; (*right*) Drill machine and horse hoe; both from the Bath and West Society's *Letters and Papers* (1802). (*Bath Central Library, Bath & North East Somerset Council*)

The emphasis on agriculture was made quite explicit in the annual lists of premiums the Society announced as a way of 'exciting a spirit of industry and ingenuity to promote the public good'. Rule XIV laid down that 'the Premiums offered shall be more immediately directed to improvements in agriculture, planting, and such manufactures and arts as are best adapted to these counties', while Rule XV added that awards might also be made for 'industry and good behaviour among servants in husbandry, and labourers'. By 1800 some 85% of the Society's expenditure on premiums (up to that date totalling £1,642) had gone to the agricultural sector rather than to improvements in manufacturing. Annual prize topics and awards were decided by three specialist committees dealing respectively with Agriculture and Planting (the largest), Manufactures and Commerce, and Mechanicks and the Useful Arts.

Year by year the lengthy lists of premiums reveal definite preoccupations – above all with promoting root crops, encouraging tree planting, and improving livestock and farm equipment – but they also took account of many other regional activities, from honey and cider production, wool combing, and papermaking to the design of farm-workers' cottages and the problem of methane in coalmines. These all reflected the Bath and West's concerns. It was, after all, an organisation of landowners and 'thinking farmers', both groups keen to increase yields and maximise profits at a time when agricultural prices, always subject to the seasons, fluctuated unpredictably under the economic strains of war (1776-83 and 1793-1815) and peace. Nor was it surprising that the Society supported land enclosure and in late 1795 even petitioned Parliament in favour of the Enclosure Bill.[3] Increasing productivity, making land use more efficient and keeping food prices low seemed more urgent than protecting the rights of poor commoners. Patriotism and philanthropy motivated the Bath and West as well as self-interest. Even the radical reformer Henry Hunt, who thought it a clique of 'rapacious landlords, grasping parsons, and shallow vain farmers', had to admit there were many honourable exceptions. A one-time sheep breeder, he even joined for a time himself.[4]

In its early decades the Bath and West proved remarkably vigorous. It established a library and a collection of models and implements – accommodated at its Bath office in Hetling House from 1787 when William Matthews became Secretary on Edmund Rack's death. It instituted annual ploughing matches in 1788, and agricultural shows, held at various sites in Bath, from 1790 onwards. It organised a two-day annual meeting and dinner for its scattered membership. It conducted a widespread official correspondence, and between 1780 and 1816 published 15 volumes of *Letters and Papers*, a journal containing substantial essays and shorter notices that earned the Society a national and international reputation. By 1800 the Duke of York and 32 other noble lords headed the parade of supporters, while the 5th Duke of Bedford, an agricultural improver well known for the annual sheep-shearings on his Woburn estate, reigned as President. He was succeeded in turn by two other reform-minded Presidents, the 6th Duke of Bedford (1802-5) and Sir Benjamin Hobhouse (1805-17).

William Matthews, portrait by an unknown artist. (*By courtesy of Royal Bath and West of England Society, Bath Record Office, Bath & North East Somerset Council*)

Yet the question needs posing: what was the real scientific value of so much activity? In reality agricultural science was at this period still in its infancy. Many of the fundamental facts about plant and animal genetics, biochemistry, nutritional and growth factors, or the causes of disease, were simply not understood. All the notable eighteenth-century advances achieved in stock breeding, crop rotation, drilling and horse-hoeing, and growing turnips and lucerne, had arisen through ordinary trial and error with very little underpinning from scientific theory. And so it was with the Bath and West's various investigations, whether Dr William Falconer's clinical trials of medicinal rhubarb, Dr C.H. Parry's systematic efforts in cross-breeding Merino sheep, or the field studies conducted from 1780 onwards at the Society's experimental farm at Weston.[5] No doubt some of the Society's research furnished statistical data worth acting on, but it yielded no proper scientific explanations nor led to important discoveries.

The most compelling instance of the Bath and West's failure as a scientific agency can be found in the minutes of its Committee of Chemical (and Geological) Research, set up in 1805, the year after Sir Humphry Davy became an Honorary Member of the Society.[6] Aware of the growing significance of 'Economical Chymistry', the Committee installed a basic laboratory (a modest version of Davy's facility at the Royal Institution) in the basement of Hetling House. This was organised by one of their number, Dr Clement Archer, who engaged a part-time assistant, Cadwallader Boyd, to analyse soils, plants and other organic substances submitted by members of the Bath and West. In 1806 Archer was partway through giving a course of chemical lectures when his sudden death obliged Boyd to step in and complete the course himself. Since pitiably few soil samples arrived for laboratory testing, Boyd occupied himself for a time analysing specimens of local rocks, but it was all very low key. In 1808 the laboratory closed and the committee stopped meeting. Then in 1819, perhaps spurred by Dr Parry's complaint that the Bath and West had forgotten its broad remit and was becoming 'an overgrown body of Agriculturalists',[7] the Chemical Committee and its laboratory flickered back to life – and this time with an extended brief that included forming a proper geological collection. But Bath and West members once more displayed little interest in soil chemistry. Lacking samples to analyse, the Committee concentrated on its other main task, creating a small museum of fossils, minerals and rocks. But here, too, despite appeals for donations (and encouragement from the distinguished geologist Rev J.J. Conybeare), the collection grew so slowly that in 1825 it was agreed to hand it over to the newly established BRLSI, which might be expected to do a better job. The demoralised Chemical Committee then disbanded. The Bath and West seemed to have lost its edge, with a shrinking membership, falling income, and more competition from bodies like the Wiltshire Society for the Encouragement of Agriculture (1813-60). Decades later, when it eventually staged a remarkable recovery under Sir T.D. Acland, the direct link with Bath was severed and from 1852 the agricultural shows became peripatetic. Three years later the Bath and West demonstrated a renewed interest in agricultural science by appointing an expert chemist, Dr Augustus Voelker, as consultant, proselytiser and analyst.[8]

The First Bath Philosophical Society, 1779-c.1787

Other Bath societies with a clearer scientific focus had meanwhile come and gone. The first sprang to life just two years after the emergence of the Bath and West, and once again Edmund Rack became its founding Secretary.[9] This time the idea came not from Rack but from Thomas Curtis, a cultivated local man with a country house at Wickwar and a town house in Bath, already actively engaged with the Bath and West and the General Hospital. In a subsequent tribute to Curtis after his early death in 1784, Rack called him the 'Father' of the Society, its original proposer and the main author of its constitution.[10] Nevertheless, in late December 1779 both men shared the task of drawing up a tentative list of 30 potential members. What they had in mind was not a large, semi-public body on the pattern of the Bath and West, but rather a private discussion group, a select gentlemen's club for lively minds. They would know of provincial examples. The Spalding Society (founded in 1712) still survived, as did the stimulating Lunar Society at Birmingham (c.1765) with its offshoot at Derby. Versions of the same concept could be found in the intellectual circles of Warrington and Liverpool, in the clubs north of the border reflecting the Scottish Enlightenment, and in the societies that subsequently formed in the 1780s and 1790s at Newcastle, Leeds, Manchester, Norwich, Exeter, and other places.[11] Egalitarian and open-minded groups, they offered Dissenters and Anglicans alike a tolerant, intellectual forum for debate and self-improvement where only merit counted. Adopting the formula 'literary and philosophical' in their titles, as many of them did, signalled a curiosity about all the humanities and sciences. In theory nothing was barred from discussion but party politics, dogmatic religion, and the professional doings of their members.

The first Bath Philosophical Society fitted the mould well, except that its tendency was always more 'philosophical' than 'literary'. Rack's frustrated attempt to enlist a man-of-letters like William Melmoth as a member owed more to his unfeigned admiration for Melmoth himself, 'the Addison of this Age', than any desire to change the emphasis.[12] Curtis's personal objective was clear from the start, even in Rack's rather contradictory wording, namely to create

> a Select Literary Society – for the purpose of discussing Scientific and Phylosophical subjects & making experiments to illustrate them.[13]

In fact the spark that lit the tinder might well have been a course of experimental science lectures concurrently in progress at Bath that winter, especially since the lecturer in question, John

Arden, immediately joined the new society. Recruited along with him were others whom Rack characterised as 'Men of known Abilities & Learning in the different branches of science'. Fourteen attended the first meeting on 30 December 1779, and a few more soon brought the total towards the intended limit of 25 members. It was an eclectic group. Among the core members resident in Bath were several medical practitioners including John Symons, Harry Atwood, William Watson and William Falconer – the first three all Bath City Councilmen. They also numbered a 'walking Library' in James Collings, a well-read Anglican clergyman (Rev Samuel Rogers), a Methodist naturalist (John Walcott), a draper and soapmaker (John Bryant, owner of a powerful electrical machine), a brewer and coal merchant (William Matthews), a practised science lecturer (John Arden), and town gentry like Thomas Curtis. A particularly happy acquisition was the music master and obsessive stargazer William Herschel – thanks to a chance encounter between him and William Watson. The initial mix of members was a little *ad hoc* in character. After the first fortnight though, when 18 had joined, further candidates were formally subject to secret ballot.[14]

Already the new Bath Philosophical Society's combined expertise ranged from mathematics, astronomy and physics to geology, botany and, of course, medicine. All that was backed up by an assortment of scientific apparatus, cabinets of specimens, and fine specialist books owned by members and supplemented by items they funded as a group. Furthermore they had a web of useful contacts in and out of Bath. Watson's own father, for example, was an eminent London physician, electrical experimenter, and FRS. Collings had attended the Lunar Society. Arden knew fellow scientists across the country. Some of the medical members had trained in Scotland. A deliberate reaching out beyond Bath seems evident in the society's election of non-resident or corresponding members such as the philanthropic Quaker physician J.C. Lettsom, the physician Charles Blagden (FRS and later Royal Society secretary), the Welsh philosopher John Lloyd FRS, the entomologist Matthew Martin of Exeter, John Walsh FRS (famous for his research on electric fish), and the botanist physician Richard Pulteney living in Dorset. Of all the non-residents Joseph Priestley, another FRS, then enjoying the 2nd Earl of Shelburne's Bowood patronage, could most easily attend meetings in person. He was certainly present at a special four-hour daytime meeting on 22 March 1780 appointed for experiments on 'Phosp[h]orial Light and Electricity'. According to Rack:[15]

> Some new discoveries in Electricity were made, & Notes taken. And it was found that divers kinds of Bodies being exposd a Minute to the Suns Rays and instantly drawn into the dark Room – Would retain their Light near A Minute, particularly a Sheet of writing paper which on being drawn in appeard very Light for half a Minute. I then wrote a Word upon it & pressd it with a hot smoothing Iron. On exposing it again & drawing it in before it Coold it Appeard for near a Minute all on fire & the writing Diamond was very legible. Many other Substances were tryd – the next in brightness was a peice of Stalactites, which was as luminous as a Coal. Dr Watson had a Diamond Ring, which shone so bright for near half a minute, as to enable him to Read by it. ... We also tryd Live fish – Mosses, Funguses, bread, Lump Sugar – Leeks, dryd Wood, Red Herring – silk Handkerchiefs, Allum – Garden Roots – Fossils – Spar, & Minerals.

This session – like a similar one four days earlier – was unusual in being held in daytime, the venue on both occasions being the society's 'dark Room'. The room in question may well have been in Rivers Street close to where Herschel then lived. Caroline Herschel later remembered the society having a room there where they kept Bryant's powerful electrical machine and other scientific instruments.[16] But their normal meeting place was more centrally located at No.11 Milsom Street, the address of Martha Bally's bookshop and circulating library.[17] Starting at 7.00pm and chaired by rota, the evening meetings might involve the reading and discussion of papers and correspondence, the inspection of specimens, and sometimes experiments. The details we have for early 1780 show that on 7 January the members discussed electricity, on 14 and 21 January (at Rack's suggestion) the growth of corallines (calcareous seaweeds), and on 28 January 'petrifactions' or fossils. In February Herschel introduced the topic of light and on 11 February carried out his experiments on the subject. The following week a number of members described their own experiments, there was a hands-on examination of fossils, and Herschel handed in a paper for later debate on 'the central powers of the particles of matter'. On 16 March they heard Herschel speak about measuring mountains on the Moon and debated a paper by Rack on the concept of civilisation. All this was impressive and Rack began to think of publishing the society's transactions, an equivalent to *Letters and Papers*, his new series for the Bath and West. In the end, unlike the comparable societies at Manchester and Exeter,[18] the Bath Philosophical Society regrettably never did publish. As a result, once the revealing entries in Rack's private journal cease in March 1780, we have only scanty records of its proceedings beyond the 31 papers that Herschel delivered in 1780 and 1781, four of which, thanks to William Watson, found a home in the Royal Society's *Philosophical Transactions*. They included his celebrated account in March 1781 of a newly discovered heavenly body, the first observation of the planet Uranus.[19]

Rack had once used an astronomical analogy to characterise societies like theirs. Solitary minds, however cultivated, merely twinkle at a distance, but assembled together 'they form a Glorious Constellation'.[20] Undoubtedly the Bath constellation dimmed somewhat with Herschel's departure for London in 1781, even if he did still correspond and pay occasional return visits. Meetings went on briskly for a time, but by 1784 the picture was looking less rosy. 'We are here rather flat', John Bryant wrote to Herschel that September, 'nothing new going forward in Science & our Society misses you, for we not only decline in Numbers but in amusement'.[21] The losses were grave. By 1785, out of the resident members at least five had gone: the founder Thomas Curtis and the physician John Staker were dead, and Joseph Priestley, John Arden and the naturalist John Walcott had all moved away. In December 1786 William Watson was quite blunt about the situation. He fully expected to see the society dissolved 'after having barely subsisted for a year or two'.[22] It was clear that neither he nor Rack could save it, and Rack, moreover, had not long to live.

The Second Bath Philosophical Society, 1798–c.1805

For a dozen years the first Bath Philosophical Society had no successor. Except for occasional public science lectures, scientific communication languished. It is unlikely that William Watson had instituted his weekly house assemblies of 'scientific residents and learned visitors' by then, though such *conversazioni* were becoming fashionable in London and Watson certainly held them sometime after 1800.[23] So too did the Bath physician John Haygarth, who arrived in Bath from Chester in 1798. Once settled at No.1r Royal Crescent, Haygarth resumed his friendship with his old medical colleague William Falconer, an inquiring doctor of the same stamp. They may well have hatched the scheme for a second Bath Philosophical Society together, Falconer having participated in its predecessor, and both men being familiar with the Manchester Literary and Philosophical Society that now appears to have inspired them.[24] Support soon mustered, the society was inaugurated on 11 December 1798 and proceedings began in earnest on 3 January.[25] Besides Falconer, both Watson and the absent Herschel joined (as did Watson's elderly father, now Sir William Watson, a key figure in London scientific circles), but the majority of known members were new – among them the enterprising physician George Smith Gibbes.[26] Watson himself had reservations about the society (perhaps its lack of an experimental focus), as he mentioned to Herschel in October 1800;

I hope our society here will go on prosperously – I do not quite like the plan it is founded upon, nevertheless it serves to bring together men of science, and make them know one another.[27]

The essence of the plan was straightforward enough – weekly meetings where members spoke on a pre-announced theme.[28] Nothing more is known, but William Smith's latest geological findings must surely have been one subject of keen discussion.[29] Whatever the scientific content of the early meetings, Watson was telling Herschel by March 1804 that they now offered only fleeting entertainment. The society was unlikely to add much to the stock of scientific knowledge, he added, because 'we have no Herschel among us'.[30] Since early 1801 they had met at Marshall's circulating library at the top of Milsom Street, where an independent scholarly library, Bath Publick Library, had also just been formed.[31] The twin organisations had much in common – the diffusion of information and 'the collision of minds' – yet neither lasted long. There is no record of the Philosophical Society after 1805, and in 1807 the learned library dissolved too.[32]

The Third Bath Philosophical Society, 1816–c.1821, 1830

Charles Hunnings Wilkinson, founder of the third Bath Philosophical Society, was then still off stage,[33] administering galvanic medical therapy in London, lecturing around the country, writing on electricity and medical topics, and doubtless absorbing the influential lesson of the new Royal Institution (established in 1799) that serious science, fashionable lectures, and a Utilitarian philosophy could all be combined under one roof. By 1809[34] he had moved to Bath, and in the next few years he acquired and improved the Kingston Baths, initiated galvanic treatments there, built a private lecture room alongside, investigated the Bath waters and published his results, and, not least, instituted annual courses of science lectures. In 1812 he first floated the idea of 'a Bath Philosophical Institution',[35] but while this plan matured, the entrepreneurial Wilkinson directed his energies elsewhere. He became active in the Bath and West Society,[36] added a pump room to his medical establishment, and embarked on the ambitious project of introducing gas street-lighting to Bath – a scheme eventually realised, after much effort and despite opposition from the Corporation, in 1819.[37]

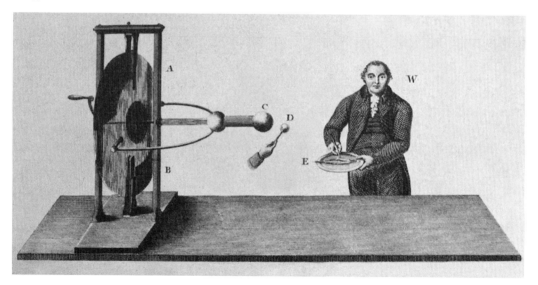

Illustration from C.H. Wilkinson, *Elements of Galvanism in Theory and Practice* (1804) probably depicting Wilkinson himself. (Annals of Science, *December 1967, Bath Central Library, Bath & North East Somerset Council*)

In the midst of all this, in December 1815, Wilkinson at last issued his proposals for a new philosophical society, pointing out the merits of such institutions in London, Manchester, Liverpool, and Newcastle. It came into being on 8 January 1816, doubtless with support from devotees of his lecture courses,[38] and thereafter met every Monday evening at Wilkinson's own Kingston Lecture Room, which was already fitted up with apparatus and furnaces. Unlike the two former societies this was not a gentlemen's scientific club but an open subscription society, one that encouraged women to join as well as young people, manufacturers, respectable tradesmen, and even Bath visitors.[39] To stimulate participation, meetings normally began with oral communications from members before moving on to a lecture on some aspect of science or technology. How this worked in practice can be gauged from the informative, sometimes quite detailed, reports published in the local press up to May 1817[40] – after which, in the nervous atmosphere of the government's Seditious Meetings Act, they abruptly ceased. These reports covering the first two seasons provide the names of over 40 different participants and associates, including the physicians Edward Barlow and G.S. Gibbes, the geologists Rev J.J. Conybeare and Robert Bakewell, the astronomer Rev [John?] Chamberlain, the mathematicians [P.?] Bush and W.G. Horner, the antiquary John Cranch, and the stationer/printseller Robert Ricards (at this time still Secretary of the Bath and West). Among other named contributors were at least two artists (Orme and Hulley), three civil engineers (Brough, Hill, Smith), and three women (Grose, Hawes, Hepburn). The involvement of clergymen must have reassured any doubters that these meetings were not out to undermine belief in a divine Creation – a fear of investigative science (of geology especially) that still persisted in some quarters.[41] As it turned out, the society had a decidedly technological character thanks to Wilkinson's enthusiasm for applying scientific knowledge to solving practical problems. Subjects addressed in the early years dealt with many down-to-earth matters: the repair of roads, the shoeing of horses, improved optical instruments, tests for arsenic, uses for bitumen, breadmaking, Davy's safety lamp, Newman's blowpipe, the dampness of Bath vaults. More speculative were the discussions on the geological sources of the hot springs, the saltiness of the ocean, sunspots, electricity and magnetism, capillary action, the properties of matter, and algebraic equations, with occasional sorties into 'literary' territory in papers dealing with Roman antiquities, the progress of engraving, or artificial memory. Sometimes experiments were performed, sometimes letters from distant correspondents or items brought along by members sparked off general debate, but Wilkinson was always the presiding genius, ever ready with information and ideas.

At the end of the 1816/17 season he reviewed the society's achievement so far, highlighting the stream of original material it had produced and its success in attracting young people, and he went on to suggest forming a library after the summer recess. The start of the third season was duly advertised in October 1817,[42] but beyond that we have a documentary void. It is thought that the society lasted until c.1821. It had definitely lapsed before winter 1824/25 which Wilkinson passed in Geneva.[43] Yet it was not quite done with, because in February 1830 Wilkinson very briefly resurrected it under the banner of the Bath Philosophical Society for the Diffusion of Knowledge. Happily blending (as was claimed) instruction and amusement, the revived meetings at the Kingston Pump Room covered a mixed bag of topics – electricity, the mechanism of the eye, Italian literature, Pestalozzi's educational system, and a new barometric theory (by R. Saumarez, Esq. of Bath). During one lecture on the physics of heat Wilkinson dramatically demonstrated the fireproofing properties of asbestos by holding a lump of red-hot iron in his gloved hand.[44] This, however, may have been at a public lecture at the Kingston Pump Room rather than one strictly for society members. Because the distinction is not always clear, it remains uncertain whether Wilkinson's revived society survived much beyond 1830.

The Bath Mechanics' Institute, from 1825

This era of the so-called 'march of mind' saw a proliferation of new organisations for self-improvement, many of them – like the Society for the Diffusion of Useful Knowledge (or 'Steam Intellect Society'[45]), the new University of London, and numerous mechanics' institutes – directly inspired by Utilitarian principles of popular education. This was the air that Wilkinson breathed and he naturally found himself involved in the Bath Mechanics' Institute, founded in summer 1825 at a gathering of mechanics, tradesmen and supportive patrons. Begun with high hopes,[46] it contributed less in fact to scientific education than might have been expected, in spite of presenting the odd course of science lectures and accumulating a small museum. Its more valuable features were a miscellaneous lending library and a warm reading room. Over the years it lost most of its 'mechanic' members, evolved into the loftier-sounding 'Athenaeum', and in the end merged with BRLSI, an organisation founded about the same time as the Mechanics' Institute but after a longer gestation.[47]

The Bath (Royal) Literary and Scientific Institution, from 1825

From the date it opened in 1799, the metropolitan Royal Institution had exerted a strong influence, most notably in the impetus it gave to public lecturing. Its tiered, heated, lecture theatre, capable of seating 700, had been designed from the start for popular lecturing to genteel audiences of both sexes, as well as for serious courses targeted at professional men, manufacturers, and artisans. To begin with, scientific topics prevailed, with Humphry Davy's entertaining demonstrations proving a particular crowd-pleaser. But within a few years the need to generate more income dictated a change in the Royal Institution's policy, so that, from 1803/4 onwards, outside speakers on art, music, history, and other non-scientific subjects were also engaged in order to boost the number of fashionable subscribers. Soon a speaker such as the scintillating Rev Sydney Smith, lecturing on moral philosophy, found himself addressing packed audiences that outstripped even Davy's. The lesson was not lost on others. Almost every institution founded or rejuvenated in the wake of the Royal Institution henceforth boasted a lecture hall of sorts and made organising a varied lecture programme one of its principal duties.

There were, of course, other possible institutional priorities – a scholarly library, a museum, an exhibition room for works of art, a laboratory, a botanic garden, even an associated school. The initial requirement at Bath was a good library. It is true the spa's commercial circulating libraries could offer plenty of worthy reading in theology, history, travel, and foreign classics, not to speak of magazines, pamphlets, popular novels and plays. On the other hand they carried relatively little science, few heavyweight works of reference, and no runs of learned journals at all. Only a private subscription library would have serious 'academic' literature on its shelves, and this Bath had entirely lacked since the failure of the Bath Publick Library around 1807. A fresh proposal came forward in 1812 from a relative newcomer to Bath, the Unitarian minister Joseph Hunter, who wanted a good library as a focus for what he called 'intercommunication among studious persons'. Pessimists advised him the time was not ripe and the matter dropped. Seven years later Dr Edward Barlow, yet another recent arrival, tried once more (*see Colour Plate VIII*). His prospectus, circulated in 1819, set forth a grander vision encompassing a library, museum of natural history, cabinet of antiquities, lecture hall, laboratory, botanic garden and, in time, an exhibition room, all rolled into one. Here was the germ of the Literary and Scientific Institution, but was it, as Joseph Hunter feared, altogether 'too magnificent'?[48] Costed at £30,000, a princely sum, the scheme found unexpected favour all the same, perhaps spurred by the knowledge that Bristol too had an ambitious institution project in hand.[49] Directors were appointed and a public campaign for subscribers got under way, only to disappointing effect. By late 1820, with less than £4,000 promised, the grand conception was already being watered down.[50] At this point chance intervened. The old-fashioned Lower Assembly Rooms on Terrace Walk burned down overnight, leaving a sad ruin on a prominent site but also signalling a golden opportunity. Within days the naturalist Henry Woods had written to the press suggesting it be rebuilt to house the proposed institution.[51]

Protracted negotiations with the Manvers estate then ensued over leasing the site and the planned reconstruction. While these were in progress Bath Corporation had to be convinced of the scheme's viability, a substantial capital sum raised (through an issue of 400 twenty-guinea shares), trustees elected, an architect found, and noble patronage secured. The nature of the institution-to-be was still in some doubt as late as mid-1823 when 'H.W.' [Henry Woods again?] argued the case for a non-elitist, useful establishment, of real benefit to trade and manufacturing, welcoming even to apprentices, attorneys' clerks and medical students, and certainly not, as some had proposed, a place for concerts and card parties.[52] In the event the outcome was something in between. Built quickly to a rather humdrum design (but retaining the Doric portico that had survived the fire), the Literary and Scientific Institution opened with some ceremony – and large debts – in January 1825. In his inaugural address Sir George Smith Gibbes described knowledge as the ultimate source of national prosperity, cited various successes of modern technology, reminded his audience of famous scientists (not forgetting the local hero, Herschel) and assured them, as usual on such occasions, that the study of natural history, geology and comparative anatomy did nothing but reinforce belief in a beneficent, divine creation.[53] This address, which emphasised the 'scientific' at the expense of the 'literary', was followed in the next 12 months by courses of lectures exhibiting the same bias

on the steam engine, on zoology, and on chemistry, electricity and magnetism (given by Robert Addams of the Royal Institution). The Literary and Philosophical Association, set up in late 1825 as a separate organism within the BLSI, would in time redress the balance towards the 'literary', but it began with a programme strongly weighted towards science and, in the use of 'philosophical' in its title, seemed to hark back to the earlier societies.[54]

Four sub-committees had been formed with responsibility for the library, the collection of antiquities, the natural history museum, and the laboratory, but it appears that stocking the library had greater priority than equipping a laboratory hidden away in the vaults. The first *Annual Report* revealed that £1,700 had already been spent on books, and according to Joseph Hunter, one of the selectors, many of these were large expensive items.[55] Other books arrived as donations, and donations also formed the nucleus of the other collections. The antiquities section soon had casts of ancient sculpture and showcases of medals, coins and seals on display, and in 1827 received a deposit of Roman archaeological finds from the Corporation. A small museum of local natural history and geology was similarly being assembled, catalogued and arranged by the outstanding young geologist, William Lonsdale, with the help of Henry Woods, the Institution's first secretary. The geological items given by the Bath and West Society, already mentioned, joined this collection.

The next few years were a period of consolidation amid constant worries about the balance sheet. The inadequate base of shareholders and subscribers left the Institution perennially short of funds, and adding the 'Royal' tag to its name around 1830 (thanks to William IV's patronage) brought no financial advantage. No longer was there talk of expansion, of operating a laboratory, or of creating a botanic garden.[56] The most prominent activities were the lecture series (open to the paying public) and the private meetings of the Literary and Philosophical Association. The lecture programme had quickly diversified. One course in 1827, followed by another c.1830, dealt with the controversial topic of phrenology, doubtless staged at the wish of Edward Barlow, still influential and himself a devoted student of the subject.[57] Otherwise, the *Annual Report* for 1830

Exterior view of BRLSI by T.H. Shepherd, from John Britton, *Bath and Bristol* (1829).
(*Bath Central Library, Bath & North East Somerset Council*)

and 1831 mentions courses in elocution, poetry, Stonehenge, geology, botany, and comparative anatomy – not a complete list.[58] Popular lectures might be repeated for different audiences. When John Britton spoke on architectural antiquities in winter 1832-3, he delivered each of his eight lectures twice: first in the afternoon to 'the fashionable' and then in the evening to 'the professional and trading part of the community'. He found the institution's rooms 'commodious and handsome', the library well stocked, the museum full of interest, the views from its windows delightful, but he regretted that it was 'not flourishing equal to its deserts'.[59] Indeed, enthusiasm was waning even for the independent Association, and from 1836 this ceased to meet. Some of the old stalwarts had died or moved away, and Hunter and Lonsdale, both gone to important posts in London, were especially missed. In 1838 the number of shareholders had fallen to around 160, with only 30 extra subscribers, though lectures were well enough attended, especially a double series on the ever-popular subject of phrenology.

Successive *Annual Reports* from the mid-1830s to the 1850s depict an institution mainly marking time. The library grew slowly, helped by a deposit of books, maps and prints on Bath from J.J. Chapman, but it was little used by most members who preferred the magazines and daily newspapers to shelves of scholarly reading. Lecture courses tended to be much briefer now, usually only three lectures long instead of the eight, ten or twelve formerly. In the four sessions 1850-1853 speakers on science and technology (including geology, astronomy, applied chemistry, the electric telegraph, and the wonders of microscopy) matched in total those on other subjects. The financial profit from public lectures was now relatively small, and the expansion of the museum into the lecture room in 1854 put a stop to them altogether.

This represented a significant shift in emphasis for the institution. After discussions with other interested parties (the Athenaeum in particular), BRLSI proposed in May 1853 that part of its

Interior view of BRLSI, from James Tunstall, *Rambles about Bath* (1847).
(*Bath Central Library, Bath & North East Somerset Council*)

building should be sublet to the administrators of a new 'city museum'. When Manvers ruled this out, BRLSI went ahead on its own.[60] Two important receipts at this period favoured the museum venture – a mineral collection acquired from Frederick Field and a 'noble' geological collection deposited in 1854 by Charles Moore, the leading authority on the strata of the Bath area. Field and Moore both lent BRLSI invaluable support and curatorial aid as the whole museum came together. With the earlier holdings of natural history and antiquities there was now more than enough material to display in the old lecture room and even to overflow upstairs. More exhibition cases were ordered, but before these were yet in place a trial run for the museum had seen nearly 9,000 visitors pass through the building during the 1854 Bath and West meeting. From 1856 it opened free to the public on three (later four) days a week and was soon increased by the Godfrey collection of over 1,000 stuffed birds, obtained with the help of Bath Corporation and in future one of the museum's main attractions.[61]

Besides the development of the museum there were other signs of progress. The Literary and Philosophical Association revived in late 1856 after a gap of 20 years. Historical and literary topics now dominated its meetings, but over the next decade or two science featured occasionally, with lectures (sometimes accompanied by demonstrations) on, for example, geology, electricity, photography, spectrum analysis, and glass-blowing. A braver decision led BRLSI to purchase its premises in 1859 from the Manvers estate for 2,000 guineas, a sum raised partly by mortgage and partly through a public appeal. A year or so later the Institution Gardens were acquired as well for another 200 guineas, and here in 1865 Leonard Jenyns set up a meteorological station equipped with thermometers and rain gauge to take daily readings.[62] A distinguished naturalist with many scientific friends, Jenyns, like Moore earlier, stirred the institution into activity. In 1869 he donated his scientific library and comprehensive herbarium. This meant extending the building and creating a Jenyns room, but the gift immediately enhanced BRLSI's reputation and doubtless encouraged later donations from Francis Lockey, C.E. Broome, and indeed Jenyns himself who presented the institution with his cabinet of shells and continued to add to the Jenyns library. He had already induced the Bath Natural History and Antiquarian Field Club to hold its meetings at the institution. Although the encroaching museum[63] had no doubt prevented BRLSI being used for sectional meetings of the British Association's Bath conference in 1864, there was no reason why smaller organisations should not meet there, as the Literary and Philosophical Association had long done. The Field Club made it their headquarters in 1865, and much later the Selborne Society, Microscopical Society, and Photographic Society also met there, all contributing to the impression of BRLSI as a cultural centre.

The Later Victorian Societies

The Field Club arose out of the weekly botanical rambles that Jenyns and an old friend, the mycologist C.E. Broome, had been taking, with a few others, around Bath for some years. It had precedents too in the Berwickshire, Tyneside, and Cotswold Field Clubs that Jenyns certainly knew.[64] Formally established in February 1855, the club's stated purpose was 'to make excursions round Bath, with view of [*sic*] investigating the Natural History, Geology, and Antiquities of the neighbourhood'.[65] Its early history is not well documented, but Jenyns, Broome and Moore must have quickly discovered that excursion parties afforded limited scope for serious observation and recording, and that they still needed to make their own expeditions.[66] Once Jenyns had resumed as President in 1864, the club moved its collections and indoor meetings to BRLSI, formulated a plan for four to six excursions a year augmented by regular nature walks, and published its first volume of *Proceedings* (covering 1867-9), which recorded the first outing – to Dyrham Park in 1866 – in which women had participated. Excursions were mainly to places of historical or archaeological interest, notwithstanding the club's rule that natural history should be paid equal attention. Jenyns came to regret this overemphasis on antiquities, while recognising that train excursions brought in more new members than nature rambles round Bath ever did. He rejoiced all the same to find a botanising trip to the Somerset Levels on the programme as late as 1893.[67] The club's journal, besides printing several valuable pieces by Jenyns himself, reveals the spread of members' biological interests, with listings of local fungi (C.E. Broome), molluscs (Henry Bird), and insects (Col. Blathwayt), and articles on mammals, birds, and even the algae present in the spa waters. The volumes of *Proceedings* equally displayed the Field Club's ever-increasing preference for archaeology and architecture as its more scientific members were lost (Broome died in 1886, Jenyns in 1893) and not replaced. The final three volumes, published 1901-09, contain few items of serious natural history.

A rather similar trajectory is evident in the Bath branch of the national Selborne Society which flourished for over three decades from its foundation in 1887 and had a membership eventually topping 300, three times that of the Field Club.[68] As a pressure group for the protection of wildlife the Selborne Society can be bracketed with other Victorian organisations for the protection of birds, open spaces, footpaths, and historic buildings. Indeed the Field Club shared the same protectionist sentiments (as well as some members).[69] Nature was under threat, whether from the widespread shooting and trapping of birds and mammals or the indiscriminate collecting of birds' eggs, butterflies, rare plants, and aquarium specimens. The Bath Selbornians bewailed the activities of 'the professional fern gatherer … exterminating wherever he goes', saw with dismay the sale of wild orchids at Bath market, tried to discourage the sale of bird skins, campaigned against quarrying at Cheddar, and published a column in the *Bath Chronicle* to raise public awareness.[70] Their effectiveness in saving endangered species was probably limited, but the society went some way towards fulfilling its other aim, that of promoting the study of natural history, through lantern-slide lectures at BRLSI, field trips, a small library and herbarium, and specialist sections covering ornithology, botany and geology. It also socialised at annual gatherings held at Claverton,

(*left*) A portrait of H.D. Skrine. (*Bath Central Library, Bath & North East Somerset Council*)

(*right*) One target of the Selborne Society campaigning was the slaughter of birds for fashion accessories. (*Author's collection*)

home of its founder and President, H.D. Skrine, until his death in 1901. Female members were regarded as equals and often gave papers at meetings, among them Lucy Wheatcroft, one of their most zealous secretaries and ramble leaders. However, like the Field Club, they had always included archaeology and historic buildings in their purview, and as with the Field Club the original enthusiasm for natural history gradually ebbed away. In 1903-4 lectures on rood screens and Bath architecture drew packed audiences, and by 1910 even nature rambles had lost their appeal.[71] The same phenomenon of natural history succumbing to antiquarian interests can be observed too in the Somerset Archaeological and Natural History Society, whose Bath branch, founded in 1903, had a similar leaning towards antiquities, even if a minority did want 'more natural history thrown into the proceedings'.[72]

No such backslidings affected the Bath Microscopical Society, a group of keen microscopists who met to share their discoveries in natural history, general science and medicine.[73] The group came together around 1858 and survived for at least 36 years, meeting first at the Public Library, then from 1881 at the Mineral Water Hospital, and finally at BRLSI, and acquiring meanwhile a useful collection of books, journals and slide specimens. Optical instruments were improving all the time, offering much increased magnification and resolution of detail. The investigations of the society's members were accordingly impressive, ranging from the study of plant and animal parasites, blood corpuscles, the mouth parts of snails, and the microstructure of rocks to analysis of the Bath mineral water – in which one member detected arsenic at 1 part in 14 million. The society's long-term secretary, J.W. Morris, advanced the scientific classification of ferns by examining their minute fibro-vascular bundles; others specialised in mosses and insects, and others again were said to be 'confirmed pond-hunters'. Private though much of this activity was, the Microscopical Society went public to particularly dramatic effect when it hosted grand soirées for the British Association conferences held at Bath in 1864 and 1888. Before the 1864 soirée it organised trial displays at the Guildhall, the second of which attracted 300-400 Bathonians, including many 'too inquisitive ladies in crinolines [who] monopolised the entire space before the microscopes'.[74] Colleagues from Bristol were enlisted to help with the soirée proper, held at the Assembly Rooms. In the ballroom, 68 microscopes covered plant and invertebrate life; in the tearoom, another 37 showed vertebrate and inorganic specimens; and the octagon contained a display of the latest scientific instruments. The 1888 event was organised on similar lines, except that this time the card room was used as well to show transparencies of pond life illuminated by gas jets.[75] After this second endeavour the society experienced a drop in active membership. By 1893 they were wishing for a fresh infusion of talent – in vain as it turned out, for average attendance in the next season was down to seven, and the society probably expired in 1896. Doubtless they should have admitted women sooner than they did,[76] as Bath's female microscopists now demonstrated by founding the Ladies' Microscopical Society in January 1897. Presided over by Miss Jarrett of Camerton and meeting at members' houses, this small group was still just functioning 15 years later in 1911.[77] From the slim documentation that survives, plants and insects seem to have been their dominant subjects.

Decline of BRLSI

In the late 1880s BRLSI, under its long-serving chairman, Jerom Murch,[78] once again tried to broaden its appeal, for it was as financially fragile as ever and its ageing membership still hovered stubbornly around 200. Its library remained a valuable asset, dispersed though it was throughout the reading room, four other rooms and a corridor. The 1879 catalogue, which excluded the Jenyns and Chapman books, listed some 8,000 volumes, strongest in history, antiquities and theology but with a respectable showing, too, of natural history and geology – supplemented in 1886 by Broome's botanical library. The museum likewise continued to grow and was on full display at the Literary and Philosophical Association's *conversazione* in 1886 when the whole building, smartened up for the occasion, was thrown open to members and guests.[79] The Association had not wholly abandoned science, as witness a demonstration of a dynamo at the *conversazione* and its annual lecture programme. Thomas Cole's paper on bird migration in 1889 roused particular interest and was serialised in the *Bath Chronicle*.

Once the Moore collection had been expensively moved to the upstairs gallery, the main hall became available to the various independent organisations BRLSI wished to shelter under its roof. These included the recently formed Selborne Society and the still newer Bath Photographic Society, founded c.1889. The latter organised excursions, held regular indoor meetings, and set up a dark room – presumably at BRLSI. And it was here that the Bath commercial photographer William Friese-Greene – a pioneer in the developing technology of cinematography – delivered a highly pertinent address at the society's second AGM in February 1890 on 'photography in an age of movement'.[80]

Making BRLSI into what the Selbornians' chairman, George Norman, envisaged as a grand scientific club failed to arrest its downhill slide in the 1890s. Another Bath institution, the Athenaeum – still flourishing in 1889[81] – was also now in decline and facing too the loss of its premises in the redevelopment of Orange Grove. A merger with BRLSI seemed the best solution to both parties, discussions took place, and terms were agreed. The Athenaeum's books would be specially housed at BRLSI, its members given free access, and BRLSI's microscope room turned into a smoking lounge. The thought of invasion by 'commercial people' and disruptive youths was a bitter pill for some of the institution's members to swallow,[82] but hard necessity forced the issue and the two bodies amalgamated in 1899. In the long run it made little difference. The Athenaeum members soon fell away and had all gone by 1910. By 1915, with BRLSI's own membership reduced to 175, the possibility of closure was already in the air.[83]

The sites of scientific research and technological advance had vastly changed since the days of Priestley, Herschel and William Smith when Bath had been at the cutting edge of discovery. Professionals – in industry, government departments, and universities – now largely dominated the field. Small provincial societies might still play a modest part – in recording their local natural environment, for example, as Moore, Jenyns and their colleagues had shown – but in other respects, even in education, their role was being eroded. The opening of the Bath City Science, Art and Technical Schools in 1892, and their move in 1896 into a purpose-built extension to the Guildhall, illustrates the point exactly. The British Association conference of 1888 had left the city with over £900 towards this rather prestigious project.[84] The struggling BRLSI, which had received civic support in the past, on this occasion got nothing.

Further reading

Hudson, Kenneth, *The Bath and West: a Bicentenary History,* Bradford-on-Avon, Moonraker Press, 1976

Hunter, Joseph, *The Connection of Bath with the Literature and Science of England*, Bath, R.E. Peach, 1853

Lim, H.L.H., 'Bath and the Bath and West of England Society, 1777-1851', *Bath History*, vol.vi, Bath, Millstream Books, pp.108-31

Turner, A.J.(ed.), *Science and Music in Eighteenth Century Bath: An Exhibition in the Holburne of Menstrie Museum, Bath, 22 September 1977-29 December 1977*, Bath, University of Bath, 1977

Proceedings of the Bath Natural History and Antiquarian Field Club, Bath, 1869-1909

13: The Bath Royal Literary and Scientific Institution Reborn

Robert Draper

The late nineteenth-century decline of the Bath Royal Literary and Scientific Institution (BRLSI), discussed in the previous chapter, continued into the twentieth century. A serious blow was the death of the Honorary Curator, H.H. Winwood, in 1920. Although 1925 was BRLSI's centenary the Institution was not in a fit state to hold any events to mark it. It did, however, stimulate the start of a fund for repair work and the collections were re-catalogued by Dr F.S. Wallis of Bristol Museum.

The nineteenth-century BRLSI building obstructed traffic coming up from Bath Spa railway station into the city centre since the only roadway around it was the narrow one currently running in front of the row of shops at Terrace Walk ('Bog Island'). To allow construction of the present roadway above the edge of the Parade Gardens following demolition of the BRLSI building, the Institution moved to its present premises on the west side of Queen Square, Nos.16-18, where it re-opened on 17 November 1932. Three adjacent substantial terrace houses were purchased by Bath City Council and knocked together, the middle staircase being taken out. A separate single-storey building (still known as the Moore Room) was erected at the rear to house the Moore Collection. All the collections had to be packed up, moved and redisplayed.

The Second World War

Following the outbreak of the Second World War the Queen Square building was requisitioned by the Admiralty in 1940. Only 48 hours' notice was given, an extraordinarily short time in which to pack up all the collections once again and dismantle all the displays. Everything was dispersed: books were stored at St Catherine's Court in Batheaston and fossils taken to Bristol Museum where they were kept in a basement. A great deal of other material was dispersed without record.

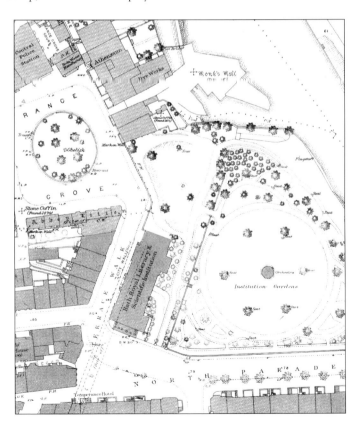

Parts of two sheets of the 1886 1:500 Ordnance Survey of Bath, showing the positions of the original BRLSI building on Terrace Walk and the Bath Athenaeum on Orange Grove. (*Bath Record Office, Bath & North East Somerset Council*).

Demolition of the BRLSI building in Terrace Walk, 1932;
view looking west towards the terrace of shops that still exists.
(*BRLSI collection*)

The Admiralty did not vacate the building until 1959, by which time, of course, all the members had died, lost interest or moved away and the Institution had ceased to function. So it was resolved that '... the Institution shall be dissolved and that all the property shall be vested in [Bath] Corporation for the advancement of Literature and Science in the City of Bath.'

Local Authority Control

As a consequence of this development, Bath City Council had somehow to incorporate BRLSI into its structure. Since the Institution had books, it was put under the Library Committee. In 1960 all the BRLSI collections were returned from wartime stores but a decision was made (not surprising from a Library Committee) not to develop the museum, but to adapt the building for use as the City Reference Library.

In 1967[1] an article appeared in the *Bath Chronicle* instigated by Peter Pagan, the Director of Libaries. It posed the question as to whether the collections should be disposed of and related that 'the storage was like a cracked brain glory hole'. The article was illustrated by a photograph of Ron Pickford, outside No.18 Queen Square, holding the thigh bone of a mammoth. This led to a letter being written to the *Bath Chronicle* by the founder members of Bath Geological Society – Anne Davison, Phil Hewitt, Jeremy Lavis and including its first chairman, Bob Whitaker. Shortly afterwards Whitaker was asked to meet with Peter Pagan and was appointed as Hon. Advisor for

169

Bob Whitaker and Ron Pickford. (*BRLSI collection*)

the Collections, a post he held until Avon County Council took control of BRLSI in 1974. Ron Pickford was appointed curatorial assistant at about the same time. With the support of Councillor Mary Rawlings, funds were obtained to set up museum displays on the second floor and purchase storage boxes, racks etc. Whitaker and Pickford then battled with Pagan and elected members to ensure that as much of the collections as possible remained.

In recognition of this, Ron Pickford, employed as a joiner but also a keen amateur geologist, was made FGS in 1985. Despite his best efforts, a great deal of material was loaned to other museums, to schools, given away or sold. The Bath Reference Library opened to the public in the Queen Square building in 1964. Three years later, in 1967, Bath Geological Society was founded: it was to become one of the main organisations lobbying on behalf of the Institution's interests. There followed a period of 'pass the parcel' as trusteeship was transferred first to the new Avon County Council (Education Department) and subsequently to the Community Leisure Department. In 1982, due to representations to the Charity Commissioners by the Bath Society and Bath Geological Society (in the persons of Lord Raglan, Major Anthony Crombie and Bob Whitaker), Avon County Council was thwarted in its plans to move the Library's administrative offices into the Queen Square building.

1986 saw the appointment of a curator, Diana Smith, who had previously worked for the Norfolk County Museums Service.

In August 1987 council and museum officers held discussions in the Bath City Solicitor's Office regarding Avon County Council taking a lease in the Podium Development for library space. Before undertaking that, assurances were sought that Avon would co-operate to the full in transferring BRLSI property into the custody of new trustees. The future administration of the trust's exhibits and disposition of the trust's financial affairs were matters with which the Charity Commission would be concerned. There was no intention to display as a distinct unit the exhibits belonging to the trust.

Five concerned individuals[2] wrote to the Chief Charity Commissioner on 5 August 1987 to articulate the 'uncertainties and anxieties' raised by then current proposals for a change of trusteeship that would have entailed 'transfer of the trusteeship exercised by Avon County Council to Bath City Council, and the sale or lease of the Queen Square building'. Their letter (which is to be found in the BRLSI archives) provides a succinct history of BRLSI, its collections, and some of the misfortunes that befell the Institution's property during local authority trusteeship.

The Friends of BRLSI
On 23 March 1988[3] a new body was formed: 'Friends of the Bath Royal Literary and Scientific Institution'. An American (Karl Jaeger) who had heard of the Institution and who tried to join it, and a lawyer (Michael King) whose grandfather had been involved in the earlier days of the

Institution, provided the unlikely combination that proved to be a catalyst for action. At an open meeting in the Pump Room, Roger Rolls introduced the history of the Institution and Michael King discussed legal issues. Simultaneously the Bath Society set up its own working group to consider the future of BRLSI.

Reporting to the meeting, Karl Jaeger recorded strongly held opposing views from members of the 'RLS Steering Group' operating within Bath City Council. On the one hand it was thought that there was no need for the Friends until the Institution had been revived and that Avon should be allowed to get on with its proposals, whereas an opposing view was that Bath City Council's plan to sell the Queen Square premises and place the Institution's collections within the new Bath City Museum at Bridge Street would safeguard the collections in a way that could not happen if the collections remained at Queen Square. Despite these views it was decided to make representations to the trustees, Avon County Council, seeking the involvement of the Friends in any discussions of the future of BRLSI.

The (local authority) cuckoo in the BRLSI nest: cartoon by a Friend of BRLSI, 1988. (*Michael King*)

One of the first actions of the Friends was to respond to a discussion paper produced by Avon County Council on 12 April 1988. In their response they stated that 'The Friends see themselves as the embryo members of the Institution and wish as a body to become members as soon as possible and certainly before any new trustees are appointed'. On the matter of trustees they were cautious: 'In view of the potential conflict of interests (non-payment of rent, past sales of assets and possession of parts of the collections, etc.) we would strongly object to any Councillor or Officer of Avon or Bath being a trustee during the initial period of re-establishment of the Institution.' Avon County Council responded to this by suggesting a list of 17 organisations[4] that should appoint trustees of BRLSI.

It was stated that the first tasks would be to locate, list, assess, value and catalogue the collections, the library and the archive. Avon County Council had changed their view on whether the identity of the BRLSI collections could be maintained and now thought that it could.

In May 1990 Mr J.F. Claricoat and Mr Stephen Slack at the Charity Commission were getting a rather larger postbag than normal. The Friends had put out an urgent appeal for its members to write to the Commission urging it to take action after Avon County's decision to ignore the Steering Group's report and instead disperse the Institution's collections and sell the Queen Square building. In response, the Commission reported that several disparate groups were writing to them with ideas for the charity's future and encouraged Michael King to draw these groups together. A Steering Group was thus set up to move matters forward with the Charity Commissioners, Michael King's detailed knowledge of charity law and practice proving invaluable in its subsequent work.

Shadow Trusteeship

In April 1992 there was a meeting of the wonderfully titled 'Urgency Sub-Committee' at which the Steering Group and Bath University put forward a joint proposal for the establishment of an interim Trustee Body. Events clearly moved quickly, for the inaugural meeting of the BRLSI Shadow Trustees took place on 24 April 1992. The Shadow Trustees comprised:

- Three nominees from Bath University: Prof. Rodney Quayle FRS (Vice-chancellor), Richard Mawditt OBE, Professor Angus Buchanan
- Six nominees of the ad hoc Steering Group: Edgar Avent, Rodney Cross, Dr David Dunlop (chairman), Michael King, John Skipper, Robert Whitaker MBE

The BRLSI Shadow Trustees suggested a future composition of the BRLSI board of trustees, essentially the same as the current one. They proposed that the trustees should comprise:

- Four nominees of national bodies: the British Academy, the British Museum (Natural History), the Royal Society, and the Geological Society/Geologists' Asssociation
- Four nominees from local academia: three from Bath University, one from Bath College of Higher Education (BCHE), now Bath Spa University
- Two nominees from the Area Museum Service
- Two nominees from Local Authorities
- Five elected from the membership of BRLSI

The July 1992 briefing notes of the Trustees make stark reading. They accepted the need to sell off or rent part of the Queen Square building to fund the Institution (which had a building and collections but no income at all) and also to find alternative homes for some of the collections (but not the Moore or Jenyns which were specific to Bath) in order to reduce expenditure. Accountants Pannell Kerr Forster produced an interim report saying that, even by selling off one of the three buildings and letting two floors of the remaining two, insufficient capital and revenue would be produced.

In January 1993 three of the Friends – Micky Brown, Dr Peter Ford and Bob Draper – were tasked with looking at similar organisations around the country. They were to look at their organisation, activities and finances and see what useful lessons could be learnt.

A re-launch exhibition was held in May 1993 with a catalogue written by former curator Roger Vaughan and display material produced by the students of the BCHE Art Department at Sion Hill under the supervision of David Beaugard. The first new members for over 50 years joined BRLSI. At this stage everything was being fuelled by faith and optimism rather than money. Painful efforts were being made to extract money from Bath City Council and Avon County Council. Membership stood at 215, receiving a boost after an article in *The Times*.

At a meeting in June 1993 the idea of renting out part of the premises took on a more realistic tone as government money was being made available to local councils to provide training for the unemployed. Premises would be needed for this and the Institution was centrally located, even if it was in a poor state of repair. Bath City Council was setting up an Employment Training Unit (ETU) and by June negotiations were looking promising. The clincher (suggested by Clive Abbott, then Chief Executive of Bath City Council) was getting the ETU to agree to pay a lump sum in lieu of rent up-front which could then be used to pay for refurbishment of the premises before ETU moved in. Brooks Chartered Surveyors prepared specifications of works to be carried out and Crisp Cowley negotiated rental terms. The top two floors were solely for use by the new tenants (actually Bath City Council): in addition they had daytime use of the first floor and two offices on the ground floor. Local Authority funding was still being sought before the Shadow Trustees would agree to take over the trusteeship. Some concern was expressed that, as the main users would be young adults, potential wear and tear could be significant! Budget costings were available to concentrate thinking – a quarter of a million pounds was the first estimate for the refurbishments.

By July 1993 all the strands were coming together. The Director of Leisure and Tourist Services, reporting to the Spa and Recreation Committee, advised the appointment of a Development Officer for a four-year period, jointly funded by the Area Museums Council for the South West and recommended a one-off grant of £10,000 for start-up costs. The Shadow Trustees were under pressure to take over the trusteeship but were resisting until adequate funding was reasonably certain. In August 1993 the BRLSI Property Committee recommended acceptance of the letting to Bath City Council on behalf of the ETU, as a consequence telling Avon that the trusteeship could be passed over. This was approved by the Shadow Trustees on 5th August 1993. The same month, on 19 August and with a membership of 250, BRLSI held its first meeting of members since 1939. Then on 27 September 1993 the BRLSI trustees were incorporated at Companies House, and two days later the Charity Commission 'Scheme' took effect. Instructions were issued to all holders of parts of the collections that these were now under the control of BRLSI. The second *Friends Newsletter* gave the good news to supporters and announced a programme of monthly talks, to be held at the Bath and County Club while the Queen Square building was in the hands of the builders. The building renovation was accomplished by moving all the collections into the Moore Room while work was carried out in the main building, and then back again afterwards. Work parties of volunteers in groups of about a dozen toiled endlessly, moving all the boxes and artefacts.

The BRLSI premises in Queen Square after the 1995 restoration. (*BRLSI collection*)

In the newly refurbished and re-roofed buildings, tenants Training Services occupied the top floors of the building and 'time shared' some of the rooms on the first floor. This enabled evening and weekend meetings to be held in the Institution for the first time since the Second World War. Various 'Discussion Groups' were formed and local societies such as Bath Geological Society, Bath Natural History Society and the Bath and Camerton Archaeological Society used the premises for meetings. A Development Manager, Linda Wigley, was appointed and serious work started again on conserving and cataloguing the collections using volunteers. The growth of IT was harnessed from an early stage with work on creating a website and a 'Virtual Museum', and a weekly email *Bulletin* inaugurated. The re-launched BRLSI held the first of its regular Annual General Meetings on 11 October 1996, and in 1998 the Institution's activities were recorded for the first time in a new series of *Proceedings*, published annually since then.

The long-running story of the Institution's claim against the former Avon County Council reached its final act in November 2001 when a compromise settlement was reached, although the money due (including interest) was not paid to BRLSI until April 2002. After expenses were met, the Institution had £600,000 to invest to provide for the refurbishment of the building once Training Service's lease expired. The aim was to preserve the listed building and to enable a modest expansion of activities. The Institution acknowledged those who did the original researches with dogged determination which made it possible to pursue the claim – Stella Pierce, Marta Inskip and Dr Dorothy Speed – and also the London solicitors, Bates, Wells & Braithwaite who negotiated the settlement.

Conclusion

Following its successful rebirth, BRLSI has flourished. The number of meetings has grown to around 300 annually and BRLSI has achieved a deserved reputation (as hoped by the people who strived for its resurrection) as a 'cultural village hall'. This reputation has been enhanced by the fact that local societies and Institutions such as those of Physics, Mechanical Engineers and Structural Engineers have used BRLSI for regional meetings. As well as very wide-ranging popular lectures, 'hands-on' scientific activities for children have proved very popular, as has the 'Bath Taps into Science' science fair that takes place in Green Park station as part of National Science Week. The latter has even attracted schools from abroad to come and give demonstrations. Another aspect of education in which the Institution has been involved is in providing some stimulation for brighter children, with maths masterclasses sponsored by the London Mathematical Society and APEX (Able Pupils Extending Opportunities) for the local authority.

As this book makes abundantly clear, Bath has a very long history of scientific involvement. An academic quadrangle of Bath, Bristol and Bath Spa Universities and the University of the West of England, and a science park in the offing, gives a concentration of thoughtful minds. Finding lecturers to inform and inspire has hardly proved a taxing task. Local employment for those of a scientific and engineering bent includes such fields as software, structural engineering, telecommunications and pharmaceuticals. Bath University's steady output of very bright graduates who find the area an attractive place in which to live augurs well for the future.

Further Reading
Material related to the history of BRLSI and its relaunch is to be found in the BRLSI archives.

14: The British Association in Bath

Trevor Fawcett and Colin Axon

The British Association for the Advancement of Science ('the BA') was founded in 1831 in response to the perceived failure of the learned societies, the universities, and the government to promote British science. Its primary aim was to foster research that would otherwise never be undertaken, helped by the award of financial grants. Despite always holding its Annual Meeting outside London – each time in a different city – the BA focused on the national picture. Encouraging science in the various provincial centres in which it met was only a by-product of the bigger objective. All the same, the annual September gatherings clearly had a galvanising effect on the host cities. They required much advance planning and fund-raising, brought local scientists to public notice, and produced a flurry of civic excitement and long newspaper reports during the week or more that the event lasted. First York, and then in turn Oxford, Cambridge, Edinburgh, Dublin, Bristol, Liverpool, Newcastle and Birmingham provided the earlier venues (1831-9), and Bath, it seems, was eventually penciled in for 1845, doubtless with the backing of P.B. Duncan, keeper of the Ashmolean at Oxford and a stalwart supporter of BRLSI.[1] Yet Cambridge was selected for 1845 instead.

The 1864 Meeting

In the end Bath had to wait its turn until September 1864,[2] the Association having overcome its long-held scruples as to the spa's suitability and accepted the recommendation of the influential Roderick Murchison, president of the Royal Geographical Society. Making the detailed arrangements for this meeting would have been an onerous task, with Charles Moore, C.E. Davis and Rev H.H. Winwood playing key roles as the local secretaries and with the mayor-elect, the enthusiastic Jerom Murch, persuasive behind the scenes. A week of social events (including two Guildhall banquets, one sponsored by Murch, now mayor in person, the other by William Tite, the city's MP), together with visits and field excursions, general lectures, plus a full programme of sectional meetings, all had to be catered for. The sections for Mathematics/Physics, Chemical Sciences, and Geology were respectively accommodated in the Bluecoat School, the Corridor Rooms, and the Guildhall, while both Biology/Physiology and Geography/Ethnology squeezed into the two wings of the Mineral Water Hospital, Economics/Statistics into the Milsom Street Rooms, and Mechanical Science into the Grammar School in Broad Street.

Obvious venues for the general meetings were the Theatre Royal (newly rebuilt after a devastating fire) and the Assembly Rooms. The latter held two major evening events – a crowded *conversazione* for members, and the Bath Microscopical Society's soirée and exhibition. It was also used for the BA's AGM on the final afternoon. The theatre was more suited to the three general lectures: the eminent geologist Sir Charles Lyell's presidential address, David Livingstone's account of his recent Zambesi expedition, and Henry Roscoe's lecture demonstration on the chemical action of light. Such was the demand to hear Livingstone that his lecture had to be read simultaneously to an overflow audience at the Mineral Water Hospital. Among hundreds of sectional papers, maybe a dozen had specifically local interest, including Charles Moore on the geology of Southwest England, Charles Daubeny on the thermal waters, Leonard Jenyns on Bath meteorology, J.E. Daniel on molluscs of the area, and J.L. Stothert on a machine for testing girders. Isaac Pitman handed in a technical paper about his shorthand system that was not actually read. One of the most

Sir Charles Lyell lecturing at Bath Theatre Royal during the British Association meeting in 1864, from the *Bath Chronicle* reports.

keenly anticipated sessions on the programme, a confrontational debate between the explorers J.H. Speke and Sir Richard Burton concerning the disputed source of the White Nile, never took place. Speke fatally shot himself the day before on a partridge shoot at his uncle's estate, Neston Park, near Corsham, Wiltshire. Whether an accident or suicide no-one could be sure.[3]

This tragic event apart, the Bath meeting proved a great success. It attracted an attendance of some 2,800 members and associates (37% of them women) – three times the number at earlier gatherings in Plymouth, Southampton, and Swansea, for instance, and not many fewer than recent meetings at Oxford and Newcastle. It brought in a welcome influx of new members for the BA, and it had been a scientific feast. Charles Moore felt by the end that he had experienced 'a sort of mental intoxication'. Another measure of the meeting was that John D. Hooker, who was to become the Director of Kew Gardens the following year, wrote to Charles Darwin before the meeting had ended commenting on the mixed reception of Lyell's address and other events.[4]

The 1888 Meeting

More than 20 years later, the BA's nine-day meeting at Bath in 1888, while worthy in every respect, went off with less éclat.[5] There were fewer national celebrities to match the stars of 1864 like Lyell, Murchison, and Livingstone, and the overall attendance of just under 2,000 members was significantly down. This time an extra section had to be accommodated, Anthropology having meanwhile hived off from Geography. Some of the sectional venues were also new – Mathematics/Physics housed in St James's Memorial Hall, Chemistry in the Friends' Meeting House, and Economics/Statistics in Christchurch Hall. The site for the main lectures now became the Drill Hall on the Lower Bristol Road which could take an audience of 2,000, but turned out to have poor acoustics and ventilation. Here the BA's president, Sir Frederick Bramwell, delivered an opening address extolling his own profession of mechanical engineering. The other big evening lecturers were W.E. Ayrton on the topical theme of electrical power transmission, and T.G. Bonney speaking about 'the foundation stones of the Earth's crust'.

The substantial part of the meeting lay as usual in the many section events, but apart from a few papers on local geology there was little of immediate Bath relevance. What gave a better impression of Bath and its neighbourhood were the score of carriage and train excursions laid on for the two free days. The most prominent here was the official visit conducted by the city surveyor, Major C.E. Davis, to the recently excavated and controversially rebuilt Roman Baths. Among the more social occasions the soirées at the Assembly Rooms again rated highly, the second of them producing another rich exhibition from the Microscopical Society. Taking stock of the whole meeting, the *Bath Herald* singled out one other popular hit, the demonstration in the Masonic Hall of Edison's improved phonograph.

As in 1864, BRLSI had no active role, though plenty of BA members must have looked in to see its museum. Over 50 Bath notabilities had been on the organising committee; some £2,000 had been raised in donations; hotels, shops and restaurants had benefited from the extra influx of visitors; and there was one useful residue from the meeting in a special *Handbook to Bath* (edited by J.W. Morris) prepared for the occasion. Bath had a second time acquitted itself pretty well.

The 1978 Meeting

It was a further 90 years before the BA's third, and most recent, visit to Bath. Much had changed in the intervening years – to science, Bath, and the BA. Professional science was only emerging in 1888, but by 1978 was essentially the only way new fundamental discoveries were made. The dramatic expansion of higher education in the post-Second World War period included specifically technical institutions – Bath's amongst them. Furthermore, school education had expanded and changed. So the BA too had evolved. The 1978 Annual Meeting[6] was held on the still young Bath University of Technology's Claverton Down site, and only a small number of special events took place in the city. Also evident was the start of a major shift of the BA's focus to younger people, with a special programme of events and lectures for sixth formers and students. These included events of global concern such as the use of technology in the developing world. Even so, the purpose of the Annual Meeting remained consistent with its origins – the engagement of non-experts with some of the latest ideas and discoveries in all aspects of science, engineering, and medicine. Consistent too with the past was the eminence of the 1978 President – Professor Dorothy Hodgkin (Nobel Prize for Chemistry, 1964). New Sections had been added to keep abreast of various emerging subjects, for example Forestry, Biomedicine, and Sociology. Crucially though, the subjects for discussion continued to be the important ones of the day: the effects of the Torrey Canyon oil spill disaster, and an address by the Secretary of State for Energy, Tony Benn, analysing the impact of science and technology.

While there was increased administrative support, the events and lectures were still arranged and organised by local scientists. As scientific endeavour had become a worldwide competition, very few lectures were specifically on 'local' science. This can be summed up by saying that whereas in the nineteenth century local scientists spoke on local science (obvious examples being geology and botany), in the twentieth century they spoke on global science. But topics which did have strong local resonance included lectures or sessions on rheumatism and arthritis, physics and music, excavations of cave deposits in the Mendips, and conserving urban Bath. Two other topics with strong local, historically important, connections were the 'exploitation of sheep and cattle in local industries', and the 'role of botany in meeting food, energy, and environmental needs'. The latter remains a globally important theme 30 years on. Some topics would have seemed alien to a nineteenth-century audience, though nonetheless are direct descendants. This was literally true for the session on the molecular biology of inherited disorders. Others would not have seemed out of place, for example, 'The Structure of the Earth's Crust'. Local scientific history and industrial archaeology were represented by talks on water power, Brunel, and William Smith. Twentieth-century technology allowed the introduction of new features such as films, even if the content of *Big Bill – The story of the Heron* would have been at home in the previous meetings. One technological achievement which apparently was 'just round the corner' but that has still not been managed was 'One Thousand Miles per Gallon: Novel Ways of Saving Fuel'.

Visits to local sites of scientific interest were easier to make in 1978, and some would have been familiar a hundred years earlier, others entirely inconceivable. For example, visits to wine merchants (Harveys in Bristol), hospitals (Royal United, and Mineral Water), and industrial installations (Stothert & Pitt, and the Somerset coalfields) to see the latest technologies were standard stuff. But visits to the Ministry of Defence, various chemical works at Avonmouth, and in particular the laboratories at the nuclear power station at Berkeley showed how far science and engineering had changed since the first two meetings in Bath. Perhaps reassuringly, many of the social events would be wholly recognisable and comforting to any nineteenth-century time-traveller. Concerts, walking tours, dinners, and play readings were all programmed for the evening entertainment of the delegates. Familiar, too, would have been many of the museums and galleries. Although BRLSI had yet to be reborn, the City Reference Library used 18 Queen Square to display a selection from Charles Moore's fossil collection. One other major difference from the first two meetings was the level of media coverage. Television and radio had since been invented and become ubiquitous, and the print media had expanded considerably. Seemingly commonplace techniques such as photographic reproduction in newspapers had transformed the way science and scientists were reported and portrayed. Media interest in the 1978 event was greater than ever before, but this was as nothing compared with the coverage Annual Meetings have attained following the invention of the internet and the world wide web.

The BA Today

The BA continues its transformation into the twenty-first century with nationwide engagement via science clubs in primary and secondary schools, the organisation of National Science Week, and a new emphasis on dialogue with the public over the ethical issues raised by new science.[7] Reflecting these changes, the 'Annual Meeting' has now become the 'Annual Festival' with a resurgence of city-based activities which mix education and entertainment as never before. However, the core activities, peripatetic nature, and purpose remain unchanged in a way that Moore, Winwood, Stothert, and Morris would have recognised.

Further Reading

Howarth, O.J.R., *The British Association for the Advancement of Science: a Retrospect 1831-1931*, 2nd edition, London, British Association, 1931

MacLeod, Roy M. & Collins, Peter (eds.), *The Parliament of Science: the British Association for the Advancement of Science 1831-1981*, Northwood, Science Reviews, 1981

Morrell, Jack & Thackray, Arnold, *Gentlemen of Science: Early Years of the British Association for the Advancement of Science*, Oxford, Clarendon Press, 1981

Briggs, Dr Peter, *The BA at the end of the 20th Century – a Personal Account*, London, British Association, 2004; available electronically at www.the-ba.net

15: University Science and Technology in Bath

Angus Buchanan

The development of the ancient professions of the law, medicine and theology in England was dominated for many centuries by the universities of Oxford and Cambridge, but this situation has been transformed in the last 200 years by the rapid growth of industrialisation, with its demand for expertise in new fields of scientific knowledge and the acquisition of novel technical skills. The first institutional expression of this change was the foundation of University College London in 1826. Elsewhere, attempts were made to set up new university colleges on the collegiate principles of Oxford and Cambridge, like the one which became the University of Durham in 1832. Others, like the grandiose scheme of 1839 for what was to be called 'Queen's College' on Claverton Down in Bath, never got off the drawing board.[1] Bath had to wait for over a hundred years for the foundation of its first university, and then the initiative came from the neighbouring city of Bristol.

Bath's first University Project. One of the drawings prepared by the architect, James Wilson, for 'Queen's College, Bath'. Nothing came of this ambitious project, but it represents an early aspiration to develop university-level education in the city. (*Author's collection*)

Early Developments in Bristol

The pressure for better scientific leadership and technical instruction from a society that saw itself as 'the workshop of the world' led to a spate of provincial foundations in the second half of the nineteenth century. Amongst these, the Bristol Trade School, set up in 1856, was a comparatively small venture but one of great significance for the future development of higher education in Bath and the rest of the south-west. The Bristol Trade School took over the premises of a defunct diocesan school in Nelson Street, in the middle of the city. Supported by national spokesmen for technical education such as Canon Henry Moseley and Lyon Playfair, the School grew steadily under the headmastership of Thomas Coomber. The Bristol Society for Merchant Venturers (SMV), a wealthy body of businessmen with a long tradition of philanthropic benefactions in Bristol, came to take an interest in it and in 1885 assumed full responsibility for the School, constructing new premises for it in Unity Street, where it became known as the 'Merchant Venturers' School'. At this point in its development the School consisted of a teaching staff of 12, including the Headmaster. The general objectives of the School were neatly encapsulated in the Prospectus as providing 'a complete, continuous, and thoroughly sound preparation for an industrial career'.[2]

Thomas Coomber retired as Headmaster in 1890, after 33 years of service in which he had acquired the reputation of being the 'father of technical instruction in Bristol'. He was replaced by Julius Wertheimer, BSc, who had previously held a post at the Leeds School of Science. Under him, the School was able to take advantage of a new commitment to technical education by the state. Ever since 1870, successive governments had recognised that the provision of elementary education could no longer be left entirely to private and voluntary efforts, and had taken the initiative in establishing compulsory elementary education for all children. This had encouraged attempts to make similar provision for secondary education, and especially technical education, so that the Technical Instruction Act of 1889 gave local authorities powers to develop technical education. However, these were permissive rather than compulsory powers, and no special provision was made to raise rates for the purpose. Fortunately for technical education, the proceeds from a tax on spirits – 'whisky money' – were made available the following year for expenditure on such developments. In Bristol this amounted to the handsome sum of £5,700 per annum, part of which was allocated to the Technical School. So the School expanded, assuming a new style in 1894 as the Merchant Venturers' Technical College (MVTC), with Julius Wertheimer becoming Principal and taking the title of Professor of Chemistry and Metallurgy.

Another institution to benefit from the 'whisky money' was the University College of Bristol, which had been founded in 1876 and developed an ambitious programme of courses in higher education. It was reasonable to expect some collaboration between the MVTC and the University College, and negotiations were conducted intermittently in the 1890s to explore the possibility of a federation between the two bodies. A deal was eventually brokered by the Wills family which made a large benefaction to the University College, enabling it to acquire its Charter as the University of Bristol in 1909. But as prominent members of the SMV, the Wills family were able to secure a concession whereby the MVTC would provide the Faculty of Engineering in the University, even though in other respects the two institutions preserved their separate identities.

This curious arrangement worked tolerably well for 40 years. Professor Wertheimer became Dean of the University Faculty of Engineering, as well as Principal of the MVTC, and when he died in 1923 he was succeeded in both posts by Professor Andrew Robertson, who also held the Chair of Mechanical Engineering in the Faculty until his retirement in 1949. At this point a major reorganisation occurred. The SMV, anxious about the escalating costs of higher education, handed over the College to the Bristol Local Education Authority (LEA). At the same time, the University established its own Department of Engineering, distinct from that of the College, and the two institutions went their separate ways. The LEA recognised that the Unity Street premises were no longer adequate for the expanding College of Technology, Bristol, as it was now styled, and began to seek alternative accommodation. This was found in Mullers' vacant Orphan Houses in Ashley Down, and the transition was made in stages under its new Principal, F.W. Partington (1949-1954) and his successor, George H. Moore (1954-1968).

Before the transition was complete, another change was inaugurated. Following the decision by the government in 1956 to establish several new Colleges of Advanced Technology (CATs) to pursue higher technical education to university level, the higher level work of the Bristol College was hived off to form the Bristol College of Science and Technology, leaving the remainder to become Bristol Technical College.[3] The former then acquired the CAT designation and expanded its higher level work under the supervision of the National Council for Technological Awards. The new Diploma in Technology was awarded to students who successfully completed four-year 'sandwich courses' that included periods of practical experience. There was also an insistence on the inclusion of non-specialised studies, which were to comprise one tenth of the examinable work.

Hot on the heels of these changes came another revolution. In 1963 the government accepted the recommendation of the Robbins Report on *Higher Education* that the CATs should be raised to full university status.[4] This created a major problem for the Bristol CAT, because the Ashley Down site, in the middle of a heavily developed suburban district, was manifestly inappropriate for a new university. Attempts had already been made to move within Bristol, sites at King's Weston and Rockwells being prepared for the purpose, but all were subject to irksome restrictions. The hunt for a new site, giving freedom to expand, was on.

The Founding of Bath University

The problem was resolved in 1964, when the CAT accepted a generous offer from the City of Bath to take over the playing fields on Claverton Down, so that Bath at last acquired its putative university. The College architects, Robert Matthew, Johnson-Marshall & Partners, moved swiftly to prepare an outline plan for the new campus,[5] and to establish a 'Preliminary Building' on the site (subsequently known as the South Building of the university). This was occupied in 1965, and building continued steadily thereafter for several years so that most of the institution, now called – under the Charter of 1966 – the 'University of Bath: A Technological University', was housed on Claverton Down by the mid-1970s. The name was changed briefly to Bath University of Technology, but then settled down as the University of Bath.

The University of Bath. The first 'permanent' building on Claverton Down was the Chemistry block, seen here under construction in 1967. Ironically, this block has now been demolished and its replacement is under construction. (*Photograph by the author*)

Springtime at the University of Bath. With the completion of the main Parade, the Great Hall (on the left) and the first residential building (on the right), and with the campus landscaping taking shape the University had begun to settle in to Claverton Down by the spring of 1973. (*Photograph by the author*)

The varied nomenclature reflected the wish, strongly felt by many of its founder members, to retain a clear association with its roots as an institution of higher scientific and technological education. Even though the present title appears to have abandoned this aspiration, the reality is that the University of Bath retains a strong emphasis on science and technology. Of the original 'Schools' designed in 1966, virtually all took over the structure and personnel of departments from the CAT: there had been Departments of Aeronautical and Mechanical Engineering; Electrical Engineering; Applied Chemistry; Applied Physics; Mathematics; Pharmacy; Architecture; and General Studies. All of them translated, in varying degrees of complexity, into 'Schools' with professorial heads. Dr Joseph Black, who had come over from the University of Bristol in 1960 to become Head of the Department of Aeronautical and Mechanical Engineering, was appointed as the first Professor of the School of Mechanical Engineering. Further, the new university signalled its determination to promote research by appointing several readerships, including Mr M.W. Hardisty, of the School of Biological Sciences, for his pioneering study of lampreys, and Mr Gerald Walters, for his work in the humanities.

The overwhelming strength of the University, in teaching and research, remained engineering and applied sciences. It was here that it built up in subsequent decades its enviable rating for outstanding work, under three successive vice-chancellors who were all Fellows of the Royal Society – Dr Leonard Rotherham, an electrical and nuclear engineer (1968-1976); Professor Paul Matthews, a physicist (1976-1983); and Professor Rodney Quayle, a microbiologist (1983-1992). Architecture and Building Engineering, Management Studies, Mathematical Sciences, Modern Languages and Social Sciences have made a creditable contribution to this record. The fact remains, however, that there is a partial vacuum in the coverage of the arts and humanities in the University of Bath, even though any deficiency in this respect in the civic life of Bath has been met to some extent by institutions such as Bath Spa University moving into the gap.

Other Developments in Bath

The city had established a sound educational system in the nineteenth and twentieth centuries, with some excellent schools and other institutions. It had been the home base for the Bath and West Agricultural Society from its foundation in 1777, and had promoted a flourishing intellectual life through bodies such as BRLSI, which opened in 1825. In 1864 and 1888, the city had hosted meetings of the British Association for the Advancement of Science, and other intellectual organisations had found it a congenial meeting place. A Technical College had been set up in 1896 in response to the Technical Instruction Act of 1889, taking advantage of the same 'whisky money' that had been so useful in Bristol. This had been housed first in a wing of the Guildhall (marked still by the educational frescoes round the parapet), and then in the building that had been a hospital in Beau Street, before it moved to the uncompromisingly modern buildings in Avon Street in the 1960s. A small School of Pharmacy had been set up in Bath in 1907, and this had moved to Bristol in 1929 to become part of the MVTC. As such it became responsible for the strong Pharmacy component in the new university, when it returned to Bath in 1966.

An Emergency Teacher Training College had been established at Newton St Loe after the Second World War. This became the Bath Training College, and subsequently Bath Spa University. In the early 1990s, serious negotiations were conducted to merge the College with the University, but these broke down for various reasons and the two institutions went their own ways. But logistic considerations of scales and shared resources suggest that the possibility may be explored again.

Meanwhile, two university institutions flourish in the city of Bath, alongside a substantial amount of intellectual activity in other organisations, various international festivals, and a wealth of local societies. The University of Bath remains the city's leading institution in scientific and technological education, with an outstanding national and international reputation for research that draws students from all over the world. It is clear, however, that the big challenges and difficult decisions which have been tackled in the past are by no means the last, and that the twenty-first century will be an exciting period for the development of scientific and technological education in Bath.

Further Reading

Buchanan, R. Angus, 'From Trade School to University: a microcosm of social change' in Gerald Walters (ed.), *A Technological University: an experiment in Bath*, Bath, Bath University Press, 1966, pp.12-26

Buchanan, R. Angus, 'Bath: University City' in *Bath History*, vol.ix, Bath, Millstream Books, 2002, pp.160-180

Notes

Preface

1   Hunter, Joseph, The Connection of Bath with the Literature and Science of England, Bath, R.E. Peach (Pocock's Library) & London, J.H. Parker, 1853.
2   Williams, W.J. & Stoddart, D.M., Bath – Some Encounters with Science, Bath, Kingsmead Press, 1978.

Introduction

1   300 have been found in Britain, Gaul and Northern Provinces, see Nutton, V., *Ancient Medicine*, Abingdon, Routledge, 2004, p.31.
2   The author first learned of Junianus when attending a lecture at the BRLSI by Stephen Clews, who then provided all the information in the remainder of this note together with much useful background information. The inscription on the stone is recorded in the minute book of the Society of Antiquaries vol iv (1744) p.210. and vol viii (1757) p.29. The first formal published description of the stone was in *Archaeologia*,1788, in an article entitled 'Observations on certain Stamps and Seals used anciently by oculists', written by a Mr Gough. Junianus' medicine-stamp is described in Scarth, H.M., *Aquae Solis, or Notices of Roman Bath*, London, Simpkin Marshall & Bath, R.E. Peach, 1864, pp.32-34: this nineteenth-century paper is the source of all the information given here concerning the eighteenth-century history of the stone and its eighteenth-century documentation.
3   The latin word *scientia*, from which the English word *science* is derived, always simply meant 'knowledge'.
4   The author is extremely grateful to Jill Frederick of Moorhouse University for help with this section. Translations of the poem into modern English may be found in many anthologies of early English poetry. Two prose translations well-accepted as scholarly versions are those to be found in S.A.J. Bradley, *Anglo-Saxon Poetry*, London, Dent, 1995 and R.K. Gordon, *Anglo-Saxon Poetry*, London, Everyman's Library, Dent, 1954. The translation is reproduced by permission of Alfred A. Knopf.
5   The discussion of the characteristics of the poem and the strength of the claim that it refers to Bath has been extracted from R.F. Leslie, *Three Old English Elegies*, Exeter, University of Exeter, 1988, pp.22-28. This is an extremely comprehensive scholarly study that includes both the original old English text of the poem and a detailed discussion of the claim that it refers to Bath.
6   Sources for Adelard used in this chapter are Burnett, C., 'Bath, Adelard of', *DNB*; Burnett, C., *Adelard of Bath, Conversations with his Nephew: On the Same and Different, Questions on Natural Science, and On Birds*, Cambridge, Cambridge University Press, 1998 and Cochran, L., *Adelard of Bath: The First English Scientist*, London, British Museum Press, 1994.
7   Ramsey, F., 'Tours, John of', *DNB*.
8   See Burnett, *op.cit.*, for translations of these with commentaries.
9   *De Eodem et Diverso = On the Same and Different.*
10 *Questiones Naturales = Questions on Natural Science.*
11 See, for example, Gribbin, J., *Science: A History 1543-2001*, London, Allen Lane, 2002.
12 Gribben, *op.cit.*, p.134.
13 Glanvill's replies to Boyle's queries on mining are 'Answers to Some of the Inquiries Formerly Published Concerning Mines' in *Philosophical Transactions of the Royal Society*, vol.2, pp.515-527 (1667) and 'Additional Answers to the Queries of Mines' in *Philosophical Transactions of the Royal Society*, vol.3, pp.767-771 (1668).
14 Cope, J.I., *Joseph Glanvill: Anglican Apologist*, St Louis MO, Washington University Studies, 1956, p.23n.
15 'Observations Concerning the Bath-Springs' in *Philosophical Transactions of the Royal Society*, vol.4, pp.977-982 (1669).
16 Burns, W.E., 'Joseph Glanvill', *DNB*.
17 Hankins, T.L., *Science and the Enlightenment*, Cambridge, Cambridge University Press, 1985, p.11.
18 Hankins, *op.cit.*, p.9.
19 See for instance Golinski, J., *Making Natural Knowledge: Constructivism and the History of Science*, Cambridge, Cambridge University Press, 1998.
20 Butterfield, H., *The Origins of Modern Science*, Cambridge, Cambridge University Press, 1949; second edition, 1957, p.11.
21 Wroughton, J., *Tudor Bath: Life and Strife in the Little City, 1485-1603*, Bath, The Lansdown Press, 2006.
22 Wroughton, J., *Stuart Bath: Life in the Forgotten City, 1603-1714*, Bath, The Lansdown Press, 2004.
23 Fawcett, T., private communication, July 2005.
24 The classic work on the Georgian architecture of Bath is Ison, W., *The Georgian Buildings of Bath*, London, Faber & Faber, 1948; revised edition Bath, Kingsmead Press, 1980. For a general survey of nineteenth-century Bath architecture, see Jackson, N., *Nineteenth Century Bath: Architects and Architecture*, Bath, Ashgrove Press, 1991; paperback edition 1998. A comprehensive, up-to-date guide to all the noteworthy architecture of modern Bath is Forsyth, M., *Pevsner Architectural Guides: Bath*, New Haven CT & London, Yale University Press, 2003.
25 Fawcett, T. and Bird, S., *Bath: History and Guide*, Stroud & Andover NH, Alan Sutton Publishing, 1994.

1: **Airs and Waters**

1 There are three hot springs in Bath - the King's Spring (at the Roman Baths), the small Hetling (or Hot Bath) Spring, and the very small Cross Bath Spring. See W.I. Stanton, 'Hydrogeology of the hot springs of Bath', in G.A. Kellaway, *Hot Springs of Bath*, Bath, Bath City Council, 1991. The collection of articles edited by Kellaway is a mine of technical information about the hot springs.

2 Turner, W., *A Booke of the Natures and Properties as well of the Bathes in England as of other Bathes in Germanye and Italye*, Cologne, Arnold Birckman, 1562.

3 Jorden, Edward, *A Discourse of Naturall Bathes and Minerall Waters ... with examples of Particular Bathes ... especially of our Bathes at Bathe in Sommersetshire*, London, 1631.

4 Jorden, *op.cit.*, p.76.

5 Thorburn Burns, D., 'Edward Jorden MD (1569-1632): Early Contributions to Solution Analysis', *Proceedings of the Analytical Division of the Chemical Society*, vol.16, No.8, August 1979.

6 Glanvill, Joseph, 'Observations Concerning the Bath-Springs, Communicated by Mr. Joseph Glanvill, in a Letter to the Publisher Dated June 16, 1669', *Philosophical Transactions (1665-1678)*, vol.4, 1669, pp.977-982.

7 For a summary of the literature see Kellaway, G.A.(ed.), *op.cit.*, pp.57-65.

8 Coley, N.G., 'Cures without cares - Chymical physicians and mineral waters in seventeenth-century English medicine', *Medical History*, vol.23, no.2, 1979, pp.191-214.

9 Falconer, William, *An Essay on the Bath Waters, etc.*, London, 1770.

10 Smollett, Tobias, *An Essay on the External Use of Water in a Letter to Dr....., with Particular Remarks upon the Present Method of Using the Mineral Waters at Bath in Somersetshire and a Plan For Rendering Them More Safe, Agreeable and Efficacious*, Bath, D. Wilson & London, Leake & Frederick, 1752.

11 Waterhouse, R., 'The spa treatment of disease', *British Medical Journal*, 12 January 1929.

12 Kellaway, *op.cit.*

13 Williams, W.J. & Stoddart, D.M., *Bath – Some Encounters with Science*, Bath, Kingsmead Press, 1978, p.88.

14 This information is due to Robert Whitaker, one of those who dived a metre or so into the hot spring wearing a wetsuit!

15 Ford, P.J. & Saunders, G.A., *The Rise of the Superconductors*, London, CRC Press, 2004, pp.7-11.

16 Williams & Stoddart, *op.cit.*, p.88.

17 Williams & Stoddart, *op.cit.*, pp.88-9.

18 Hatton, J., *The Radium Waters of Bath*, Bath, Bath City Corporation, c.1920s.

19 Heywood, A., Waldron, H.A., O'Hare, P. & Dieppe, P. A., 'Effect of immersion on urinary lead excretion', *British Journal of Industrial Medicine*, 43, 1986, pp.713-715.

20 Heywood, A., 'A trial of the Bath Waters: the treatment of lead poisoning', *Medical History Supplement*, 10, 1990, pp.82-101.

21 Mayow, J., *Medico-physical Works: Being a Translation of Tractatus Quinque Medico-Physici*, Edinburgh, Alembic Club Reprints, No.17, 1907, *passim*.

22 Wood, Anthony, *Athenae Oxonienses*, New York, Johnson Reprint Company, new edition ed. P. Bliss, vol.3, 1967, p.1119.

23 The American academic, politician and scientist who was present at the signing of the American Declaration of Independence.

24 An apothecary by profession who made important discoveries in electricity and whose son William lived in Bath. The younger William Watson, a member of the Bath Philosophical Society, became a friend of William Herschel.

25 Another scientist born in the west country at Stroud, Gloucestershire, in whose honour the Institute of Physics erected a blue plaque on his old schoolhouse in Stroud.

26 Tudor-Jones, Goronwy, 'In praise of Joseph Priestley – the Particle Physicist', *Physics Education*, vol.26, no.3, 1991, p.148.

2: **Looking for Evidence**

1 Guidott, T., *The Register of Bath or Two Hundred Observations Containing an Account of Cures Performed and Benefit Received by the Use of the Hot Waters of Bath, etc.*, London & Bath, Henry Hammond, 1694; Peirce, R., *The history and memoirs of the Bath - containing observations on what cures have been there wrought, both by bathing and drinking those water, etc.*, London, printed for Henry Hammond, Bath, 1713.

2 Mayow, J., *Medico-physical Works: Being a Translation of Tractatus Quinque Medico-Physici*, Edinburgh, Alembic Club Reprints, No.17, 1907; Guidott, T., *A Discourse of Bathe and the Hot Waters there, and on the St Vincent Rock, near Bristol*, London, 1676.

3 Peirce, R., *op.cit.* The five autopsies mentioned were those of Sir Thomas Mauleverer, Sir Robert Craven, Mrs Sherwin, Henry O'Brien (7th Earl of Thomond) and Robert Grierson.

4 Tropical sprue: a disease caused by malabsorption of nutriments from the small bowel leading to weight loss, diarrhoea and ulceration of the intestines. Hillary's description would also fit a chronic bowel infection such as giardiasis.

5   Hillary, W.A., *A Rational and Mechanical Essay on the Smallpox*, London, G. Strahan, 1735. For an excellent biography of Hillary, see Booth, C.C., 'William Hillary – A pupil of Boerhaave', *Medical History*, vol.7, no.4, October 1963, pp.297-316.

6   Later renamed the Mineral Water Hospital and now the Royal National Hospital for Rheumatic Diseases.

7   Tröhler, Ulrich, *To Improve the Evidence of Medicine*, Edinburgh, Royal College of Physicians, 2000, p.88.

8   Letters and Papers of the Bath and West of England Society held in the University of Bath Library.

9   Smollett, Tobias, *An Essay on the External Use of Water in a Letter to Dr...., with Particular Remarks upon the Present Method of Using the Mineral Waters at Bath in Somersetshire and a Plan For Rendering Them More Safe, Agreeable and Efficacious*, Bath, D. Wilson & London, Leake & Frederick, 1752.

10 Parry, C.H., 'Experiments relative to the medical effects of Turkey Rhubarb, and of the English Rhubarbs, No.I and No.II made on patients of the Pauper Charity', *Letters and Papers of the Bath Society*, III, 1786, pp.431-453. For a full transcript of this paper see http://www.jameslindlibrary.org/trial_records/17th_18th_Century/parry/article/parry_article_1.html.

11 A condition characterised by over-activity of the thyroid gland and bulging eyes.

12 An abnormal enlargement of the large bowel, more usually known as Hirschspung's Disease.

13 Parry, C.H., *Collections From the Unpublished Writings of C.H. Parry*, London, Underwood, 1825.

14 Dobson, M. 'Experiments and observations on the urine in diabetes' in *Medical Observations and Inquiries*, vol.5, London, 1774.

15 Booth, *op.cit.*, p.102. See also Creaser, T., *Evidences of the Utility of Vaccine Inoculation: Intended for the Information of Parents*, Bath, R. Cruttwell, 1801.

16 Kingsdown House, Box.

17 Haygarth, J., *Of the Imagination as a Cause, and as a Cure of Disorders of the Body*, Bath, R. Cruttwell, 1800.

18 Fothergill, A.A., *A New Inquiry into the Suspension of Vital Action, in Cases of Drowning and Suffocation*, Bath, S. Hazard, 1795.

19 Hamilton, F.G., *The Bath Humane Society 1805-1955*, Bath [printed by Wyatt & Reynolds], n.d.

20 A passage running between the throat and the middle ear cavity, allowing air pressure to be equalised on the inner side of the ear drum.

21 Rolls, R., 'Archibald Cleland c1700-1771', *British Medical Journal*, 288 (6424), 14 April 1984, pp.1132-4.

22 *ibid.*

23 Soden, John Smith, 'On inguinal aneurysm, cured by tying the external iliac artery', *Medical Chirurgical Transactions*, vol.vii, 1816, p.536.

24 Bougie. A slender surgical instrument used for dilating bodily passages, for example the urethra.

25 The first surgeon to perform this operation was George Freer of Birmingham who taught Pring as a student.

26 Pring, D., 'History of a case of the successful formation of an artificial anus in an adult', *Medical and Physical Journal*, vol.45, 1821.

27 Nooth, J., *Observations on the Treatment of Scirrhous Tumours, and Cancers of the Breast*, Bath, R. Cruttwell, 1803; Ewart, J., *The History of 2 Cases of Ulcerated Cancer of the Mammae*, Bath, 1794.

28 Nooth, J., *ibid.*

29 Kersley, G.D., *The Three Rs – Rheumatism, Rehabilitation, Research – as Viewed from Bath*, Bath, n.d., p.43.

3: Of Canals and Quarries

1   McCann, C., 'Geophysical Investigations of the Hot Springs of Bath', *Proceedings of the Bath Royal Literary and Scientific Institution*, 3, 1999, pp.36-37

2   Winchester, S, *The Map that Changed the World*, London, HarperCollins, 2001.

3   Walcott, J., *Descriptions and Figures of Petrifactions found in the Quarries, Gravel Pits etc. near Bath*, Bath, Samuel Hazard, 1779.

4   *ibid.*

5   Torrens, H.S., 'Walcott, John (1754-1831)', *DNB*.

6   A prominent physician and father of William Parry, the Arctic explorer.

7   Torrens, H.S., *op.cit.*

8   Desmond, R., *Dictionary of British and Irish Botanists and Horticulturalists, Including Plant Collectors and Botanical Artists*, London, Taylor and Francis, 1977.

9   Torrens, H.S., 'Smith, William [called Strata Smith] (1769-1839)', *DNB*.

10 Torrens, H.S., 'An Introduction to the Life and Times of William Smith (1769-1839)', in *Memoirs of William Smith, LL.D., author of the 'Map of the Strata of England and Wales' by his nephew and pupil, John Phillips, F.R.S., F.G.S.* (first published in 1844), reissued Bath, Bath Royal Literary and Scientific Institution, 2003.

11 Cox, L.R., 'New Light on William Smith and his Work', *Proceedings of the Yorkshire Geological Society*, 25, [1], 1942, pp.1-99.

12 Phillips, J., *Memoirs of William Smith, LL.D., author of the 'Map of the Strata of England and Wales'*, Murray, London, 1844; reissued Bath, Bath Royal Literary and Scientific Institution, 2003.

13 Torrens, H.S., 'An Introduction', *op.cit.*

14 Eyles, J. M., 'William Smith', in Gillispie, C.C. (ed.), *Dictionary of Scientific Biography*, New York, Charles Scribner's Sons, 1974.

15 Pollard, D., 'Bath Stone Quarry Railways, 1796-1830', *Bristol Industrial Archaeological Society Journal*, 15, 1982, pp.13-19.

16 Torrens, H.S., 'An Introduction', *op.cit.*

17 The information given here on the Bathonian Stage is from Hugh Torrrens. See H. Torrens, 'The Bathonian: A Case History', in 'From d'Orbigny to the Devonian: Some Thoughts on the History of the Stratotype Concept *Comptes Rendus Palevol*, vol..1, Fasc.6, December 2002, pp.335-345.

18 The Inferier Oolite was later placed by the French geologist Alcide d'Orbigny (1802-1857) in his Bajocian Stage, named after Bayeux, France.

19 Pierce, S.W., 'Lonsdale, William (1794-1871)', *DNB*.

20 W.T.(?), 'Local Celebrities, William Lonsdale F.G.S.' *The Bath & County Graphic*, 3, (7), 1898, pp.1-2.

21 *First Annual Report of the Committee of The Bath Royal Literary and Scientific Institution for the year 1825*, printed by M. Meyler, Abbey Church-Yard, 1826.

22 *Second Annual Report of the Committee of The Bath Royal Literary and Scientific Institution for the year 1826*, printed by M. Meyler, Abbey Church-Yard, 1827.

23 Mitchell, W.S., 'Notes on early geologists concerned with the neighbourhood of Bath', *Proceedings of the Bath Natural History and Antiquarian Field Club*, 2, [3], 1892, pp.303-341.

24 Mitchell, W.S., *op.cit.*

25 Lonsdale, W., 'On the Oolitic District of Bath', *Transactions of the Geological Society of London*, 2, (3), 1829, pp.241-276.

26 Lonsdale, W., 'Report of a Survey on the Oolitic Formations of Gloucestershire', *Proceedings of the Geological Society of London*, 1, 1832, pp.413-415.

27 Pierce, S.W., *op.cit.*

28 Lonsdale, W., 'On the Age of the Limestones of South Devonshire', *Transactions of the Geological Society of London*, 2, (5), 1840, pp.721-738.

29 Prestwich, J., 'Presidential Address', *Quarterly Journal of the Geological Society of London*,28, [1], 1872, pp.xxxv-xxxvi.

30 *ibid.*

31 Winwood, H.H., 'Charles Moore F.G.S., and his work', Bath, *The Bath Herald*, 1892; also published in *Proceedings of the Bath Natural History and Antiquarian Field Club*, 7, pp.232-292.

32 *ibid.*

33 Moore, C., 'On the palaeontology of the Middle and Upper Lias', *Proceedings of the Somersetshire Archaeological and Natural History Society*, 3, [2], 1853, pp.61-76.

34 Duffin, C.J., 'The Bath Geological Collections. The Moore Collection of Upper Liassic crocodiles: a history', *Newsletter of the Geological Curators Group*, 2, 1979, pp.59-67.

35 Baker, P.G. & Copp, C.J.T., 'Terebratulide affinity of the brachiopod Spirifera minima Moore', *Palaeontology*, 18,(4), 1975, pp.879-882.

36 Savage, R.J.G., 'Moore, Charles (1815-1881)' *DNB*.

37 Copp, C.J.T., Taylor, M.A. & Thackray, J.C., 'Charles Moore (1814-1881), Somerset Geologist', *Proceedings of the Somersetshire Archaeological and Natural History Society*, 140, 2000, pp.1-36.

38 Winwood, H.H., *op.cit.*

39 Moore, C., 'On the zones of the Lower Lias and the Avicula contorta Zone', *Quarterly Journal of the Geological Society of London*, 17, 1861, pp.483-516.

40 A fuller exploration of this subject can be found in Swift, A. & Martill, D. (eds.), *Fossils of the Rhaetian Penarth Group*, Palaeontological Association Field Guide to Fossils No.9, 1999.

41 Savage, R.J.G., *op.cit.* The technique of sieving for microfossils was probably developed by Etheldred Bennett earlier in the nineteenth century, see Torrens, H.S., 'Bennett, Etheldred (1775-1845), *DNB*.

42 Moore, C., 'Vallis Vale and Holwell Quarries', *Proceedings of the Somersetshire Archaeological and Natural History Society*, 22, (1), 1876, pp.40-42.

43 Butler, P.M. and Macintyre, G.T., 'Review of the British Haramiyidae (? Mammalia, Allotheria), their Molar Occlusion and Relationships', *Philosophical Transactions of the Royal Society: Biological Sciences*, 345, [1314], 1994, pp.433-458.

44 Moore, C., *Handbook to the Geological Collection of Charles Moore Esq., F.G.S., deposited at the Royal Literary and Scientific Institution, Bath*, Bath, *Bath Chronicle*, published for the British Association meeting of 1864.

45 Copp, C.J.T., Taylor, M.A. & Thackray, J.C., *op.cit.*

46 Moore, C., 'On the zones of the Lower Lias and the Avicula contorta Zone', *op.cit.*

47 Moore, C., 'On abnormal conditions of Secondary deposits when connected with the Somersetshire and South Wales coal-basin; and on the age of the Sutton and Southerndown series', *Quarterly Journal of the Geological Society of London*, 23, 1867, pp.207-208 & 429-568.

48 Pengelly, W., *A Memoir of William Pengelly of Torquay FRS Geologist*, Murray, London, 1897.

49 Copp, C.J.T., Taylor, M.A. & Thackray, J.C., *op.cit.*

50 Moore, C., *Handbook to the Geological Collection of Charles Moore Esq., F.G.S., op.cit.*

51 Winwood, H.H., *Handbook to the Geological Museum, Bath*, Bath, William Lewis and Sons, 1888.

52   ibid.

53   For a fuller account of the history of Moore's collection see: Copp, C.J.T., Taylor, M.A. & Thackray, J.C, op.cit.

54   Tite, C., 'Rev. H.H. Winwood, M.A., F.G.S.', Proceedings of the Somersetshire Archaeological and Natural History Society 66, 1921, pp.159-160.

55   Oldham, R.D., 'The Anniversary Address of the President', Quarterly Journal of the Geological Society of London 77, [1], 1921, pp.lxvii-lxviii.

56   Moore, C., Handbook to the Geological Collection of Charles Moore Esq., F.G.S., op.cit.; Winwood, H.H, Handbook to the Geological Museum, Bath, op.cit.

57   Oldham, R.D., op.cit.

58   Anon., 'Death of the Rev. H.H. Winwood, an Eminent Bath Geologist', Bath Chronicle, 1 January 1921.

59   Walcott, J., op.cit.

60   Torrens, H.S., 'Notes on 'The Amateur' in the development of British Geology', Proceedings of the Geologists' Association, vol.117, part 1, 2006, pp.1-8.

4: Telescopes and Astronomy

1   Lubbock. C.A., The Herschel Chronicle, Cambridge, Cambridge University Press, 1938; reprinted Bath, The William Herschel Society, 1997, pp.1-41.

2   Brown F.S., William Herschel, Musician and Composer, Bath, The William Herschel Society, 1990.

3   See Moore P., Caroline Herschel, Reflected Glory, Bath, The William Herschel Society, 1988, p.7 and Lubbock, C.A., op. cit., pp.42-43.

4   See Asimov I., Eyes on the Universe: A History of the Telescope, London, Andre Deutsch, 1976 and Learner R., Astronomy Through The Telescope, London, Evans, 1982.

5   Moore P., William Herschel, Astronomer and Musician of 19 New King Street, Bath, Bath, The William Herschel Society, 1981.

6   Lubbock. C.A., op.cit., pp.78-86.

7   Edmund Rack, MS B920, Bath Central Library, quoted in Fawcett, Trevor, Voices of Eighteenth-century Bath, Bath, RUTON, 1995, p.118.

8   In Classical mythology, Uranus was the father of Saturn, Saturn the father of Jupiter, and Jupiter the father of Mars.

9   Asimov, op.cit., p 81.

10   See Miner, Ellis D. & Wessen, Randii R., Neptune: the Planet, Rings and Satellites, Chichester, Springer-Praxis, 2001.

11   See Moore, P., William Herschel, op.cit., p.11 and Lubbock, op.cit., pp 78-86.

12   Hervey, W., Journals, entry for 12 March 1782 in Fawcett, Trevor, Voices of Eighteenth-century Bath, Bath, RUTON, 1995, p.327.

13   Herschel, Mrs J., Memoir and Correspondence of Caroline Herschel, London, Murray, 1876; second edition 1879; reprinted Bath, The William Herschel Society, 2000.

14   Lubbock, C.A., op.cit., pp.169-173.

15   Hoskin, M., The Herschel Partnership, Cambridge, Science History Publications, 2003.

16   Moore P., Caroline Herschel, Reflected Glory, Bath, The William Herschel Society, 1988, p.17.

17   Hoskin M., The Herschels of Hanover, Cambridge, Science History Publications, 2007.

18   King-Hele, D.G. (ed.), John Herschel 1792-1871: A Bicentennial Commemoration, London, The Royal Society, 1992.

19   Ring, E.F.J., 'The Discovery of Infrared Radiation in 1800', Imaging Science Journal, vol.48, 2000, pp.1-8.

20   Hoskin, M., 'Herschel's 40ft. Reflector: Funding and Functions', Journal for the History of Astronomy, vol.34, part 1, 2003, 1-32.

21   Maurer, A., 'A Compendium of All Known William Herschel Telescopes', Journal of the Antique Telescope Society, vol.14, 1996, pp.1-12.

22   These remarks on Herschel and Romanticism are based on comments by Allan Chapman.

5: Bath Naturalists

1   Allen, D.E., 'Localised records from the fourteenth century' in BSBI News, No.88, London, Botanical Society of the British Isles, 2001, p.23.

2   Turner, William, A New Herball, reprinted Cambridge, Chapman, G.T.L. & Tweddle, M.N. (eds.), Cambridge University Press, 1995; a facsimile edition with modern transcript and a biography of the author.

3   Turner, William, A New Herball, part 1, London, 1551; part 2, Cologne, 1562; part 3, Cologne, 1568.

4   BRLSI Annual report ... for 1879, Bath, 1880: donation listed, p.14.

5   Turner, William, Common Place Book, ms., 2 vols., c.1560; one volume covers Church and religious matters, the other predominantly contains notes and drawings relating to herbs and medicine.

6   Turner, William, Booke of the Nature and Properties of the Bathes in England, Cologne, 1562. Published with part 2 of his A New Herball, op.cit.

7   *BRLSI Annual report ... for 1845*, Bath, 1846: deposit listed, p.13.

8   'L'Obel, Matthias de' in *DNB*.

9   Pena, Pierre & l'Obel, Matthias de, *Stirpium Adversaria Nova*, London, 1570.

10   'Lyte, Henry' in *DNB*.

11   Lyte, Henry (trans.), *A Niewe Herball*, London, 1578.

12   Clusius, Carolus, *Histoire des Plantes*, Antwerp, 1557.

13   Dodoens, Rembert, *Crüijdeboeck*, Antwerp, 1552; the source for Clusius' *Histoire des Plantes*, which in turn was the source for Henry Lyte's *Niewe Herball*.

14   Dodoens, Rembert, *Stirpium Historiae Pemptades Sex*, Antwerp, 1583; the Latin edition of Dodoens' *Crüijdeboeck*, the source reference used for John Gerard's *Herball*.

15   'Gerard, John' in *DNB*.

16   Gerard, John, *The Herball or Generall Historie of Plants*, London, John Norton, 1597.

17   'Johnson, Thomas' in *DNB*.

18   Gerard, John, *The Herball or Generall Historie of Plants*, ed. Thomas Johnson, London, A. Islip, 1633.

19   Johnson, Thomas, *Mercurius Botanicus*, London, T. Cotes, 3 volumes, 1634-41.

20   White, J.W., *The Flora of Bristol*, Bristol, John Wright, 1912; reprinted Bristol, Chatford House Press, 1972; this contains an extensive chapter on 'The History of Bristol Botany', including details of botanists residing in, or visiting, Bath.

21   Ray, John, *Catalogus Plantarum Angliae*, London, J. Martyn, 1670.

22   'Ray, John' in *DNB*.

23   Ray, John, *Synopsis Methodica Stirpium Britannicarum*, ed. J.J. Dillenius, London, 1724.

24   'Dillenius, Jacob' in *DNB*.

25   Dillenius, Johann Jacob, *Diary*, ms., 1726.

26   'Walcott, John' in *DNB*.

27   Williams, W.J. & Stoddart, D.M., *Bath – Some Encounters with Science*, Bath, Kingsmead Press, 1978.

28   Walcott, John, *Descriptions and Figures of Petrifactions, found in Quarries, Gravel-pits, &c. near Bath*, Bath, S. Hazard, 1779.

29   Walcott, John, *Flora Britannica Indigena, or Plates of the Indigenous Plants of Great Britain*, Bath, 1778-9.

30   Walcott, John, *Synopsis of British Birds*, 1789.

31   'Collyer, Joseph' in *DNB*.

32   'Hibbert, William' in *DNB*.

33   'Sole, William' in *DNB*.

34   *ibid.*

35   Sole, William, *Menthae Britannicae*, Bath, 1798.

36   Desmond, R., *Dictionary of British and Irish Botanists and Horticulturists*, London, Taylor & Francis, 2nd edition, 1993.

37   Sole, William, *An Account of the Principal English Grasses, with Descriptions of their Respective Excellencies and Defects to Agricultural Uses ...*, ms. in the library of The Royal Bath and West of England Society, 1799.

38   'Sole, William' in *DNB*.

39   Hudson, William, *Flora Anglica*, 3rd edition, London, 1798.

40   Sole, William, *Flora Bathonica*, ms., 1782, at one time in the possession of T.B. Flower, but now apparently lost.

41   Warner, Richard, *History of Bath*, Bath, R. Cruttwell, 1801.

41   Collinson, John, *History and Antiquities of Somerset*, Bath, 1891.

43   'Stackhouse, John' in *DNB*.

44   Stackhouse, John, *Nereis Britannica*, Bath, 1795-1801.

45   Explanatory notice in the BRLSI archives, dated 3/8/1928.

46   Correspondence and catalogues in the BRLSI archives. Walker's business and home addresses have been checked in the Bath directories and copies of church registers in Bath Central Library, but nothing is currently known of Walker's collecting activities.

47   McLaughlin, David & Gray, Michael, *Shadows and Light: Bath in Camera 1849-1861, Early Rare Photographs*, London, Dirk Nishen Publishing, 1989.

48   *BRLSI Annual report ... for 1874*, Bath, 1875. Donations include models, ethnological material, Lockey's meteorological journals (including notes on his photographic techniques and subjects), and natural history collections ranging from minerals, fossils, shells and insects to stuffed fish, birds and animals.

49   Taylor, Richard (ed.), *The Annals and Magazine of Natural History ...* 2nd series, vol. 4, London, R. & J.E. Taylor, 1849, pp.424-5.

50   Clark, William, *A History of British Marine Testaceous Mollusca*, London, J. van Voorst, 1855.

51   *Alumni Oxoniensis*, and various websites, e.g. www.acny.org.uk ('A church near you', Church of England), www.freshford.com and www.leebay.co.uk.

52   Tugwell, George, *A Manual of the Sea Anemones Commonly Found on the English cCast*, London, J. van Voorst, 1856.

53   *BRLSI Annual report ... for 1904*, Bath, 1905: donations list.

54   'Babington, Charles Cardale' in *DNB*.

55   Babington, Charles Cardale, *Memorials, Journal and Botanical Correspondence*, Cambridge, Macmillan & Bowes, 1897.

56 Babington, Charles Cardale, *Flora Bathoniensis*, Bath, E. Collings, 1834, supplement, 1839.

57 'Davis, John Ford' in *DNB*.

58 'Henslow, John Stevens' in *DNB*.

59 Babington, Charls Cardale, *Manual of British Botany*, London, J. van Voorst, 1843.

60 Babington, Charles Cardale, *The British Rubi*, London, J. van Voorst, 1869.

61 White, J.W., *op.cit.*

62 Grose, J. Donald, *The Flora of Wiltshire*, Devizes, Wiltshire Archaeological and Natural History Society, 1957; this contains 'Biographical Notices', pp.30-45, which includes details of botanists residing in, or visiting Bath.

63 Swete, E.H., *Flora Bristoliensis*, London, Hamilton, Adams & Co., 1851.

64 Flower, Thomas Bruges, 'The Flora of Wiltshire, comprising the Flowering Plants and Ferns Indigenous to the County' in *Magazine of the Wiltshire Archaeological and Natural History Society*, Devizes, 1858-1874.

65 Blomefield (previously Jenyns), Leonard, '[Presidential] Address to the Members of the Bath Field Club, in reference to the death of C.E. Broome, Esq., F.L.S.' in *Proceedings of the Bath Natural History and Antiquarian Field Club*, vol. 6, 1889, pp.144-153; republished in Wallace, Ian (ed.), *Leonard Jenyns: Darwin's Lifelong Friend*, Bath, BRLSI, 2005.

66 Blomefield (previously Jenyns), Leonard, *Chapters in my Life*, Bath, for private circulation, 1887; reprinted with additions 1889; republished in Wallace, *op.cit.*

67 Berkeley, Miles Joseph & Broome, Christopher Edmund, 'Notices of British Fungi, and other papers', in *The Annals and Magazine of Natural History*, 1846-1885.

68 Broome, Christopher Edmund, 'Description of a new species of Melanogaster', in *The Annals and Magazine of Natural History*, vol.15, pp.41-42, 1845.

69 'Jermyn, George Bitton' in *DNB*.

70 Broome, C.E., 'On the fungi of Somersetshire', in *Somersetshire Archaeological and Natural History Society Proceedings during the year 1852*, Taunton, 1853, p.9, list of species pp.132-156.

71 Broome, C.E., 'Remarks on some of the Fungi met with in the neighbourhood of Bath', in *Proceedings of the Bath Natural History and Antiquarian Field Club*, vol.2, 1870, p.188; vol.3, p.53, 304; vol.5, p.143; vol.6, 1886, p.1.

72 Broome, C.E., 'The Myxogasters, their position in the natural system', a paper read in February 1873 before the Microscopical Society of Bath.

73 Broome, C.E., 'The fungi of Wiltshire', in *Magazine of the Wiltshire Archaeological and Natural History Society*, Devizes, 1864.

74 Sowerby, John, *Coloured Figures of English Fungi or Mushrooms*, London, 1795-1815.

75 Deduced from the contents of the herbarium of C.E. Broome at BRLSI.

76 *BRLSI Annual report ... for 1886*, Bath, 1887: donations list.

77 'Glenavon', 'Rus in Urbe', in *The Bath and County Graphic*, Bath, December 1902.

78 Toft, Simon, 'Legacy of collector is still growing' in the *Bath Chronicle*, 25 September 1987. The centenary of the Botanic Gardens in Royal Victoria Park was commemorated by extending the gardens into the Great Dell.

79 'Jenyns, Leonard' in *DNB*.

80 Blomefield, *Chapters in my Life*, *op.cit.*

81 Winwood, Henry Hoyte, 'Reminiscences of the late President and Founder of the Club', in *Proceedings of the Bath Natural History and Antiquarian Field Club*, vol.8, 1897, pp.35-55.

82 Wallace, *op.cit.*

83 Lewis, William, 'List of Excursions and Walks since the first formation of the [Bath Field] Club', in *Proceedings of the Bath Natural History and Antiquarian Field Club*, vol.4, 1881, pp.289-298. William Lewis was proprietor of *The Bath Herald*, which advertised the club's excursions and printed their proceedings. His son Harold was one of the club's secretaries.

84 *Proceedings of the Bath Natural History and Antiquarian Field Club*, 1867-1909. Jenyns' first presidential address on 2 February 1864 was the first occasion on which the club met for the reading of papers.

85 Wallace, *op.cit.*

86 Norman, George, in Allen, Alfred (ed.), *The Journal of the Postal Microscopical Society*: 'On the Saprolegnieae', vol.2, 1883, p.185; 'On the Peronosporae', vol.3, 1884, pp.186, 197; 'On Cystopus', vol.4, pp.135, 1885. Bath was influential in the affairs of this society. Alfred Allen lived at 1 Cambridge Place and was Honorary Secretary, editor and publisher of the society's journal. It was printed by Charles Seers of Argyle Street.

87 Bird, Henry, 'List of Mollusca found in the neighbourhood of Bath' in *Proceedings of the Bath Natural History and Antiquarian Field Club*, vol.1, 1868.

88 Duff, Andrew, *Beetles of Somerset*, Taunton, Somersetshire Archaeological and Natural History Society, 1993. Includes biographical notes on Col. Linley Blathwayt and Robert Gillo.

89 Blathwayt, Col. Linley Wynter, *Diaries*, ms., 1873-1914, Gloucestershire Archives (Gloucestershire Record Office) – ref. D2659/21.

90 Blathwayt, L.W., in *Proceedings of the Bath Natural History and Antiquarian Field Club*: 'Remarks on some Hemiptera Heteroptera taken in the neighbourhood of Bath', vol.6, 1889, p.315; 'List of Terrestrial Hemiptera-Heteroptera taken in the neighbourhood of Bath', vol.6, 1889, p.432; 'Certain rare beetles found in a wasps' nest', vol.8, 1897, p.136.

91 Blathwayt, L.W., 'Insects of Somerset' in Page, William (ed.), *The Victoria County History of the County of Somerset*, London, 1906, vol.1, pp.73-86, 115-120; this contains brief notes on other contributors and sources of information.

6: Drawing with Light

1   Gail Buckland, *Fox Talbot and the Invention of Photography*, Scolar Press, 1988, p.20.
2   Letter from Thomas Hooker to W.H.F. Talbot dated 12 April 1812, British Library.
3   Letter from Lady Elisabeth Therese Feilding dated 19 May 1817, British Library.
4   Letter from Sir David Brewster to W.H.F. Talbot dated 8 March 1833, British Library.
5   William Henry Fox Talbot, *The Pencil of Nature*, London, Longman, Brown, Green & Longmans, 1844.
6   William Henry Fox Talbot, 'Some Account of the Art of Photogenic Drawing', *The Philosophical Transactions of the Royal Society of London*, vol.4, pp.120-121.
7   Letter from Constance Talbot (née Mundy) to W.H.F. Talbot dated 7 September 1835, British Library.
8   King-Hele, D.G. (ed.), *John Herschel 1792-1871: A Bicentennial Commemoration*, London, The Royal Society, 1992.
9   William Henry Fox Talbot, *The Pencil of Nature*, *op.cit.*, text accompanying plate XIII.
10 Mike Chapman, 'Bath's First Photographic Studio', *The Survey of Bath & District*, no.15, June 2001, pp.41-44.
11 More of these photographs are reproduced in Wallace, Ian (ed.), *Leonard Jenyns: Darwin's Lifelong Friend*, Bath, BRLSI, 2005.
12 Mike Chapman, 'Early Photographic Studios in Bath', *The Survey of Bath & District*, no. 14, November 2000, p.23.
13 Mike Chapman, *op.cit.* (2000), p.24.

7: City and Landscape

1   Bird, S., 'The Earliest Map of Bath', *Bath History*, vol.i, Gloucester, Alan Sutton, 1986, pp.128-149.
2   Smith, D., 'The Earliest Printed Maps of British Towns', *Society of Cartographers Bulletin*, vol.27, no.2, 1995, pp.35-38.
3   Speed was a freeman of the Merchant Taylors.
4   Delano-Smith, C. & Kain, R.J.P., *English Maps: A History*, The British Library, Studies in Map History, vol.ii, 1999, pp.210-211.
5   Holland, E. & Chapman, M., *The Kingston Estate Within the Walled City of Bath*, Bath, Survey of Old Bath, 1992.
6   Chapman, M., *A Guide to the Estates of Ralph Allen around Bath*, Bath, Survey of Old Bath, 1996.
7   Penrose, J., *Letters from Bath, 1766-1767*, Gloucester, Alan Sutton, 1983.
8   Bath booksellers usually published maps and guides jointly, to cover the expense.
9   Wright, R.W.M., '1588-1816: A Descriptive List of the Published Plans of the City of Bath & its Environs', unpublished MS, 1925, Bath Reference Library.
10 In 1782, Donn decided to spell his name with a final 'e', a form he thought was used by his grandfather.
11 Ravenhill, W.L.D., 'Benjamin Donn, 1729-98, Map-maker and Master of Mechanics', *The Devonshire Association for the Advancement of Science, Literature and Art*, vol.xcvii, 1965.
12 Chapman, M., Hawkes, J. & Holland, E., *The J.Charlton Map of Lyncombe and Widcombe 1799*, Bath, Survey of Old Bath, 1998.
13 This survey was carried out in response to a prize incentive by the London-based Society of Arts, Manufacture and Commerce. The earliest award of this kind by the Society was to Benjamin Donn for his survey of Devon in 1765.
14 Harley, J.W. & Dunning, R.W., *Somerset Maps; Day & Masters 1782, Greenwood 1822*, Somerset Record Society, Vol.76, 1981.
15 Twyman, M., 'The Lithographic Hand Press, 1796-1850', *Journal of the Printing Historical Society*, vol.3, 1967, pp.19-21.
16 Bernhardt, D., 'A 19th Century Architectural Practice in Bath', 2005, unpublished thesis, Bath Record Office and Bath Reference Library.
17 Torrens, H.S., 'Early Maps of the Somersetshire Coal Canal', *Journal of the British Cartographic Society*, June 1974, pp.45-47; Torrens, H.S., 'Further Comments on the Maps of the Somersetshire Coal Canal', *Journal of the British Cartographic Society*, June 1975, p.49.
18 Judd, J.W., 'William Smith's Manuscript Maps', *Geological Magazine*, vol.iv, 1897, pp.439-447.
19 *A Catalogue of Historic Maps in Avon*, Bristol, Avon County Council, 1984.

8: Trenches and Tunnels

1   Although the old photograph shows 1754.
2   Englefield, H., 'Account of Antiquities Discovered in Bath, 1790', paper read to the Society of Antiquaries, *Archaeologia*, vol.x. 1792, pp.325-333.
3   Henig, M., public lecture at the Guildhall, Bath, 2005.
4   Lysons, S., *Reliquiae Britannico-Romanae*, London, vol.i, 1813.
5   Cunliffe, B., *Roman Bath*, Report No.XXIV of the Research Committee of the Society of Antiquaries of London, Oxford, Oxford University Press, 1969, p.207.
6   *ibid*, p.216.
7   Scarth, H.M., 'On Ancient Sepulchral Remains Discovered in and around Bath'. *Proceedings of the Somerset Archaeological Society*, vol.v, 1854, pp.53-54.

8   Cunliffe, *op.cit.*, p.216.

9   Scarth, 'On Ancient Sepulchral Remains ...', *op.cit.*, pp.49-51, 56.

10 *ibid*, p.55.

11 *ibid*, p.58.

12 Cunliffe, *op.cit.*, p.217.

13 Dowden, W.S. (ed.),*The Journal of Thomas Moore*, Newark DE, University of Delaware Press, vol.1, 1983: entry for 29 October 1818.

14 Heritage Environment Record, Bath & North East Somerset Council.

15 *Bath & Cheltenham Gazette*, 20 November 1816.

16 Scarth, H.M., *Aquae Solis, or Notices of Roman Bath*, London, Simpkin Marshall & Bath, R.E. Peach, 1864, p.98.

17 *ibid*, p.99.

18 Cunliffe, *op.cit.*, p.90.

19 *ibid*, p.90.

20 *ibid*, p.90.

21 *ibid*, p.40.

22 Irvine Papers, Bath Central Library.

23 Cunliffe, *op.cit.*, p.40

24 *ibid*, p.90.

25 *ibid*, pp.90-91.

26 *Proceedings of the Somerset Archaeological & Natural History Society*, vol xxvii, p.32.

27 *ibid*, pp.32-33.

28 Cunliffe, *op.cit.*, p.91

29 *ibid*, p.93

30 Scarth, *Aquae Solis, op.cit.*, p.48.

31 *ibid*, p.89.

32 *ibid*, p.90.

33 *ibid*, p.89.

34 Wood, J., *An Essay towards a Description of Bath*, 2nd edition, London, C. Hitch, 1749, p.270.

35 Crutchley, A. & Lewcun, M., 'An Archaeological Investigation on the site of the former Bath Chronicle Printing Works, 31-35 Westgate Street, Bath, 1997', *Bristol and Avon Archaeology*, vol.14, 1999, p.13.

36 Cunliffe, *op.cit.*, pp.151-152.

37 *ibid*, pp.39-42.

38 *ibid*, p.211.

39 *ibid*, p.210.

40 Scarth, *Aquae Solis, op.cit.*, p.9.

41 Davenport, P. & Beaton, M., 'Empire Hotel', in *Field Officers' Annual Report*, no.7., Bath Archaeological Trust, 1995, pp.1-3.

42 Davenport, P., 'Excavation at a Roman site at Julian Road, Bath', in *Archaeology in Bath, Excavations 1984-1989*, British Archaeological Reports, no.284, Bath Archaeological Trust, 1999, pp.127-151.

43 Skinner, J., *Journal of a Somerset Rector, 1803-1834*, ed. H. & P. Coombs, Bath, Kingsmead Press, 1971.

44 BL. MS.33654, 33671, 33674, 33682, 33692, 33697; copies at Somerset Record Office.

45 Somerset Record Office, DD/SAS/G/1818/4/2/2-5.

46 See Skrine, H.D., 'The Belgic Camp on Hampton Down', paper read before the Bath Literary and Philosophical Association, 1888, Bath Reference Library, B913.4238, Accession No.32.409; Skrine H.D., 'Some Account of the Belgic Camp on Hampton Down', paper read before the Bath Selborne Society, 1897; Scarth, *Aquae Solis, op.cit.*, p.9.

47 See the following: Grey, G.J., 'Exploration of Barrows, Hampton Down', *Proceedings of the Bath Branch of the Somerset Archaeological & Natural History Society*, 1904; Grey, G.J., 'Exploration of a Bank in Norwood's Field, Claverton Down', *Proceedings of the Bath Branch of the Somerset Archaeological & Natural History Society*, 1904; Winwood, H.H. 'Exploration on Claverton Down', *Proceedings of the Bath Branch of the Somerset Archaeological & Natural History Society*, 1905; Winwood, H.H., 'The Wansdyke, Hampton Down', *Proceedings of the Bath Branch of the Somerset Archaeological & Natural History Society*, 1995.

48 Knowles, W.H., 'The Roman Baths at Bath; with an Account of the Excavations conducted during 1923', *Archaeologica*, vol.XXV, 1926, pp.1-18

49 MS records of the Bath & Camerton Archaeological Society, Roman Baths Museum, Bath.

50 Cunliffe, *op.cit.*, p.9.

51 Cunliffe, *op.cit.*

52 Cunliffe, B, & Davenport, P., *The Temple of Sulis Minerva at Bath: Volume 1 (I), The Site*, Oxford, Oxford Committee for Archaeology, Monograph no.7, 1995, pp.21-22 .

53 Time Team, Channel 4 Television, 2003.

54 Beaton, M., 'An Archaeological and Historical Landscape Survey of the National Trust Skyline Properties', Bath Archaeological Trust Report, no.2003.11, 2003, unpublished report for The National Trust.

55   Sources used here for the life of Sir Leonard Woolley are his *DNB* entry and the book by H.V.F. Winstone, *Woolley of Ur: The Life of Sir Leonard Woolley*, London, Secker and Warburg, 1990.

56   Woolley, Sir Leonard, *Ur 'of the Chaldees', the Final Account: Excavations at Ur*, revised and updated by P.R.S. Moorey, London, The Herbert Press, 1982.

9: Providing Infrastructure

1   For Smeaton, see Skempton, A.W. (ed.), *John Smeaton FRS*, London, Thomas Telford, 1981 and Watson, Garth, *The Civils: The Story of the Institution of Civil Engineers*, London, Thomas Telford,1988. The account of his visit to Bath is culled from the diaries in the Smeaton Archive, held by Trinity House in London: see the entry for 24/25/26 September 1783 (Minute Book for 1782 and 1783), referring to the 'dissipation' of Bath and spending his time 'in Walking reading visiting etc.' I am grateful to the Archivist at Trinity House for permission to consult these documents.

2   For Rennie, see Boucher, C.T.G., *John Rennie 1761-1821*, Manchester, Manchester University Press, 1963. On the Kennet & Avon Canal, Clew, K.R., *The Kennet & Avon Canal*, Newton Abbot, David & Charles, 1968 remains the best general account.

3   For Padmore, see the entry by Buchanan, Brenda J., in *The Biographical Dictionary of Civil Engineers*, vol.1, London, Thomas Telford, 2002 (hereafter *BDCE*); and for the Avon Navigation, see Buchanan, Brenda J., 'The Avon Navigation and the Inland Port of Bath', *Bath History*, vol.vi, Bath, Millstream Books, 1996, pp.63-87. The claim that the Combe Down tramway can be regarded as a precursor to the railways was made by Sir Arthur Elton in 'The Prehistory of Railways – with special reference to the early quarry railways of North Somerset', *Proceedings of the Somerset Archaeological and Natural History Society*, vol.107, 1963, pp.31-59.

4   William Smith has been the subject of considerable scholarly attention by historians of science and geology: see particularly the article by Mrs J. Eyles in the *Dictionary of Scientific Biography*.

5   For the Smeatonians, see Watson, Garth, *The Smeatonians: The Society of Civil Engineers*, London, Thomas Telford, 1989.

6   On the relationship between Rennie and Telford, see Hadfield, Charles, *Thomas Telford's Temptation*, Cleobury Mortimer, Baldwin, 1993, especially pp.163-5. But Hadfield was then trying to vindicate the claims of William Jessop, whose biography he had written (with A.W. Skempton), and to whom he considered credit should be given for some of the engineering works attributed to Telford.

7   On Telford, see the article by Roland A. Paxton in *BDCE*, vol.1, and also the standard biographies, Gibb, Sir Alexander, *The Story of Telford*, London, Maclehose, 1935; and Rolt, L.T.C., *Thomas Telford*, London Longmans, 1958.

8   Curiously, Telford's business in Bath is not mentioned in any of the standard references in Note 7 above, but there is a file in Bath City Archives containing a report from Telford about his proposals, and subsequent correspondence. I am grateful to Colin Johnston, Archivist to the City of Bath, for his assistance in locating this.

9   Source material on Dredge and Motley is tantalisingly slight, but see Buchanan, R. Angus, 'The Bridges of Bath', *Bath History*, vol.iii, Gloucester, Alan Sutton, 1990, pp.16-18.

10   The careers of the MacAdam family are surveyed in Reader, W.J., *Macadam: The McAdam Family and the Turnpike Roads, 1798-1861*, London, Heinemann, 1980. See also the article by Buchanan, Brenda J., 'The Great Bath Road, 1700-1830', *Bath History*, vol.iv, Bath, Millstream Books, 1992, pp.71-94.

11   For details of the career of I.K. Brunel, see Buchanan, R. Angus, *Brunel, The Life and Times of I.K. Brunel*, London, Hambledon, London, 2002.

12   For Brunel's contribution to the Bath landscape, see Buchanan, R. Angus, 'Brunel in Bath', *Bath History*, vol.x, Bath, Millstream Books, 2005, pp. 158-186. The quotations are from the Private Diary of I.K. Brunel for March 1833, held in the Brunel Collection of Bristol University Library. I am grateful to the Bristol University Archivists, Michael Richardson and Hannah Lowery, for their assistance in access to this collection.

13   For further details of this episode, see the author's article in *Bath History*, vol.x – see note 12 above.

14   Carrs' Wood in Twerton has recently been opened up to public access, with a display board describing Brunel's contribution above the western portal of the Twerton Tunnel.

15   See Buchanan, R. Angus, 'The Bridges of Bath', *op.cit.*, pp.9-10.

16   For an account of the development of the engineering profession, see Buchanan, R. Angus, *The Engineers: A History of the Engineering Profession in Britain 1750-1914*, London, Jessica Kingsley, 1989.

17   For an account of the University of Bath, see Buchanan, R. Angus, 'Bath: University City', *Bath History*, vol. ix, Bath, Millstream Books, 2002, pp.160-180.

18   Sir Henry de la Beche, *Report on the Sanatory Condition of Bath*, 1845, set the pattern for this work.

19   Wright, G.N., *The Historic Guide to Bath*, Bath, R.E. Peach, 1864, p.149.

20   Rocke, P.N., 'The story of Bath power station', in *Western Power*, vol.1, no.2, February 1962. See also the booklet by Eyles, William E., *Electricity in Bath, 1890-1974*, Bath, Bath City Council and the South West Electricity Board, 1974.

21   See Buchanan, R. Angus, 'The Floods of Bath', *Bath History*, vol.vii, Bath, Millstream Books, 1998, pp.167-188.

10: Machines and Industry

1   Williams, W.J. & Stoddart, D.M., *Bath – Some Encounters with* Science, Bath, Kingsmead Press, 1978.
2   Desaguliers, J.T., *A Course of Experimental Philosophy*, London, W. Innys, 1744.
3   Torrens, Hugh, *Stothert & Pitt: The Evolution of a Family Firm*, Bath, Hugh Torrens, 1978, p.8.
4   Fawcett, Trevor, 'Mechanical Enterprise in Eighteenth-Century Bath', *BIAS Journal*, vol.30, 1998, p.14.
5   Torrens, *op.cit.*, p.26.
6   *The Engineer*, 31 August 1934.
7   British Patent No.22,704.
8   British Patent No.15,632/18.
9   Cummins, L, *Internal Fire*, Lake Oswego OR, Carnot Press, 1976, p.132-156.
10 British Patent No.4080.
11 Clerk, Dugald, *Gas, Petrol & Oil Engines*, London, Longmans, 1916, pp.212-214.
12 Burroughs, Stuart, unpublished manuscript, 2003.
13 British Patent No.18513.
14 Torrens, Hugh, *Joseph Day 1855-1946*, Bath, Bath Industrial Heritage Trust, 1991, pp.9-12.
15 British Patent No.373,660.
16 Cross, R., unpublished manuscript, 2006.
17 White, I., *Clock and Watchmakers of Bath*, Ticehurst, 1996, pp.156-159.
18 British Patent No.2353.
19 British Patent No.27,290.
20 Burroughs, Stuart, unpublished manuscript, 2002.
21 British Patent No.263,925.
22 Ellis, M.J. Hall, *The Early History of the Telephone in Bath*, Bristol, British Telecom, 1986.
23 U.S. Patent No.174,456.

11: Science Lecturing in Georgian Bath

1   This chapter is lagely based on Fawcett, Trevor, 'Science Lecturing at Bath, 1724-1800', *Bath History*, vol.vii, Bath, Millstream Books, 1998, pp.55-77. For individual lecturers see also under Desaguliers, Donn, Ferguson, Martin, Walker, Warltire, etc. in *DNB*.
2   Printed letter from Bath dated 11 May 1724 in *Weekly Journal or British Gazetteer*, 16 May 1724.
3   *Gloucester Journal*, 9 September 1730.
4   Desaguliers, J.T., *A Course of Experimental Philosophy*, 2nd edition, London, W. Innys, 1745, vol.1, p.xi.
5   *ibid.*, vol.1, pp.283-8, plates 12, 21 & 22.
6   *Gloucester Journal*, 20 September 1737.
7   *ibid.*, 26 April 1743.
8   Martin, Benjamin, *An Essay on Electricity*, Bath, for the author, 1746.
9   Martin, Benjamin, *A Supplement Containing Remarks on a Rhapsody of Adventures of a Modern Kight-Errant in Philosophy*, Bath, for the author, 1746.
10 *Bath Journal*, 18 November 1751.
11 *ibid.*, 22 October & 12 November 1750; 18 & 25 November 1751.
12 *Bath Advertiser*, 27 December 1755.
13 *Bath Chronicle*, 22 January, 12 February, 26 March, 16 & 23 April 1767.
14 *ibid.*, 1 & 29 December 1768; 5 January & 23 November 1769; 22 February 1770.
15 *ibid.*, 28 December 1769; 5 April & 6 December 1770; 4 March, 29 April, 6 & 13 May 1773.
16 McKie, Douglas, 'Mr. Warltire, a good chymist', *Endeavour*, vol.10, 1951, pp.46-9.
17 *Bath Chronicle*, 5 September 1776.
18 Fawcett, Trevor, 'Selling the Bath waters', *Somerset Archaeology and Natural History*, vol.134, 1990, pp.193-209.
19 *Bath Chronicle*, 23 October 1777 (Warltire); 19 December 1776; 3 & 10 April, 13 November, 25 December 1777 (Arden).
20 *ibid.*, 1 January, 26 February, 2, 9 & 16 April 1778.
21 Rack, Edmund, 'A disultory journal of events &c at Bath', Bath Central Library, ms.1111.
22 *Bath Chronicle*, 17 June 1784, 14 January 1790 (Smith); 8 March 1781; 9 January & 25 December 1783; 6 & 13 January 1785; 31 December 1795; 7 & 14 January 1796 (Donn); 7 September 1786, 6 [i.e. 7] & 21 March 1788.
23 *ibid.*, 13 December 1781; Harrison, J.A., 'Blind Henry Moyes', *Annals of Science*, vol.13, 1957, pp.109-25.
24 *Bath Chronicle*, 2 & 9 January 1783.
25 *ibid.*, 1 November 1787; 21 February, 28 March, 10 April, 10 July, 13 November 1788; 3 December 1789 (Didier); 20 & 27 November 1788 (Lloyd).
26 *ibid.*, 14 & 21 November 1793; 1 December 1796; 26 January, 16 February, 30 November, 14 December 1787; 8 February 1798.

27 *ibid.*, 18 & 25 April, 2 & 16 May 1799; 6, 13 & 20 February 1800 (Lloyd); 16 & 23 October, 6 November 1800 (Walker).

28 *ibid.*, 15 May 1800.

29 Balderston, K.C. (ed.), *Thraliana: the Diary of Mrs. Hester Lynch Thrale (later Mrs. Piozzi)*, Oxford, Clarendon Press, 1942, pp.1073-4.

30 Wilkinson, C.H., *Analytical Researches into the Properties of the Bath Waters*, Bath, Wood & Cunningham, 1811, advertises his lectures on experimental philosophy, chemistry (including the new electro-chemistry) and mineralogy, held annually from November to May. His course starting early in November 1816 is referred to in the *Bath & Cheltenham Gazette*, 2 October 1816. See also Shelley, Mary, *Frankenstein, or The Modern Prometheus*, revised edition by M. Hindle, Harmondsworth, Penguin, 2003.

31 *Bath & Cheltenham Gazette*, 7 June, 18 October, 13 & 27 December 1820.

12: Bath Scientific Societies and Institutions

1 Among the basic sources for this chapter are Williams, W.J. & Stoddart, D.M., *Bath – some Encounters with Science*, Bath, Kingsmead Press, 1978, 55-80; and Torrens, Hugh, 'The four Bath philosophical societies' in Rolls, R., Guy, J. and Guy, J.R. (eds.), *A Pox on the Provinces*, Bath, Bath University Press, 1990, pp.181-8. The *DNB* also has entries for some of the key figures referred to. As regards the Bath and West, its archive is held at Bath Record Office and its library at the University of Bath. Its history has been related in Lewis, William, *A Century of Agricultural Progress ... [a] History of the Bath and West of England Society*, Bath, for the Author, 1879; Plowman, T.F., *Edmund Rack: the Society he founded and the Company he kept*, Bath, Bath and West Society, 1914; Hudson, Kenneth, *The Bath and West: a Bicentenary History*, Bradford-on-Avon, Moonraker Press, 1976; and Lim, H.L.H., 'Bath and the Bath and West of England Society, 1777-1851', *Bath History*, vol.vi, Bath, Millstream Books, pp.108-31.

2 *Bath Chronicle*, 11 September 1777.

3 Bath and West of England Society, *Letters and Papers on Agriculture, Planting, &c.*, 2 volumes, Bath, the Society, 1802, vol.2, pp.285ff.

4 Hunt, Henry, *Memoirs ... written in His Majesty's Jail at Ilchester*, 3 volumes, London, T. Dolby, 1820, vol.2, pp.465-73.

5 A more ambitious proposal for an experimental farm and agricultural college was put forward in 1811 but came to nothing. See the Bath and West of England Society's *Prospectus for an Agricultural College ...* , Bath, the Society, 1811, held in Bath Central Library.

6 Bath and West of England Society, 'Minutes of the Committee of Chemical [and Geological] Research 1805-08, 1819-25', Bath Record Office, Acc.38/2/21-22.

7 Report of Bath and West AGM in the *Bath & Cheltenham Gazette*, 16 December 1818.

8 Williams & Stoddart, *op.cit.*, pp.64-7.

9 Sources for the first Bath Literary and Scientific Society include Williams & Stoddart, *op.cit.*, plus Torrens, Hugh, *op.cit.* and especially Turner, A.J.(ed.), *Science and Music in Eighteenth Century Bath: An Exhibition in the Holburne of Menstrie Museum, Bath, 22 September 1977-29 December 1977*, Bath, University of Bath, 1977, pp.81-95. The latter, with its list of the then known members, was based on an archive assembled by Hugh Torrens and now deposited in Bath Record Office, Acc.465/1-2. Also crucial for the society's early history are the entries in Rack, Edmund, 'A disultory journal of events &c. at Bath' [22 Dec 1779-22 March 1780], Bath Central Library, ms. transcript B920.

10 Rack, Edmund, *A Respectful Tribute to the Memory of Thomas Curtis Esq.*, Bath, 1784.

11 Fawcett, Trevor, 'Self-improvement societies: the early Lit and Phils' in *Life in the Georgian Town: Papers given at the Georgian Group Annual Symposium 1985*, London, The Georgian Group, 1986, pp.15-25.

12 Rack, Edmund, 'Disultory Journal', 1 January 1780. While Melmoth declined, his intimate friend Samuel Pye did join.

13 *ibid.*, 27 December 1779. Though the society's bias was scientific, its rules allowed discussion of 'the History of Nations, or any branch of Polite Literature' together with essays on morality and the social virtues, and candid criticism of any new publication.

14 *ibid.*, 28 & 30 December 1779; 7 & 14 January 1780. Several likely candidates never joined, e.g. Rack's Bath friend Robert Madden who had long studied science and made collections of scientific instruments and books on natural history.

15 *ibid.*, 22 March 1780.

16 Hoskin, M. (ed.), *The Herschel Partnership*, Cambridge, Science History Publications, 2003, p.60. Sooner or later they also had a furnace, apparently used in 1783 for experiments with manganese and bismuth – Thomas Curtis to Charles Blagden, 28 March 1783, Bath Record Office, Acc.465/2/11.

17 Martha Bally, widow since 1774 of the bookseller William Bally, has previously been confused with her brother-in-law John Bally, a hairdresser and perfumer at No.3 Milsom Street from 1778. Letters for the society might be addressed to Mrs Bally: see Turner, op.cit., p.89, item 159.

18 *Memoirs of the Literary and Philosophical Society of Manchester*, vol.1-, 1785- and *Essays by a Society of Gentlemen, at Exeter*, Exeter, 1796.

19   Dreyer, J.L.E. (ed.), *The Scientific Papers of William Herschel*, 2 volumes, London, Royal Society and Royal Astronomical Society, 1912. Copies of a very fragmentary ms. containing Rack's transcript of other papers delivered, can be seen at Bath Record Office, Acc.465/1/1.

20   Rack, Edmund, 'Disultory Journal', 20 January 1780.

21   Turner, *op.cit.*, p.87, item 153 (quotation slightly amended from Bath Record Office, Acc.465/2/12).

22   *ibid.*, p.95.

23   Monkland, G., *The Literature and Literati of Bath*, Bath, R.E. Peach, 1854, p.43, speaking of Watson's post-1800 address in Great Pulteney Street. Watson ran a hospitable house anyway: according to his niece it was 'a rendezvous equally of persons of benevolence, talent, wit, and fashion', see Hankin, C.C. (ed.), *Life of Mary Anne Schimmelpenninck*, 2 volumes, London, Longman Brown, 1858, vol.1, pp.6–8.

24   Warner, Richard, *An Historical and Descriptive Account of Bath*, Bath, R. Cruttwell, 1802, pp.81-2. Falconer had been made an honorary member of the Manchester society in 1782.

25   The then extant minute book is recorded in Shum, Frederick, *A Catalogue of Bath Books ...* , Bath, S.W. Simms, 1913, p.20, which also cites a letter to Haygarth, then presumably acting as chairman or secretary.

26   Gibbes was projector of the Gibbesium, a factory at Conham, near Bristol, that converted animal waste into Prussian blue, ammonia, and a kind of spermaceti – see Graves, Richard, *Excursions from Bath*, Bath, R. Cruttwell, 1801, pp.274-6. He published two treatises on the Bath waters, 1800–03. Gibbes included, 13 members of the second Bath Philosophical Society have been identified: see Torrens, *op.cit.*, p.183.

27   Watson to Herschel, 9 October 1800, Bath Record Office, Acc.465/2/23.

28   Warner, *op.cit.*, pp.81-2.

29   Torrens, *op.cit.*, pp.183-4.

30   Watson to Herschel, 10 March 1804 (also 13 February 1801), Bath Record Office, Acc.465/2/23.

31   Kite, V.J. 'Libraries in Bath, 1618-1964', unpublished FLA thesis, London, Library Association, 1966, pp.77-8. The Publick Library's secretary was Dr G.S. Gibbes and its treasurer William Matthews, further indications of the overlapping personnel of Bath's cultural institutions.

32   The Library's books were auctioned off in late 1807 and the proceeds divided among the subscribers, see *Bath Journal*, 7 December 1807 and *Bath Chronicle*, 18 February 1808.

33   Wilkinson's life is sketched in Thornton, J.L., 'Charles Hunnings Wilkinson, 1763/64-1850', *Annals of Science*, December 1967, pp.277-86

34   *Bath Chronicle*, 3 May & 21 December 1809, mention his lectures and the improved Kingston Baths.

35   *The New Bath Directory corrected to May 1812*, Bath, Wood & Cunningham, 1812, p.122.

36   In 1815 he exhibited William Smith's geological survey map to the Bath and West and in 1818 served briefly as the society's Secretary and then as supervisor of the chemical laboratory. He often addressed the society on topics as various as the preservation of meat, animal digestion, and the causes of Bath floods.

37   Wilkinson was Superintendent of the Bath Gas Light & Coke Company. The project required an Act of Parliament, considerable high-risk funding, and technical expertise to build a gas works and the associated miles of mains piping.

38   *Bath Journal*, 11 December 1815; Egan, Pierce, *Walks through Bath*, Bath, W. Meyler, 1819, pp.104-7.

39   Women were admitted as full members rather than as accompanied guests from the start of the second season; up to June 1816 the society had 70 male subscribers, each entitled to bring one visitor, see the *Bath & Cheltenham Gazette*, 2 June & 2 October 1816.

40   *Bath & Cheltenham Gazette*, 24 January-2 June 1816 and 2 October 1816-May 1817 *passim*.

41   The defence case – that true natural philosophy confirmed rather than questioned scripture – was urged by 'Theophilus' on behalf of the Philosophical Society in the *Bath & Cheltenham Gazette*, 17 January 1816.

42   *Bath & Cheltenham Gazette*, 1 October 1817.

43   For the date c.1821 see Torrens, *op.cit.*, p.184. For Geneva see Wilkinson, C.H., *An Enquiry into ... the Rock Oil ...* , London, J. Ridgway, 1830, p.46; and the *Bath & Cheltenham Gazette*, 21 December 1824, report of the Bath and West AGM.

44   *Bath Chronicle*, 4 & 18 February, 13 & 20 May, 2 December 1830.

45   T.L. Peacock's satirical name for the SDUK in his novel, *Crotchet Castle*.

46   But also amid great controversy – see Kite', *op.cit.*, pp.113-7.

47   The best account of the Bath Mechanics' Institute and Athenaeum is in Kite, *op.cit.*, pp.111-39, but see also Bath directories from 1829 onwards. The Institute occupied various addresses before moving to Orange Grove in 1841 and becoming the Athenaeum, c.1845. A different organisation, the Bath Commercial and Literary Institution, existed from 1839 to 1874 to promote arts, sciences and literature, but as its other name, the Tottenham Library, suggests it served principally as a library and reading room.

48   Sources for the history of BRLSI include its run of *Annual Reports*; Kite, *op.cit.*, pp.77-111 & 280-90.; Hunter, Joseph, *The Connection of Bath with the Literature and Science of England*, Bath, R.E. Peach, 1853; Spender, J.K., *Some Account of the History of the Bath Royal Literary and Scientific Institution*, Bath, Bath Chronicle, 1875; and assorted material at Bath Record Office.

49   The Bristol Institution was first projected in 1809. The foundation stone for the Park Street building was laid in March 1820 and the Institution opened in 1823. Merged in 1871 with the Bristol Library Society, it came under municipal control in 1894 and evolved into the Bristol City Museum and Art Gallery.

50   The chief piece of publicity was a pamphlet by Hastings Elwin, *Reasons for Establishing an Institution at Bath*, Bath, 1820. Hastings, a tireless advocate for the BLSI, shouldered most of the legal and financial negotiations. One watered-down scheme reduced the concept to just a library once more – see Hunter, *op.cit.*, p.8.

51   *Bath & Cheltenham Gazette*, 27 December 1820.

52   *ibid.*, 10 June 1823.

53   *ibid.*, 25 January 1825.

54   Bath Literary and Philosophical Association, *Annual Report[s] for 1825[-1835]*, Bath, 1826-36.

55   Many of the books must have been acquired through Upham's bookshop, just opposite the BLSI, where the Library Sub-committee met: see Spender, *op.cit.*, p.11.

56   A botanic garden was laid out in Royal Victoria Park, c.1840, as noted in Hanham, F., *A Manual for the Park*, London, Longman Brown, 1857. On C.E. Broome's death in 1886 his important plant collection from Batheaston formed the basis of a new botanic garden designed by the curator J.W. Morris and others.

57   Barlow, Edward, *An Apology for the Study of Phrenology*, Bath, Wood & Cunningham, 1825, pp.9-12. The lecturer on both occasions was the celebrated Spurzheim.

58   Newspapers of the time advertise other lecture series at BRLSI in 1830 on coins, optics, French literature (given in French) and physiology, see *Bath Chronicle,* 14 January, 25 March, 15 & 29 April 1830.

59   Britton, John, *The Auto-Biography of John Britton*, London, for the author, 1850, pp.221-2.

60   BRLSI, *Report of the Museum Sub-Committee, May 1853*; BRLSI, *Annual Report for 1853*, Bath 1854.

61   For the geological holdings and contemporary Bath collectors see the special Bath issue of *Geological Curators Group Newsletter*, April 1975, 1, 3.

62   For Jenyns see Wallace, Ian (ed.), *Leonard Jenyns, Darwin's Lifelong Friend*, Bath, BRLSI, 2005.

63   Jenyns praised the museum in 1865 for its collections of geology, minerals, birds and antiquities but thought it especially lacked 'a collection of the mammals, reptiles, fishes, and insects of the neighbourhood'. He wanted it to concentrate on local natural history, see Jenyns, Leonard, *Natural History Museums*, Bath, S. Hayward, 1865.

64   Wallace, *op.cit.*, p.129.

65   For Bath Natural History and Antiquarian Field Club see its printed *Proceedings*, 11 volumes, 1869-1909, and the collection of its minutes and newspaper cuttings, 1866-93, in Bath Central Library.

66   Blomefield [i.e. Jenyns], Leonard, '[Presidential] Address to the Members of the Bath Field Club, in reference to the death of C.E. Broome, Esq., F.L.S.' in *Proceedings of the Bath Natural History and Antiquarian Field Club*, vol. 6, 1889, pp.144-153.

67   Blomefield [i.e. Jenyns], Leonard, '[Valedictory letter]' in *Proceedings of the Bath Natural History and Antiquarian Field Club*, vol.8, pp.1-8. This excursion and a similar one to the limestone combes near Wrington are described in *ibid.*, pp.56-60.

68   The activities of the Bath branch are charted in the Selborne Society's national magazine, *Nature Notes*, *passim*, as well as in the branch's *Annual Reports*, June 1903-Jun 1910.

69   See for instance George Norman's paper on the fauna of Bath in *Proceedings of the Bath Natural History and Antiquarian Field Club*, vol.7, pp.1-13. Norman was also an active Selbornian, and Jenyns too thought well of the society, see Wallace, *op.cit.*, p.247.

70   Norman, George, *The Selborne Society: its Present Position and Future Prospects*, Bath, Bath Chronicle, 1889; *Nature Notes*, vol.2, no.19, July 1891, pp.139-40; Selborne Society Bath Branch, *Annual Meeting at Claverton Manor, June 23, 1893*, Bath, 1893.

71   *Annual Reports* 1903-4 and 1909-10.

72   *Proceedings of the Bath & District Branch [of the] Somerset Archaeological and Natural History Society*, 1909-13, pp.236-9.

73   For its activities see Bath Microscopical Society, *Extracts from the Minutes ...* , Bath, 1862 and 1866, and *Reports*, 1881-95, and also Morris J.W., *The Annual Address to the Bath Microscopical Society, February 4th, 1873*, Bath, 1873. Parallel to it ran the Postal Microscopical Society, formed in 1873 in order to circulate boxes of slides among its national membership. The business was largely conducted from Bath by its secretary, Alfred Allen, aided by a Bath sub-committee. Allen also edited the society's *Journal*, started in 1882.

74   *Bath Journal*, 13 February 1864.

75   The society also arranged a soirée for the Royal Horticultural Society's Bath show in 1873.

76   A ladies' night was first instituted c.1885.

77   Bath Ladies' Microscopical Society, *14th and 15th Annual Reports for 1910-11*, Bath, ?1911.

78   Leader of Bath's Liberal party, seven times Mayor, municipal reformer, staunch Unitarian, Murch assisted many local institutions besides BRLSI, including the Bath and West, the Mechanics' Institute/Athenaeum, and the Mineral Water Hospital. He played a major role at the time of the British Association's conference in 1864.

79   *Bath Herald*, 9 January 1886.

80   *Bath & Cheltenham Gazette*, 26 February 1890, which gives his name as C.[not W.] Friese-Greene.

81   *ibid.*, 27 February and 6 March 1889. It then boasted c.1,000 regular and casual subscribers to its library of 7,000 volumes and had a debating society.
82   *Bath Daily Chronicle*, 10 Feb 1899. The vote for the merger was 26 to 14.
83   Kite, *op.cit.*, p.280.
84   *Bath Chronicle*, 31 January 1889. At that date the existing Government School of Art and Science at No.33 Paragon taught fewer than 120 pupils; the expanded school in 1892 opened with 514.

13: The Bath Royal Literary and Scientific Institution Reborn

1   Robert Whitaker, private communication.
2   These were: Basil Greenslade, Research Fellow, University College, London; Mrs Stella Pierce, History of Science and Technology research worker; Hugh Torrens MA, PhD, Lecturer in Geology, University of Keele; R.J. Whitaker MBE, Member of Executive Committee, The Bath Society and formerly Chairman, Bath Geological Society; Roger Rolls MA, MB Medical Practitioner and Secretary, Bath Medical History Group.
3   A constitution was adopted at a General Meeting of the Friends on 23 March 1988.
4   The 17 organisations were: Avon County Council; Bath City Council (with no casting vote); Area Museum Council for the South West; Museums & Galleries Commission; Geological Curators' Group; Biological Curators' Group; Museum Ethnographers' Group; British Museum; City of Bristol Museum and Art Gallery; Bath Society; Bath Geological Society; Palaeontological Association; Bath University; Royal Botanic Gardens, Kew; Royal Society; Museums' Association; Geological Society.

14: The British Association in Bath

1   Murchison to Whewell, 1 Mar 1844, in Morrell, J. & Thackray, A. (eds.), *Gentlemen of Science: Early Correspondence of the British Association for the Advancement of Science*, London: Royal Historical Society, Camden Fourth Series No.30, 1984, pp.360-2. Here Murchison refers to Duncan in person.
2   British Association for the Advancement of Science, *Report of the Thirty-fourth Meeting ... held at Bath in September 1864*, London: John Murray, 1865. British Association for the Advancement of Science, *Authorised Reprint of the Reports in the Special Daily Editions of the Bath Chronicle*, Bath, T.D. Taylor, 1864. See p.250 of the latter for Charles Moore's statement that earlier invitations had been rejected by the BA on the grounds that Bath would be a failure.
3   Entry for John Hanning Speke in *DNB*.
4   Hooker to Darwin, 19 Sept 1864, in Burkhardt, F. & Smith, S. (eds.), *The Correspondence of Charles Darwin*, vol.12, Cambridge, Cambridge University Press, 2001, p.330.
5   British Association for the Advancement of Science, *Report of the Fifty-eighth Meeting ... held at Bath in September 1888*, London: John Murray, 1889; *Bath Herald*, 5-14 September 1888.
6   British Association for the Advancement of Science, *Final Programme of the Annual Meeting at University of Bath*, London, 1978.
7   www.the-ba.net.

15: University Science and Technology in Bath

1   The plans were for a 'Queen's College, Bath, Auxiliary to the Universities of Oxford and Cambridge', with the primary aim being to combat 'the alarmingly rapid increase of Popery in this Island'; see Buchanan, R. Angus, 'Bath: University City' in *Bath History*, vol.ix, Bath, Millstream Books, 2002, pp.160-180. There is a small collection of papers about this project in Bath Reference Library, together with some architects' drawings.
2   The *Preliminary Prospectus* for the School, issued in 1885. The *Prospectus* was issued annually and later became the *Year Book*. These and other early documents were held in the joint Library on Ashley Down, but then passed to the University of the West of England. In 1885 the School was organised in five departments – Primary, Secondary, Mining and Technical, Chemical and Metallurgical, and an Evening Class which was open to both sexes. This ban on sexual discrimination was gradually extended to other departments, becoming one of the pioneering features of the School.
3   For the Report on *Technical Education*, see HMSO Cmnd. 9703, February 1956. Bristol Technical College remained in Ashley Down until it acquired the Coldharbour Farm estate on Pur Down. It became Bristol Polytechnic and then the University of the West of England. Professor R.W. Bolland transferred from the post of Head of the School of Chemistry at the University of Bath to become the first Director of the Polytechnic.
4   The Robbins Report of October 1963 was published as *Higher Education*, HMSO Cmnd. 2154. The Bristol College was one of ten recommended for promotion to university status, of which only Brunel College had fewer students at the time.
5   For the architects' report on the Claverton Down site, see Robert Matthew, Johnson-Marshall & Partners, *The Proposed University of Bath, a Technological University: Development Plan, Report Number 1*, Bath, Bath University Press, 1965.

Biographical Notes and Gazetteer of Bath Scientists

Colin Axon

Sometimes it can be easy to lose sight of the fact that the people we have been discussing had lives beyond their discoveries, inventions, and in some cases utterly extraordinary achievements. Some were born in Bath, many decided to live in Bath; others came and went. Most had families; all of them had to live somewhere. Many of their homes and work places remain – places in which we still live, work, or walk past every day.

It can be difficult to distinguish between those who had a private income from inherited wealth to allow them to pursue scientific endeavours, and those who earned enough to free themselves from the need to work. This is particularly true of nineteenth-century characters; the eighteenth century is more clear-cut. Generally, clerics and 'professionals' (such as physicians) had to attend one of four or five British universities, and therefore usually needed private wealth. Unlike now, surgeons and engineers were not 'professionals', purely because they served an apprenticeship and not because they were less skilled. However, many went on to become wealthy. The inventors, entrepreneurs, craftsmen, traders, and merchants usually had to work throughout their lives consequently allowing them much less time to pursue their studies. Perhaps this makes their achievements all the more remarkable.

Defining the labels for particular topics is riddled with traps; our ideas of what science actually is have changed dramatically over the last 1,000 years. For example, up until perhaps 1600, natural history would have included archaeology, mineralogy, and chemistry. This makes describing the activities of Bath scientists very difficult, since they cover the whole of the last millennium! The professionalisation of science did not come about until the late nineteenth century. If our characters were to take a view at all, most would have thought of themselves as 'natural philosophers' or 'natural historians'. Philosophy was far more than having thoughts about the nature of human existence, it was about experimental science, mathematics, and probably medicine too. Those concerned with plants and animals (except humans) were generally termed natural historians. As many people were simply interested in the world around them, their most easily distinguishable interests have all been listed below. The subtleties of interdisciplinarity have not been drawn out in order to demonstrate the various patterns of study and ingenuity. Likewise, any distinction between inventors and engineers is not worthwhile for our purposes. Therefore the list of scientific interests of our characters reflects a view of the twentieth-century division of 'the sciences'. Our use of the term 'natural history' will cover botany, zoology, mycology, algology, marine biology, conchology, and entomology – to name but a few. The exception is where an individual strongly concentrated on a single aspect of natural history.

Apart from a Nobel prize, the highest honour a British scientist or engineer can attain is FRS. This has not always been the case. Since its founding in 1660, the Royal Society has recognised brilliant scientists for sure, but until the mid to late nineteenth century there was an element of a 'Gentleman's Club' about its membership. Whilst it helped, scientific eminence was not always a necessary criterion for election. As science became professionalised, so did the Fellows of the Royal Society. Furthermore, achievements should be judged against the standards of their time.

A reference list has not been included with this section of the book as there are many citations within the main text. So the only source identified here is the *DNB* – all authors have used this where possible. The addresses are correct as far as we can ascertain, but are not exhaustive; some of those featured lived at as many as 20 locations during their time in Bath. The various *Bath Directories* are the principal source. A question mark preceding a piece of information, i.e. ?item, indicates some uncertainty about that single piece of information. Normally this means that there are reasonable grounds to support the assertion, though conclusive evidence for the statement has been lost or become untraceable. Great care has been taken to ensure that all of the information is accurate: the author accepts responsibility for any remaining errors.

Entries are arranged thus:
Surname, First name(s), [FRS]; birth year, birth place – death year, death place; occupation (where relevant); list of scientific interests; [*DNB*].

The following abbreviations are used throughout:

BAS	Bath Agricultural Society
BAFC	Bath Antiquarian and Field Club
BCID	Bath City Infirmary and Dispensary (*see Note 1*)
BPS	Bath Philosophical Society (there were three before BRLSI was formed)
BRLSI	Bath (Royal) Literary and Scientific Institution (*see Note 2*)
DNB	*Oxford Dictionary of National Biography*, Oxford, Oxford University Press, 2004
FGS	Fellow of the Geological Society (London)
fl.	flourished, i.e. known to be active between these dates
FRS	Fellow of the Royal Society
GSL	Geological Society of London
L/M/FRCP	Licentiate/Member/Fellow of the (Royal) College of Physicians
M/FRCS	Member/Fellow of the (Royal) College of Surgeons
MWH	Mineral Water Hospital (*see Note 3*)

Note 1: The current Royal United Hospital (RUH) at Combe Park (site opened in 1932) is a result of many mergers. The Bath City Infirmary and Dispensary (founded in 1747 in Wood Street then moved to Lower Borough Walls) and the Bath Casualty Hospital (founded in 1788 at 38 Kingsmead Street) merged to become the Bath United Hospital (1826 at Beau Street). The Royal title was bestowed in 1864. The Ear, Nose, and Throat Hospital (founded in 1837 in Marlborough Buildings) moved to the RUH in 1959, as did the Bath Eye Infirmary in 1973 (founded in 1811 at 1 Pierrepont Street and later moved to 1-2 Belvedere on Lansdown Road).

Note 2: As related in Chapter 12, the Bath Literary and Scientific Institution opened in 1825, adding the style 'Royal' to its name around 1830 thanks to the patronage of William IV. The abbreviation BRLSI is used for the Institution throughout the period from 1825 to the present.

Note 3: The Bath General Hospital was opened in 1742 and remains so today at its original location, Upper Borough Walls. However, the name evolved through (Royal) Mineral Water Hospital to its current title The Royal National Hospital for Rheumatic Diseases, affectionately known as 'The Min'.

Abraham, Jacob; b. ?Exeter (Devon) – d. ?1845, ?Bath; engineer; scientific instruments.
Lived at: 1 St Andrews Terrace.
Lived and worked at: 7 Bartlett Street.
Arrived in Bath in 1800 and traded until the 1840s. He is known to have made orreries, thermometers, sundials, microscopes and telescopes. His son, Abraham, also became a highly successful instrument maker, but chose to set up in Liverpool (from 1818). JA started a branch in Cheltenham, and claimed that he had received the royal warrant having undertaken work for HRH the Duke of Gloucester and His Grace the Duke of Wellington.

Acland, Sir Thomas Dyke, FRS; b. 1809, Killerton (Devon) – d. 1898, Killerton (Devon); chemistry and agriculture; *DNB*.
Principally known as a politician (MP for West Somerset 1837-47 and 1885-86) and educational reformer. Graduated from Oxford University in classics in 1831, but attended Kings College London to study chemistry after leaving Parliament in 1847. Actively promoted technical education for farmers and was one of the founders of the Royal Agricultural College. TA led the rejuvenation of the BAS in the 1850s by making the society's shows peripatetic and revamping its *Journal*. Wrote on farming and agricultural chemistry. Elected FGS.

Adelard of Bath; b. c.1080, Bath – d. c.1152; scholar; astronomy, mathematics; *DNB*.
Sometimes styled 'the first English scientist'. Travelled and studied in Europe and the Near East. Translated Euclid's *Elements* and Arabic mathematical texts into Latin. Wrote on the astrolabe, astronomy, botany, human nature, mathematics, metrology, and zoology. Not to be confused with Peter Abelard of the same era.

Alexander, Patrick Y.; b. 1867, Belvedere (Kent) – d. 1943, Windsor (Berks); aeronautics.
Lived at: 8 Portland Place; De Montalt Wood, Summer Lane, Combe Down; The Mount, Batheaston.
Worked at: De Montalt Mill; Combe Down; 24 Ballance Street; The Mount, Batheaston.
Patron and pioneer of aeronautics, particularly ballooning, and enjoyed a world-wide reputation. Also experimented with wireless telegraphy; Nikolai Tesla built on PYA's work. Built balloons for meteorological data-gathering and was elected Fellow of the Royal Meteorological Society.

Allen, Alfred H.; b. 1834, Cambridge – d. 1898, Bath; wine merchant; natural history.
Lived at: 1 Cambridge Place.
Co-founded the Postal Microscopical Society in 1873 to put slide-mounted specimens around a 'circuit' of its members. AA was Secretary and/or Treasurer until his death, and the PMS still flourishes. President of the Bath Microscopical Society in 1882.

Archer, Dr Clement; b. 1750/1, Ireland – d. 1806, Cheltenham (Glos); surgeon; chemistry.
Worked at: Abbey Church House.
Sometime army 'State-surgeon' in Ireland. Appointed Chemical Professor to the BAS in 1805 acting as superintendent to its chemical laboratory. CA gave popular lectures on agricultural chemistry.

Arden, John; b. 1702, Charford (Worcs) – d. 1791, Beverley (Yorks); lecturer; physics.
Lived at: St James's Street.
An experienced peripatetic lecturer on experimental science, JA arrived in Bath in the autumn of 1768. His lectures covered many topics including the increasingly important local topics of fossils and mineralogy. Conducted experiments on electricity with **Bryant** and **W. Herschel**. Founding member of BAS and 1st BPS.

At(t)wood, Harry; fl. 1780-1820; surgeon; medicine.
Lived at: Queen Square; Weston Lane.
Worked at: MWH.
Collaborated with **Parry** on the origins of angina. Worked at the MWH 1781-1807. Founding member of the 1st BPS. A City Councillor, Alderman, and twice Mayor (c.1800).

Babington, Charles Cardale, FRS; b. 1808, Ludlow (Shrops) – d. 1895, Cambridge; scholar; botany and archaeology; *DNB*.
Attended school in Bath. Wrote a work on the local flora before going to Cambridge University, where he eventually became Professor of Botany. CB used the work of **J. Davis**, **H. Gibbes**, **Flower** and **Broome**. Elected as president of the botany and zoology section of the British Association in 1853, 1858, and 1861. Founded the Entomological Society of London and elected FGS.

Barlow, Edward; b. 1779, Meath (Ireland) – d. 1844; physician; medicine.
Lived at: 102 New Sydney Place.
Worked at: MWH, Bath United Hospital.
In the 1820s, introduced into hospital practice the first effective drug for gout. Member of the 3rd BPS and did much to get BRLSI operating. A graduate of Edinburgh University.

Barry, Prof Sir Edward, FRS; b. 1696, Cork (Ireland) – d. 1776, Bath; scholar and physician; medicine, *DNB*.
Held the post of Regius Professor of Physic at Trinity College Dublin from 1754 until he moved to England in 1761. EB is credited with useful advances in the treatment of tuberculosis. Arrived in Bath c.1769 to improve business for his medical practice. Made FRCP in 1762.

Baylies, Dr William; baptised 1722, Evesham (Worcs) – d. 1787, Berlin; apothecary and physician; medicine, *DNB*.
Trained as an apothecary with his father, then as a physician at Aberdeen University. Made LRCP in 1765. Spent seven years in Bath as an independent physician, but was not appointed to a hospital position because of the controversy which his book on the Bath waters caused. Moved to London and then Berlin, where he became physician to Frederick the Great. Died a bankrupt.

Bell, Alexander Graham; b. 1847, Edinburgh – d. 1922, Nova Scotia (Canada); teacher and inventor; *DNB*.
Lived at: 22 Charles Street; 21 Bennett Street.
Worked at: 11 The Circus.
Inventor of the telephone. In Bath only for the academic year 1866-7 as a master at Somerset College.

Bennet, William; fl. 1782–1825; civil engineer; canals.
Lived at: 32 St James's Parade.
Probably born in Lancashire. Chief engineer to the Somersetshire Coal Canal Company and presented the engineering evidence to obtain the required Parliamentary Act. His costings, though, were very inaccurate. Later carried out one independent surveying contract jointly with **W. Smith** and **Harcourt Masters** in 1811.

Blathwayt, Colonel Linley; b. 1839, Langridge (Somerset) – d. 1919, ?Bath; soldier; entomology.
Lived at: Langridge Rectory; Eagle House, Batheaston.
A very industrious observer and collector of insects in the Batheaston and Bristol Channel areas. LB wrote extensively and became well respected. He was a strong supporter of his daughter,

Mary, a leading suffragette. MB shared her father's passion and was a member of the Bath Ladies' Microscopical Society.

Bowler, Jonathan Burdett; b. 1834, Bath – d. 1911, Bath; mechanical engineer and entrepreneur.
Lived at: 12 Monmouth Place; 2 Rivers Street; 45 Villa Fields, Bathwick.
Worked at: 12 Southgate Street; 12-13 Corn Street.
After serving an engineering apprenticeship he struck out on his own, making anything and everything for anyone – machinery, devices, products, or repairs. The Bowler collection forms a major part of the Museum of Bath at Work.

Boyd, Cadwallader; fl. 1805-1806; chemistry.
Worked at: Abbey Church House.
Assistant to **Archer** in the BAS chemistry laboratory. CB performed analyses of soils, plants, and other organic substances for BAS members. Took over as superintendent following Archer's death in 1806.

Broome, Rev Christopher E.; b. 1812, Berkhamstead (Herts) – d. 1886, London; cleric; natural history.
Lived at: Box, Wilts; Elmhurst House, Batheaston.
Sometimes styled 'the mushroom man' – a very highly respected mycologist. Left his collection of fungi to the British Museum. Honorary curator to BRLSI from 1882 (with **Winwood**). Co-founder of the BAFC (with **Jenyns**). Travelled and collected plants across Europe; donated his collection to the Botanic Gardens in Victoria Park. **Babington** used his work.

Brough, William; fl. 1800-1817; mechanical engineer; steam engines.
Lived at: Avon Lodge, Lower Bristol Road.
Worked at: Broad Quay.
Arrived in Bath c.1802 from Bristol. Accompanied the 18-year-old **G. Stothert (junior)** in 1804 on a tour of manufacturing areas of South Wales with a letter of introduction to Richard Trevithick (at the Penydarren Ironworks) written by **W. Smith**. Member of the 3rd BPS. May have been interested in mineralogy and geology.

Brunel, Isambard Kingdom, FRS; b. 1806, Portsmouth (Hants) – d. 1859, London; civil engineer; railways; *DNB*.
Little personal connection with Bath, although he had relatives in Chilcompton. His father, Marc, looked for a house in Bath, but ultimately did not move. However, IKB's legacy and effect on Bath cannot be overstated.

Bryant, John B.; b. ?Bath – d. 1793, Bath; draper and soapmaker; astronomy and physics.
Lived and worked at: Walcot Street.
Conducted experiments on electrical machines with **Arden** and **W. Herschel**. Also knew **Watson**. Founding member of the 1st BPS. Herschel acknowledged JB's help in discovering some double stars.

Carwardine, George; b. 1887, Bath – d. 1947, Bath; mechanical engineer and entrepreneur.
Lived at: 2 Church Street, Abbey Green; 7 Victoria Road; 2 Bennett Street; 17 Macaulay Buildings; Entry Hill House, Entry Hill.
Worked at: Locksbrook Road and elsewhere.
After his apprenticeship GC joined Horstman Cars Ltd. eventually becoming Works Manager and Chief Designer, specialising in suspension systems. Trialled and raced cars at Brooklands with

S. Horstmann. Went independent and invented the anglepoise lamp (patented 1932). Designed tank suspension systems which are still in use and manufactured locally.

Charleton, Dr Rice, FRS; b. 1723, Bristol – d. 1788, Olveston (S. Glos); physician; medicine and chemistry; *DNB*.
Lived at: Alfred Buildings.
Worked at: MWH.
Honorary physician to, and a governor of, the MWH. Conducted careful experiments to determine the minerals in the spa waters. RC numerically analysed patient records to gauge the genuine efficacy of various treatments; although he erroneously did not use a control group this is still one of the earliest examples of evidence-based medicine. Withdrew from the Royal Society in 1754.

Cheselden, William, FRS; b. 1688, Somerby (Leics) – d. 1752, Bath; surgeon; medicine; *DNB*. Served his apprenticeship at St Thomas's in London, qualifying in 1711. Published and lectured extensively on anatomy, physiology, and surgery, and started one of the first pre-clinical courses in Britain. Surgeon to HM Queen Caroline (wife of George IV). The foremost surgeon of his time, he was highly innovative. A frequent visitor to Bath; an RUH ward is named in his honour.

Cheyne, Dr George, FRS; b. 1671/2, Methlick (Scotland) – d. 1743, Bath; physician; medicine and mathematics; *DNB*.
Lived at: Monmouth Street.
Wrote many 'popular' and influential medical texts. In particular he was concerned about crowded urban living and large social gatherings as a way for airborne diseases to spread (though he was not aware of bacteria and viruses). GC extolled the virtues of whole foods, vigorous exercise, and clean living to cure the nervous diseases and obesity of the wealthy; though this was after he slimmed from 32 stone (200 kg). He became one of the most well-known physicians in Britain, and had many famous patients (including Samuel Johnson, Alexander Pope, Samuel Richardson, the Countess of Huntingdon, and Beau Nash). GC arrived in Bath in 1706 and spent 12 'seasons' in practice; permanently moved in 1718. One of the founders of the MWH. A close follower of Isaac Newton, GC published a general account of Newton's calculus before Newton himself. This soured his relationship with Newton and tarnished his reputation in the Royal Society. GC continued to use Newtonian philosophy (combined with mysticism) in his medical and other writing.

Cleland, Archibald; b. c.1700, Lanarkshire (Scotland) – d. 1771, abroad (but unknown); surgeon; medicine.
Worked at: MWH.
Served a five-year apprenticeship in Edinburgh. Whilst serving in the army, AC invented many medical instruments including those for eye surgery and a candle-powered device for inspecting ear drums. Arrived in Bath c.1732 as a patient, returned in 1741 to set up a practice, and left c.1754. Considered for election to the Royal Society, but was rejected.

Cogan, Dr Thomas; b. 1736, Rothwell (Northants) – d. 1818, London; physician, agriculture; *DNB*.
Lived at: Argyle Buildings; Widcombe Crescent.
Started out as a minister and preacher. Following marriage, TC studied medicine at Leiden University and practised in Holland and London. Became interested in the resuscitation of the drowned and co-founded the Royal Humane Society. Arrived in Bath in the late 1790s and started the Bath Humane Society. Later a prize-winning experimental farmer in Somerset (and elsewhere).

Cole, Dr Thomas; d. 1899/1900, ?Bath; physician; zoology.
Lived at: 28 Paragon; 18 The Circus.
Worked at: Bath United Hospital.
Graduated from London University, arrived in Bath in 1870. TC was appointed physician to the United Hospital and elected MRCP c.1872. Interested in bird migration.

Conybeare, Rev John Josias; b. 1779, London – d. 1824, London; geology and chemistry; *DNB*.
Lived and worked at: Batheaston.
Set up a chemistry laboratory at his vicarage in Batheaston. Member of the 3rd BPS. One of the original honorary members of the GSL and a very well respected geologist.

Creaser, Dr Thomas; b. ?Cheltenham (Glos) – d. 1825, Bath; surgeon and apothecary; medicine.
Lived at: 10 Miles' Court; 7 Gay Street.
Arrived in Bath by 1798. Jointly with **Haygarth** set up (probably) the first vaccination clinic for smallpox in England. Knew Dr Thomas Beddoes of Bristol and corresponded with James Watt. Member of the London Company of Surgeons.

Cross, Dr Clara; b. 1900, Sheffield – d. 1986, Bath; GP and pathologist; medicine.
Lived at: 114 Midford Road.
Worked at: St Martin's Hospital, Midford Road.
Graduated with MB from Sheffield University in 1922 (later obtained a doctorate) when there were very few women in medicine. Married **R. Cross** which brought her to Bath c.1928. Elected the first female MRCP and likewise of the Bath Clinical Society, and set up the pathology laboratory at St Martin's Hospital during WWII which was influential in public health improvements.

Cross, Roland; b. 1895, Bath – d. 1970, Bath; mechanical engineer; engines.
Lived at: 199 Wellsway; 114 Midford Road.
Worked at: 33 Midford Road.
Worked for the Bristol Aeroplane Company during WWI. RC devised a new type of valve for piston engines, though ultimately this did not go into production. RC started Cross Manufacturing in 1938 to make a spin-off of the valve development. The company survives today making rings and seals for high-performance jet (and other) engines.

Cruse, Jeremiah; b. 1758, Rode (Somerset) – d. 1819, Bath; surveyor; cartography.
Lived at: 4 then 2 Trim Street;.
Worked at: 2 Trim Bridge; 26 St James's Parade.
Employed by the 1st Marquis of Bath prior to 1793. Went into partnership with **W. Smith** in 1802. Created the so-called 'Cruse Map' – a large wall-mounted plan of the Somersetshire Coal Canal, currently in the possession of BRLSI. JC's main source of work was parish and estate maps.

Curtis, Thomas; b. c.1739, – d. 1784, ?Oxford; ?apothecary; botany.
Lived at: Belmont, Lansdown Road.
Arrived in Bath c.1775. Founder of the 1st BPS. Active within the BAS (Vice-president) and the MWH (Governor).

Daniell, Joseph Clissild; fl.1800-1851; mechanical engineer; machines.
Lived at: Limpley Stoke.
Worked at: Lower Bristol Road, Twerton.
Came from Wiltshire. Inventor and improver of machinery and processes for the cloth industry; JD held

many patents. Worked at Twerton Upper Mill, possibly as partner with Charles Wilkins. Possibly devised a new type of cloth-shearing frame. Although not the inventor of the power loom, JD experimented from the mid-1820s. The Twerton mill had a semi-powered device probably of JD's invention.

Davies, Dr Richard, FRS; b. c.1708 – d. 1761, Bath; physician; medicine, *DNB*.
A Cambridge University graduate, he investigated and published on the analysis of blood. He later withdrew from the Royal Society. RD practised medicine in Shrewsbury before moving to Bath.

Davies, Thomas Stephens, FRS; b. ?1794 – d. 1851, Shooter's Hill (Kent); teacher; mathematics and astronomy, *DNB*.
Lived at: 3 Old King Street, Queen Square.
Little is known about his early life, though he gave private tuition in Bath. His interest was geometry and its history, and he was recognised as the most able of his generation in this field. TD's main contribution was the development of a more general system of spherical geometry using spherical co-ordinates, but he made significant advances in a variety other problems in geometry. He was also interested in sundials. TD wrote general articles on maths and science for many periodicals. Resident in Bath until 1834 when he was appointed as a mathematics professor at the Royal Military Academy at Woolwich (where he wrote very successful text books). TD was elected as Fellow of both the London and Edinburgh Royal Societies, and of the Royal Astronomical Society.

Davis, Major Charles; b. 1827, Bath – d. 1902, Bath; architect and surveyor; archaeology; *DNB*.
Lived at: 55 Great Pulteney Street; Dinmore, 18 Bathwick Hill.
Worked at: Guildhall; 3 Westgate Buildings.
CD was the City Architect and Surveyor of Works from 1864 (taking over from **Manners**) until his death in 1902. Following up the work of **Irvine**, he was the first person to expose the Great Bath (in 1871). Although his schemes for improving and opening the Roman remains was controversial, CD did have the foresight to arch over the remains rather than back-fill the site. Became a City Freeman.

Davis, Dr John Ford; b. 1773, Bath – d. 1864, Bath; physician; medicine and botany; *DNB*.
Lived at: 13 Royal Crescent.
Worked at: Bath Eye Infirmary and MWH.
Studied medicine at London and Edinburgh Universities. Obtained LRCP and set up an independent practice in Bath in 1808. JD worked at the MWH 1817-1834, retiring as senior physician. Wrote on inflammation of the heart, but ignored advice of **Sherwen**. Active in BRLSI and kept botanical records which were used by **Babington**. JD was public-spirited, being elected as a councillor and at various times holding the civic offices of chief constable, bailiff, alderman, justice of the peace, and mayor.

Day, Joseph M; b. 1855, London – d. 1946, London; mechanical engineer; engines; *DNB*.
Lived at: 9 Devonshire Buildings; 14 North Parade.
Worked at: Victoria Ironworks, Upper Bristol Road; Spring Gardens (just south of Pulteney Bridge).
Inventor and pioneer of the low-power, two-stroke, internal combustion engine. Came to Bath in 1874 as apprentice at **Stothert** & **Pitt**.

Dixon, Prof Alfred, FRS; b. 1865, Northallerton (Yorks) – d. 1936, London; scholar; mathematics.
Educated at Kingswood School. At the age of 17 he took the London University entrance exams and came top in the whole country. Worked on differential equations and became professor at Queen's University Belfast. Elder brother of **Arthur Dixon**.

Dixon, Prof Arthur, FRS; b. 1867, Pickering (Yorks) − d. 1955, Folkestone (Kent); scholar; mathematics.
Educated at Kingswood School. Graduated from Oxford University. Worked on algebra and geometry and became Waynflete Professor of Pure Mathematics at Oxford from 1922-1945. Younger brother of **Alfred Dixon**.

Dobson, Dr Matthew, FRS; b. 1732, Bolton − d. 1784, Bath; physician; chemistry and medicine, *DNB*.
Lived at: Bladud Buildings.
Graduated from both Glasgow and Edinburgh Universities. Worked in Liverpool and took part in discussion meetings with other medics in the north-west, including **Haygarth**. His most important medical discovery was that the urine and blood of a diabetic contain sugar and that it was not a disease of the kidneys or liver. He carried out experiments with carbon dioxide as a disinfectant − work which **Priestley** respected and acknowledged. MD also conducted some gruesome sounding experiments on the physiological effects of extreme heat. Retired to Bath and became active in the 1st BPS.

Dredge (senior), James; b. 1794, Great Corsley (Wilts) − d. 1863, Bath; brewer and engineer; bridges.
Lived and worked at: Norfolk Brewery, Upper Bristol Road.
Lived at: Gothic Cottage, Sion Hill.
Moved his family to Bath in 1822 and turned to engineering to improve access to his brewery. Patented an improved design for suspension bridges in 1836 and entered the Clifton bridge competition, unsuccessfully. He built over 50 bridges in the UK, India and the West Indies; the largest with a 250ft span. Seven survive to date, including the Victoria Suspension Bridge across the Avon in Twerton. His sons William and **J. Dredge (junior)** became successful railway engineers.

Dredge (junior), James, CMG; b. 1840, Bath − d. 1906, London; engineer and journalist; railways; *DNB*.
Lived at: Upper Bristol Road.
Trained under his elder brother William in London, then moved offices to work on the Metropolitan District Railway. In 1866 JD became the illustrations editor at the newly formed *Engineering* magazine, became co-editor in 1870, and remained manager until 1903 when he fell ill. During this time JD travelled extensively throughout Europe and the US, promoting UK engineering at exhibitions and rose to hold high official positions including Commissioner-General for Great Britain in 1897 at Brussels. Highly respected in the engineering community, he was made an Honorary Member of the American Society of Mechanical Engineers and served on the Council of the (Royal) Society of Arts.

Dumaresq, Daniel, FRS; b. 1712, Jersey − d. 1805, Bath; cleric; *DNB*.
Lived at: 35 New King Street.
Not so much a scientist as an international fixer and facilitator of science. Graduated from Oxford University, and became chaplain at the English Factory in St Petersburg, then the Russian capital. DD corresponded with the Royal Society about the latest work presented at the Imperial Academy of Sciences, which led to exchanges of books and papers, and eventually high-level visits. Returned to England in 1766 and held various west-country curacies. Joined BAS in 1780 and contributed translations of foreign agriculture-related texts.

Edgeworth, Richard Lovell, FRS; b. 1744, Bath – d. 1817, Edgeworthstown (Ireland); educationalist and engineer; *DNB*.
Lived at: Pierrepont Street.
Made a number of mechanical devices including orreries and clocks. Invented a road building system similar to that of **J. McAdam**. RE and his daughter Maria wrote a manual for educating children from nursery to university which was translated into many languages.

Ellacombe, Henry; b. 1790, Alphington (Devon) – d. 1885, Clyst St George (Devon); cleric and civil engineer; docks, botany, and archaeology; *DNB*.
Lived and worked at: Bitton.
Assistant engineer to Sir Marc Brunel at Chatham dockyard. Brunel thought very highly of HE and considered him a 'very talented engineer'. Took holy orders and arrived in Bitton in 1817, restored the church and constructed three others in the area. HE was probably the first scholarly campanologist, and devised a mechanism to allow one person to ring multiple bells. HE was a skilled botanist and horticulturalist; he recorded over 5,000 plants which he had personally cultivated. A species of yucca is named in his honour. Became a respected local historian and ecclesiastical antiquarian. Left to return to Devon in 1850. Buried in Bitton.

Ewart, Dr John; d. 1800; Colombo (Sri Lanka); physician; medicine.
Lived at: Abbey Street.
Worked at: BCID.
Together with **James Nooth** and **White**, built apparatus to apply carbon dioxide gas to ulcerated cancerous tissue. Became Senior Medical Officer in the British army.

Falconer, Dr William, FRS; b. 1744, Chester (Cheshire) – d. 1824, Bath; physician; medicine, agriculture, and public health; *DNB*.
Lived at: Bladud Buildings; 29 The Circus.
Worked at: MWH.
Trained as a physician at Edinburgh and Leiden Universities. Close friend and neighbour of **Parry** with whom he conducted many experiments and studies concerning Bath waters, agricultural chemistry, health of agriculture workers, and the influence of climate (on the environment, behaviour, and demography). Published many other works on botany and natural history. WF was the first to identify that Bath waters contained dissolved carbon dioxide and suggested that this gave the waters an antiseptic capacity. Conducted some of the earliest known clinical trials in collaboration with **Fothergill**, **Haygarth** and **Parry**. Collaborated with **Priestley** on treating patients with various gases. Founding member of BAS and 1st BPS. Died at home, buried at Weston, Bath.

Farnell, William; b. 1748/9, Bristol – d. 1829, Bath; apothecary, medicine.
Lived and worked at: MWH.
Became resident apothecary in 1784 (until his death). Assisted **Falconer** and **Parry** in their medicinal rhubarb experiments by preparing the appropriate powders of the expensive imported Chinese and the locally grown plants. This was an early example of a clinical trial.

Fellowes, Dr William; fl. 1820-1830; physician; medicine.
Lived at: 12 Vineyards; 7 Russel Street; 4 The Paragon.
He was Physician Extraordinary to His Majesty the Prince Regent in the 1820s. Probably died in 1836.

Fisher, Dr ?Samuel; b. 1760-2, – d. 1846, Bath; physician; medicine.
Lived at: 14 Johnstone Street.
Worked at: Bath Penitentiary and Lock Hospital.
The penitentiary was for reformed prostitutes. Physician to HRH Duke of Kent.

Flower, Thomas Bruges; b. 1815, ?London – d. 1899, Bath; surgeon; natural history.
Lived at: 3 Rivers Street.
Worked at: 9 Beaufort Buildings West.
Educated at Kings College London. TF elected as Member (1841) and Fellow (1875) of the RCS. Arrived in Bath in 1851/2. Worked closely with, and provided botanical specimens to, **Broome**. Wrote extensively about the flora of Bath and more generally Wiltshire, including contributions to **Babington**'s supplement to **Sole**'s *Flora Bathonica*. TF's herbarium is now in Plymouth City Museum, with other specimens in Manchester Museum.

Forrester-Brown, Dr Maud F.; b. 1885 – d. 1970; surgeon; medicine.
Lived at: 22 Coombe Park.
Worked at: 24 then 19 Queen Square; RUH.
Studied at London University. Moved to Bath in 1929/30 eventually becoming consultant senior surgeon to the Bath and Wessex Children's Orthopaedic Hospital (on the RUH site). MFB established Bath as a leading centre for orthopaedic surgery and enjoyed a worldwide reputation. A ward is named in her honour at the RUH.

Fothergill, Dr Anthony, FRS; b. 1732 (?1735), Sedbergh (Cumbria) – d. 1813, London; physician; medicine and meteorology; *DNB*.
Lived at: 9 Walcot Parade, London Road.
Apprenticed to a surgeon in Durham, then attended Edinburgh University. Obtained LRCP in 1779 and moved to Bath in 1782. Kept a detailed weather diary and recorded temperature, wind direction, pressure, and rainfall. Wrote on lead poisoning, rabies, the 'abuse of spirituous liquors', and the effect of climate upon health (after analysing his weather data). Awarded the gold medal of the Royal Humane Society for his work on 'the resuscitation of drowned persons'. Conducted some of the earliest known clinical trials in collaboration with **Falconer**, **Haygarth** and **Parry**. Became a Commissioner to the Somersetshire Coal Canal Company to resolve disputes between the SCCC and landowners. Gave up practice in 1803 and moved to America.

Friese-Greene, William; b. 1855, Bristol – d. 1921, London; photographer; *DNB*.
Lived at: 9 Lorne Terrace (now Lorne Road), Twerton.
Worked at: 34 Gay Street; 7 The Corridor.
Worked with **Rudge** in developing kinematography. Held 80 patents, including some relating to mechanisms to capture and project moving images on a flexible photographic medium. Died impoverished, buried in Highgate cemetery (opposite Karl Marx).

Gatehouse, John W.; d. 1920, ?Bath; teacher and chemist; chemistry.
Lived at: 1 then 6 Victoria Buildings, Twerton; St Marie, Oldfield Park; 7 Livingstone Villas, Oldfield Park; 116 then 58 Lower Oldfield Park.
Worked at: 9 then 36 Broad Street.
JG was the official chemical analyst for Bath, working at the Bath City Analytical and Metallurgical Laboratory from c.1878/9. The laboratory analysed food and water samples, and assayed ores for members of the public. He also held the official city post of Inspector of Electric Light between

1892-1920. JG gave science lectures at the laboratory and taught natural science at various schools including King Edward's (then in Broad Street) and the Bath Proprietary College (Sydney Gardens), and was Professor of Science at St Cuthbert's (Lansdown). JG became a Fellow of the Institute of Chemistry.

Gibbes, Dr Sir George Smith, FRS; b. 1771, Woodborough (Wilts) – d. 1851, Sidmouth (Devon); physician; medicine and archaeology; *DNB*.
Lived at: 11 Laura Place; 14 Queen Square.
Worked at: BCID; MWH.
Studied medicine at Oxford University, elected FRCP in 1803. Wrote on natural philosophy, Bath waters, and bones found in a Mendip cave. A member of the 3rd BPS and the inaugural speaker at the launch of BRLSI in 1825. Appointed as physician-extraordinary to Queen Charlotte in 1819. GSG was elected as a free citizen of Bath in 1810 and became a magistrate for Somerset. Father of **H. Gibbes**.

Gibbes, Rev Dr Heneage; b. 1802, Bath – d. 1887, Plymouth (Devon); physician; botany.
Son of **G. Gibbes**. Graduated from Cambridge University in 1826. Practised medicine c.1830-1840, but took holy orders in 1841 and became Rector of Sidmouth. Some of his work was incorporated into **Babington's**. Wrote a number of botanical texts and discovered *Euphorbia pilosa*.

Gillo, Robert; b. 1841, ?Bath – d. 1891, Bath; wholesale photographer; entomology.
Lived at: 16 Lambridge Place; 29 Richmond Place.
RG collected extensive records of insects (particularly beetles) with his collections merged with others at BRLSI.

Glanvill, Joseph, FRS; b. 1636, Plymouth (Devon) – d. 1680, Bath; cleric; *DNB*.
Lived and worked at: Bath Abbey Church.
Rector at Bath Abbey. The only member of his family to drop the final 'e' of Glanville. Early supporter of 'the scientific method' i.e. conducting repeatable experiments. Elected FRS in 1664.

Glover, Rev Dr Josephus; fl. 1848-1877; teacher; astronomy.
Lived and worked at: 17, then 5 Lansdown Crescent.
Graduated from Cambridge University in 1848. Principal of University College (which prepared boys for university). Elected Fellow of the Royal Astronomical Society.

Griffin, Samuel; b. ?Taunton (Somerset) – d. 1929, ?Bath; mechanical engineer; engines.
Lived at: 2 then 28 Lambridge Street.
Worked at: Kingston Iron Works, Ambury; Philip Street.
Arrived in Bath in 1870 and quickly established himself as a millwright and agricultural engineer and later as a steam engine supplier. By c.1880 SG was designing gas, oil, and petrol engines for factory and marine use, eventually holding over 50 patents. SG invented a six-stroke engine, but got into trouble when adding his own valve design to Otto's patent four-stroke engine. An example of SG's work is preserved in the Museum of Bath at Work.

Griffiths, Mr; fl. 1803-1805; mechanical engineer.
Invented a machine for '... cutting down corn in a field' i.e. a mowing machine 40 years ahead of the credited inventor in the USA. His invention went before the committee of the BAS, but was rejected for support sometime between 1803 and 1805.

Guidott, Thomas; b. ?1638, Lymington (Hants.) – d. 1706, Bath; physician; medicine; *DNB*. Settled in Bath in 1667. TG's publications were kept up-to-date with his use of chemical analyses of the waters and he gained an international reputation as a writer on both the waters and Bath physicians. Edited the works of **Jorden**. He attended Oxford University but did not take his MD. Later in life he declined professorships at Venice and Leiden Universities. Buried in Bath Abbey.

Hanham, Frederick H.; b. 1806, Bath – d. 1877, Bath; surgeon; botany and public health.
Lived at: 22 Gay Street; 5 Miles' Buildings.
Edited *Natural Illustrations of the British Grasses*, one of the most incredible botanic works ever created – each of the 1,000 copies had 62 identical dried specimens stuck in by hand. FH also laid out the arboretum in the Royal Victoria Park and published an accompanying handbook. FH was MRCS of Edinburgh, so it is likely that he trained in Scotland. His medical writing was on the spread of disease and their cause, prevention and treatment with respect to diet, cleanliness and ventilation. Also a member of the Medico-Botanical Society (now the Royal Society of Medicine).

Happold, Professor Sir Edmund (Ted) F.L.; b. 1930, Leeds – d. 1996, Bath; civil engineer and scholar; buildings; *DNB*.
Worked at: University of Bath, Claverton Down; 14 Gay Street; Camden Mill, Lower Bristol Road. Initially studied geology at Leeds University, but turned to civil engineering following National Service. EH worked all over the world. He was a member of the design team of the Sydney Opera House. EH's interest in the training of engineers and his research in novel structures for buildings and large-span roofs, led him into academia in 1976 as Professor of Building Engineering at the University of Bath. EH championed courses where architecture, civil engineering, and building services students were taught together and undertook joint design projects. This remains a unique and respected feature in UK engineering education. EH was elected as Fellow of the Royal Academy of Engineering and awarded the gold medal of the Institution of Structural Engineers. Knighted in 1994 for his services to the construction industry. In 1976, EH started the engineering consultancy Buro Happold which is renowned for its innovation, and although it now has offices worldwide, its head office remains in Bath.

Harbutt, William; b. 1844, North Shields (Tyne & Wear) – d. 1921, New York; art teacher; *DNB*.
Lived at: Tyne Villa, Newbridge Road; Hartley House, Belvedere, Lansdown.
Worked at: Government School of Arts and Sciences; own school at 15 Bladud Buildings, The Paragon; 15 Alfred Place; 22 Milsom Street; factory at High Street, Bathampton.
Invented 'Plasticine' (at Alfred Place) as a reusable modelling medium in 1897 by using a garden roller to squeeze out the water from clay and then mixing the 'dry' remains with light mineral oil. Plasticine was manufactured in Bathampton until 1983 when a fire destroyed the factory. Died of pneumonia, buried at St Nicholas Bathampton.

Harington, Dr Edward, FRS; d. 1757, ?Bath; physician; medicine.
Worked at: MWH.
One of the three physicians appointed to the newly opened General Hospital. A graduate of Oxford University. Uncle of **H. Harington**, and descendant of **J. Harington**.

Harington, Dr Henry; b. 1727, Bath – d. 1816, Bath; physician; medicine; *DNB*.
Lived at: Kelston Manor; 4 Northumberland Buildings.
Worked at: MWH; Bellot's Hospital, Beau Street.
Born at the family seat of Kelston Manor; descendant of **J. Harington**, nephew of **E. Harington**. Although he graduated from Oxford University in 1752 he did not take holy orders, but set

himself up in Wells as a physician. However, Oxford only granted his MD ten years later. Moved his medical practice to Bath and became physician to the Duke of York. Elected mayor in 1793. HH was an accomplished song composer with his work regularly performed in his time: Haydn set one to music. There is evidence that he had an active interest in mechanical devices, mathematics, and astronomy. Little is known about his medical work, though he was probably the leading physician in Bath in the 1770s. Buried in Kelston church, with a monument in Bath Abbey.

Harington, Sir John; b. 1561, Kelston, nr. Bath – d. 1612, Kelston, nr. Bath; courtier and writer; *DNB*.
Lived at: Kelston Manor.
Invented the valve-operated water closet in 1593/4. Godson of Queen Elizabeth I.

Hartley, David, FRS; baptised 1705, Halifax (Yorks) – d. 1757, Bath; physician; medicine, philosophy, and psychology; *DNB*.
Lived at: Queen Square.
Worked at: MWH.
Although he did not take a medical degree whilst at Cambridge University, he practised successfully. DH moved to Bath in 1742 and was appointed to the General Hospital in 1744. Whilst working in Bury, he strongly advocated inoculation and used probability theory to aid his arguments. However, he also worked on improving a quack remedy for bladder stones (from which he suffered), and the chemical theory he and his colleague were using was based on Newton's theory of forces. DH developed a philosophical theory of neuro-physiological processes in perceptions and sensations. DH was probably the first to analyse the science of psychology and many regard him as the 'father of modern behaviourism'. He published many influential works, the last of which **Priestley** did much to popularise.

Harvey, Dr Alfred Augustus; fl. 1819–1841; surgeon; medicine.
Lived at: 5 Edgar Buildings.
Formerly surgeon to the Honourable East India Company Service. Elected MRCP and Diplomatic Member of the London Vaccine Institute.

Haygarth, Dr John, FRS; b. 1740, Swarth Gill (Yorks) – d. 1827, Bath; physician; medicine; *DNB*.
Lived at: 15 Royal Crescent; Lambridge House, London Road.
Enjoyed an international reputation as a public health practitioner and activist. A vigorous promoter of Edward Jenner's smallpox vaccination discovery and set up (with **Creaser**) in Bath (probably) the first ever vaccination clinic. Pioneered the idea of separate fever wards to slow the spread of infection (at Chester Infirmary). Conducted (with **Falconer**) in 1799 one of the first ever controlled clinical trials to determine whether a treatment was simply a placebo. Collaborated with **Priestley** on treating patients with various gases. Buried at Swainswick church.

Herschel, (Johann) Alexander; b. 1745, Hanover (Germany) – d. 1821, Hanover (Germany); musician and engineer; scientific instruments.
Lived at: 7 and 19 New King Street; 3 Margaret's Place, near Walcot Parade.
Showed exceptional talent both as a mechanical engineer and musician from an early age. Joined his elder brother **W. Herschel** in Bath in 1770 and stayed for 46 years. Like William, AH was able to excel on many instruments, but mainly played the clarinet and cello when in Bath. William used AH to complete some of the more difficult jobs which local craftsmen could not.

Herschel, Caroline; b. 1750, Hanover (Germany) – d. 1848, Hanover (Germany); musician; astronomy; *DNB*.
Lived at: 7 and 19 New King Street; 27 Rivers Street.
Joined her brother **W. Herschel** in Bath in 1772 and became a highly accomplished solo singer. As their interest and expertise in astronomy grew, she became her brother's amanuensis, calculating and cataloguing his observations including at least 2,500 new deep-sky objects. CH discovered eight comets – a record only surpassed in the 1980s – and, with Mary Somerville, was the first female member of the Royal Astronomical Society. The King of Prussia awarded her his gold medal for Science.

Herschel, Sir William, FRS; b. 1738, Hanover (Germany) – d. 1822, Slough; musician and composer; astronomy; *DNB*.
Lived at: Bell Tree Lane; Beaufort Square; 7 and 19 New King Street; 27 Rivers Street.
Came to Bath in 1766 to be the organist at the Octagon Chapel. Later became Director of Public Concerts. Probably the finest organist of his time, and a well-respected composer. Active in the 1st BPS. After discovering the planet Uranus in 1781, he became Court Astronomer to George III. He and his sister **C. Herschel** moved to the Slough area. There he discovered infra-red radiation. They built the largest and finest telescopes of their time.

Hillary, Dr William; b. 1697, Hawes (Yorks) – d. 1763, London; physician; medicine and meteorology; *DNB*.
?*Lived and worked at*: Lyncombe House.
Practised in Bath between 1734-46; set up a cold-water spa. Kept a moderately detailed weather diary recording atmospheric pressure which he used to infer characteristics of the spread of infectious diseases and general health matters. An early proponent of using data analysis to discover real effects in clinical studies.

Hornblower, Jonathan; b. 1753, Chacewater (Cornwall) – d. 1815, Penryn (Cornwall); mechanical engineer; steam engines and astronomy; *DNB*.
Lived and worked at: Radstock.
JH is one of the most important, but little known, figures in the development of the stationary steam engine. Intriguingly, he is at the centre of an intricate and murky story in which early historical reports contained errors which were perpetuated and became accepted. Some of these errors may have been 'encouraged', or even 'created', by James Watt and his supporters. Watt had patented his compound steam engine in 1769, but only installed one in 1777. JH patented his engine in 1781 having first built a model in 1776. JH was financially backed by the Winwood family of Bristol ironmasters, which may explain why JH's first compound engine was installed at a Radstock coal mine in 1782. One entirely erroneous story was that the courts declared that JH's engine infringed Watt's patent. In fact it was JH's brother, Jabez, who wronged Watt. In any event Jonathan Hornblower was clearly a serious rival to Watt, and has been unjustly overlooked.

Horner, William; b. 1786, Bristol – d. 1837, Bath; teacher; mathematics; *DNB*.
Lived and worked at: 18 Devonshire Buildings; 27 Grosvenor Place.
Became headmaster at Kingswood School in Bristol (which later moved to Bath) at age 19. Later opened his own school, The Seminary, and remained head until his death. Member of the 3rd BPS. He made many contributions to algebra, including an algorithm for finding the roots of polynomial equations, now named the Horner Method. Also wrote popular various articles on mathematics.

Horstmann, Gustav; b. 1828, Westphalia (Germany) – d. 1893, Bath; precision mechanical engineer; timepieces.

Lived at: 19 Vineyards; 5 Malvern Villas; Hillside, Newbridge Road; Forres, Newbridge Road West; Woodlands, Lower Bristol Road.

Worked at: 3 Bladud Buildings; 13 Union Street; Colonnade, Bennett Street; 7 George Street.

A skilled clock and watch maker. Designed the first micrometer accurate to one ten thousandth of an inch. Held over 100 patents. His son **S. Horstmann** founded Horstmann Cars Ltd.

Horstmann, Sidney, OBE; b. 1881, Bath – d. 1968, Bath; engineer; transport.

Lived at: 10 Norfolk Crescent; Onega Lodge, Albion Terrace.

Worked at: James Street West and 93 Newbridge Road; 86 Walcot Street.

Youngest son of **G. Horstmann**. Devised an automatic car gear box and started the Horstmann Gear Company to manufacture it. This failed, but SH started Horstmann Cars Ltd in 1913, taking on **Carwardine** as an engineer. Carwardine and SH raced Horstmann cars at Broadlands in the 1920s and 30s. Horstmann Cars eventually metamorphosed into Horstman (one 'n') Defence Systems.

Howse, Sir Henry Greenway; b. 1841, Bath – d. 1914, Cudham (Kent); surgeon; medicine.

Lived at: Lyncombe Hall.

Trained and then worked at Guy's Hospital in London. Made significant advances in gastric and ovarian surgery. Elected Fellow and later President of the RCS. HH was a strong advocate of women's higher education.

Ingenhousz, Dr. Jan, FRS; b. 1730, Breda (Netherlands) – d. 1799 Bowood, Calne (Wilts); physician; medicine, biology, physics and chemistry; *DNB*.

Lived and worked at: Bowood House, Calne (Wilts).

Studied at Louvain, Leided, Paris and Edinburgh Universities. He was an early supporter and researcher of smallpox inoculation. JI was a skilled experimenter and was elected to the Royal Society in 1771. He published on electricity and magnetism, gases, and soil renovation. He demonstrated that the green parts of plants emitted oxygen when illuminated by sunlight, and that it is the visible light, not a heating effect, which is the mechanism. Permanently moved to England at the start of the French Revolution in 1789, often staying with Lord Shelburne at Bowood.

Inman, Thomas Frederick; fl 1829–1906; botany.

Lived at: Apsey House, Batheaston; Kilkenny House, Sion Hill.

An active member of the BAFC, and some of his work was used by **Babington**.

Irvine, James; fl. 1864–1873; surveyor; archaeology.

Worked at: Bath Abbey.

Born in the Shetland Isles. Becoming side-tracked from his work on the restoration of the Abbey, JI was the first to take a systematic approach to the unearthing and recording of the Roman baths. In 1865 he found the main drain and dug other trial shafts to map the extent of the Roman site. Subsequently worked with **C. Davis** in exploring the main drain which led to the discovery of the Great Bath.

Jarrett, Miss; fl. 1900–1911; coalmine owner; natural history.

Lived at: Camerton Manor.

President of Bath Ladies' Microscopical Society c.1900. Sisters Anna and Emily inherited the Camerton coalmines in 1863. Emily had day-to-day control of the pits. As Emily was the younger and died at Camerton in 1911, it is more likely that she was the natural historian.

Jenyns, Rev Leonard; b. 1800, London – d. 1893, Bath; cleric; natural history; *DNB*.
Lived at: Swainswick House, Upper Swainswick; 19 Belmont, Lansdown Road.
The most eminent natural historian of his time and the first choice for the voyage of the *Beagle* – LJ declined and suggested Charles Darwin. Co-founder of the BAFC (with **Broome**). LJ later changed his surname to Blomefeld for inheritance purposes.

Jorden, Dr. Edward; b. 1569, High Halden (Kent) – d. 1632, Bath; physician; chemistry; *DNB*.
Studied at Oxford and Cambridge Universities, but obtained his MD from Padua (Italy). Became FRCP in 1597. Highly respected by King James I, he became physician to the latter's consort, Queen Anne. His work on the chemical constituents in mineral waters is acknowledged as having contributed significantly to the development of modern chemical analysis. EJ was possibly the first to describe acid-base indicators, and his innovative use of crystallisation earned him a formidable international reputation. EJ's work clearly pre-dates that of the better known Robert Boyle, and his ideas were quickly taken up by others inernationally. His comprehensive book of 1631 became a standard text; subsequent editions were edited and championed by **Guidott**.

Keate, Robert; b. 1777, Laverton (Somerset) – d. 1857, London; surgeon; medicine; *DNB*.
Attended Bath Grammar School. Trained and worked at St George's Hospital, London, earning an exceptional reputation. Became surgeon to Kings George III and IV, William IV, and Queen Victoria. One of the original FRCS.

Lambert, Aylmer Bourke, FRS; b. 1761, Bath – d. 1842, London; botany and archaeology; *DNB*.
Attended Oxford University where he met **Sibthorp**. An original member and sometime vice-president of the Linnean Society. He assisted others in their excavations of Wiltshire tumuli. An eccentric man, his large botanical collection was disordered and it was left to others to trawl his collection for specimens new to science. AL wrote a number of useful botanical works; however, his approach to publication was rather disorganised.

Lawson, Henry, FRS; b. 1774, London – d. 1855, Bath; astronomy; *DNB*.
Lived at: 7 Lansdown Crescent.
Originally served an apprenticeship in the Spectaclemakers' Company, but was left a fortune by a relative. Made a number of useful planetary and solar observations using his roof-mounted telescopes (*see frontispiece*). Won awards from the Royal Society of Arts for his inventions of a reclining medical and observing chair (the 'Reclinea') and for his thermometer stand to aid measurement standardisation. Elected Fellow of the Royal Astronomical Society in 1833 for his contributions to astronomy and meteorology. Probably related to Katherine Parr. Left his large fortune to 139 people and many Bath hospitals and institutions. He was buried at Weston.

Lee, Dr Arthur, FRS; b. 1740, Virginia (USA) – d. 1792, Virginia (USA); physician and diplomat; medicine.
Lived at: 5 Rivers Street.
Studied at Edinburgh University and became interested in the medicinal uses of plants. However, AL gave up medicine for law and in 1775 acted as agent of Virginia to present the second petition of independence to the King. The following year he became 'minister to France'. AL's brother, Richard Henry Lee, was a celebrated patriot of the US Revolution. AL withdrew from the Royal Society in 1788.

Lee, Dr John, FRS; b. Kerry (Ireland) – d. 1822, Bath; physician; medicine.
Lived at: 2 Seymour Street.
Studied at Reims (France). Elected LRCP in 1778 and FRS in 1782. Published on gout.

Lockey, Rev Dr Francis L.; b. 1796 – d. 1869, ?Bath; cleric; natural history and meteorology.
Lived at: Swainswick Cottage, Swainswick; 20 Walcot Parade.
Worked at: Bath Penitentiary and Lock Hospital.
The penitentiary was for reformed prostitutes. FL kept detailed meteorological records – temperature, pressure, rainfall, wind direction, and humidity – in addition to notes on cloud formations, and flower and insect emergence. He was a keen shell collector and a highly skilled early photographer.

Lonsdale, William; b.1794, Bath – d. 1871, Bristol; soldier; geology; *DNB*.
Lived at: Lonsdale, High Street, Batheaston
Commissioned as ensign in the 4th (King's Own) Regiment of Foot, served at Salamanca and Waterloo, and retired as lieutenant. Amassed a significant collection of fossils. Became first curator to BRLSI (1825-29) and helped form its museum. WL was elected FGS, appointed curator, librarian, and indexer to the GSL and was awarded its Wollaston medal for his work on corals. Died of TB and is buried in Arnos Vale Cemetery, Bristol.

McAdam, John Loudon; b. 1756, Ayr (Scotland) – d. 1836, Moffat (Scotland); surveyor and chemical engineer; roads; *DNB*.
JM's business interests in Scotland and Bristol started in the production of coal tar, mineral paints and oils etc. However, JM is famous for devising a new method of road building, i.e. layers of different sized stones on a well drained subsoil. He and his sons were surveyors to Turnpike Trusts across the nation, and JM was the first systematic builder and administrator of roads in Britain since the Romans. JM became surveyor for the Bath Turnpike Trust from 1826 until his death. Declined a knighthood.

McAdam, William; b. New York (USA) – d. c.1859, ?Bath; surveyor; roads.
Lived at: 13 Norfolk Buildings; The Cottage, Victoria Park.
Worked at: Westgate House, 17 Westgate Buildings.
Son of **J. McAdam**. Worked for the Black Dog Turnpike Trust. With **Brunel**, surveyed the structurally difficult route of the Bath-to-Warminster road (A36) on the side of the Limpley Stoke valley.

Macaulay, Francis, FRS; b. 1862, Witney (Oxon) – d. 1937, Cambridge; teacher; mathematics.
Worked at: Kingwood School.
Attended Kingswood School and returned there to teach after graduating from Cambridge University in 1881. He then moved to St Paul's School in London, from where he retired in 1911. He was an inspiring teacher, judging by the record of scholarships, exhibitions and performance of his former pupils. He wrote many papers on algebraic geometry and his 1916 book, *The Algebraic Theory of Modular Systems*, was reprinted in 1996 as it remains relevant today.

Malthus, Rev (Thomas) Robert, FRS; b. 1766, Wooton (Surrey) – d. 1834, Bath; cleric; political economics and statistics; *DNB*.
Lived at: Claverton Rectory; 17 Portland Place.
Attended Rev Richard Graves' school at Claverton Rectory 1778-81. Learned of **Hartley**'s work. Probably his most important work was on population dynamics. Highly respected – his ideas strongly influenced Charles Darwin. Co-founder of the (Royal) Statistical Society of London. Possibly spent the final four years of his life in Bath, but certainly died at his parents-in-law's house (Portland Place). There is a commemorative plaque in Bath Abbey.

Manners, George P.; b. 1788/9 – d. 1866, Ripley (Surrey); architect and surveyor; cartography.
Lived at: 3 Sion Row; Weston Road.
Worked at: 8 Green Street; 3 Miles' Buildings; 1 Oxford Row; 1 Fountain Buildings; 39 Rivers Street; Guildhall.
Started as assistant to Harcourt **Masters** in 1804. Set up an independent practice by 1820 and took over from Harcourt Masters at the Bath Turnpike Trust. GM was the city architect and surveyor c.1829-1863 and worked on mapping the city's water systems.

Markland, James Heywood, FRS; b. 1788, Manchester – d. 1864, Bath; solicitor; archaeology; *DNB*.
Lived at: 1 Lansdown Crescent.
Moved to Bath in 1841. Elected Fellow of the Society of Antiquaries. JM was an active member of, and wrote articles for, both the (Royal) Archaeological Institute and the British Archaeological Association (BAA). He gave the opening address at the BAA Somerset Congress (1856). He was life president of the Somerset Archaeological and Natural History Society from its foundation (1849). Buried in Walcot cemetery.

Marsh, Thomas E.M.; b. 1818, Biddlestone (Wilts) – d. 1907, Bath; civil engineer; bridges, railways, materials, and archaeology.
Lived at: 34 Grosvenor Place, London Road.
Worked at: Hawthorn House, 8 Walcot Terrace.
Started as assistant engineer on the GWR. In 1837, aged 19, he excavated a sizeable mosaic floor from a Roman villa on the course of the railway cutting between Twerton and Newton St Loe. It was placed on display at Keynsham station, but was later transferred to Bristol City Museum. TM rose to become the GWR Resident Engineer in charge of the track from Box to Bath by age 22, but left in 1841 to work around the UK on canals and railways. In 1847 **Brunel** appointed him as his Chief Assistant, putting TM in charge of all GWR track work, which included materials inspection. TM then became a consulting engineer for overseas railways in countries including Argentina, Canada, and India. He investigated the collapse of the wooden 'halfpenny' Widcombe bridge in 1877 and then designed the (current) iron replacement. TM corresponded with the Institution of Civil Engineers on materials and railway matters for many years. Although little known, TM was an engineer of the greatest ability.

Martin, Benjamin; baptised 1705, Worplesdon (Surrey) – d. 1782, London; lecturer and scientific instrument maker and retailer; *DNB*.
Lived at: Upper Orange Grove (now Guildhall/Empire complex).
Interested in optics and made microscopes. BM became a peripatetic lecturer and prolific writer on a wide variety of scientific and philosophical topics. Most ran to many reprints, and some were translated into Dutch, French, and Italian. BM was probably self-taught and as a result always tried to make his books as cheap as possible to give others easy access to learning. Made Bath his base from the mid 1740s for about a decade. Declared bankrupt in 1782. BM is recognised as one of the best and most successful science communicators of his generation.

Massingham, Henry G.; b. 1851, Guildford (Surrey) – d. 1938, Brighton; electrical engineer; power generation.
Lived at: Claremont, Oldfield Road.
Worked at: 1 The Corridor; 18 High Street; Dorchester Street.
Educated at Bristol Grammar School. HM started as a shoe and boot dealer and built up a sizeable business with many shops in the West of England. Started experimenting with steam-driven

generators and his first assignment was to provide public electricity for Taunton. In 1889 he and his partners started The Bath Electric Light Co. Ltd. They only raised 20% of the required capital, so HM decided to go it alone. He started the Bath Electric Light Works in 1890 and initially supplied power for 81 public arc lamps. The business grew so rapidly HM could not supply enough personal capital, so he sold out to the City Corporation. He became a Director of the new City of Bath Electric Lighting and Engineering Company. In 1892 the Corporation appointed **Gatehouse** as its inspector.

Masters, Charles Harcourt; b. 1759 – d. 1818; surveyor; cartography.
Lived at: 21 Orchard Street.
Worked at: Guildhall.
Possibly born in Gloucestershire. Co-creator of the prize-winning *County of Somerset* map in 1782. CM then returned to Bath to work for the City Corporation, Bath Turnpike Trust, and various local landowners. Engaged **Manners** as an assistant in 1804. Conducted a survey of Bath to create a 1:360 scale model of the city. Conducted one surveying contract jointly with **W. Smith** and **Bennet** in 1811. CM was the ?first to add a magnetic meridian to maps.

Matthews, William; b. 1747 – d. 1816; corn and coal merchant; agriculture.
Lived at: Abbey Church House.
Worked at: Bridge Street; Abbey Church House
Probably born in Somerset, but arrived in Bath in 1777. Founding member of the 1st BPS and BAS. Became paid Secretary to BAS following **Rack** between 1787 and 1800. Did much to publicise **W. Smith**'s work.

Mayow, Dr John, FRS; b. 1641, London – d. 1679, London; scholar; physiology and chemistry; *DNB*.
Fellow of All Souls College, Oxford University, but practised as a physician in the Bath summer season. Chemically analysed the waters. One of the first to properly understand the mechanism of respiration (1668). A highly skilled experimenter and protégé of Robert Hooke, JM conducted early and important analyses on the composition of the atmosphere.

Metzger, Guss F.; fl. 1893-1901; electrical engineer; power generation and distribution.
Lived at: 14 Macaulay Buildings; Fern Cottage, Batheaston.
Worked at: Dorchester Street.
Appointed permanent electrical engineer and manager to the City of Bath Electric Lighting and Engineering Company in 1893. Left Bath in 1901.

Minett, Prof Colin F.; b. 1890, Hawkesbury (Glos) – d. 1953, Dartford (Kent); vet and scholar; animal pathology; *DNB*.
Attended King Edward's School and graduated from the University of London. Conducted important work on diseases in cows and pigs which led him to work in France, Turkey and India.

Montgomerie, Colonel Thomas G., FRS; b. 1830, Ayrshire – d. 1878, Bath; soldier and surveyor; geography and astronomy; *DNB*.
Lived at: 66 Great Pulteney Street.
Best known for his trigonometric surveys of India and the Himalayas, and awarded the Founder's medal of the Royal Geographical Society. Moved to Bath in 1873. TM was Kipling's model for Colonel Creighton.

Moore, Charles; b. 1815, Ilminster (Somerset) – d. 1881, Bath; printer and bookseller; geology; *DNB*.
Lived at: 6 Cambridge Place.
Worked at: BRLSI, Terrace Walk.
Created an internationally important collection of fossils, housed at BRLSI. CM's technique of searching residues has become a worldwide standard method for fossil recovery. Elected FGS.

Morley, Prof Frank; b. 1860, Woodbridge (Suffolk) – d. 1937, Baltimore (USA); teacher and scholar; mathematics.
Worked at: Bath College.
Became a teacher after graduating from Cambridge University. After Bath, FM emigrated to the USA where he became professor at Johns Hopkins University. An excellent chess player, he once beat the then world champion, Emanuel Lasker. He worked on algebra and geometry.

Morris, J.W.; d. ?1901, Bath; teacher; natural history.
Lived at: 7 Edgar Buildings; 16 Belmont; 1 Woodside, Bathford; 40 Rivers Street; 27 Green Park.
Worked at: The Woodlands, Bathwick Hill.
Arrived in Bath c.1855 and became the long-term Secretary of the Bath Microscopical Society. JM specialised in the classification of ferns, and compiled a catalogue of the Botanical Gardens. He edited the *Handbook* to the 1888 Meeting of the British Association for the Advancement of Science. JM taught literature and history at Somersetshire College and Kirkness House Ladies' College (Bathwick).

Motley, Thomas; civil engineer; bridges.
Built an innovative bridge near the current Windsor Bridge in 1837 (which was dismantled in 1894). Motley's design was a forerunner of modern cable-stay bridges (such as the Second Severn Crossing).

Nooth, James; b. 1743, Sturminster Newton (Dorset) – d. 1815, Folkestone (Kent); surgeon; medicine.
Lived at: 13 Burlington Street.
Worked at: BCID.
Younger brother of **John Nooth**. He was a highly respected breast cancer surgeon and showed that cancer was not infectious by surgically embedding a sample of cancerous tissue in his own arm on a number of occasions. Together with **Ewart** and **White** built apparatus to apply carbon dioxide to ulcerated cancerous tissue. Left Bath sometime between 1806 and 1809.

Nooth, Dr John M., FRS; b. 1737, Sturminster Newton (Dorset) – d. 1828, Bath; physician and soldier; medicine and physics; *DNB*.
Lived at: 9 Edward Street; 12 Great Pulteney Street.
Studied medicine at Edinburgh University. Contrived a commercially successful device for carbonating water at a time when **Priestley** and **Falconer** were advocating drinking spa water containing carbon dioxide. A modified version of JN's apparatus was used to administer the ether in the first known use of a general anaesthetic. He was one of the most distinguished medics of his day, became the Superintendent General of military hospitals (in North America) and in 1800 was appointed as household physician to Edward, Duke of Kent (the father of Queen Victoria). However JN was elected to the Royal Society in 1774 for his analysis of devices to generate static electricity; one of his proposers was Benjamin Franklin. Elder brother of **James Nooth**; he is buried at St Nicholas, Bathampton.

Norden, John; b. c.1547, Somerset – d. 1625, London; surveyor; cartography; *DNB*.
JN graduated from Oxford University in 1568 and embarked on a peripatetic map-making career becoming renowned throughout Britain. Created the earliest known map of the Bath area.

Norman (senior), George; b. 1783, ?Bath – d. 1861, Bath; surgeon and midwife; medicine.
Lived at: 16 Seymour Street; 1 The Circus.
Worked at: Bath Casualty Hospital; Bath United Hospital.
Began as assistant to his father (**J. Norman**) in 1801 and succeeded him at the Casualty Hospital in 1817. Became the first surgeon to the Bath United Hospital in 1826 (remaining in post until 1857). He was a skilled surgeon and considered the best of his time in Bath, probably the best outside of London. GN wrote a number of papers detailing some of his most difficult and pioneering work. In 1843 he was elected as one of the original Fellows of the RCS. At his death he was the vice-president of the British Medical Association. Twice elected mayor of Bath and became JP for Somerset.

Norman (junior), George; b. Bath – d. c.1938, ?Bath; physician and surgeon; natural history.
Lived at: 12 Brock Street.
Worked at: Bath Homeopathic Hospital, 1 Duke Street.
An active member of both the Bath and Postal Microscopical Societies, Chairman of the former in 1886/7. Sometime Chairman of the Bath branch of the Selborne Society. Principally interested in algae and microscopic fungi. Became a City Alderman. Grandson of **J. Norman**.

Norman, James; b. 1747/8, ?Bristol – d. 1827, Bath; surgeon; medicine.
Lived at: St John's Court; 24 New King Street.
Worked at: Bath Casualty Hospital.
Trained at the Bristol Royal Infirmary where he was known as a very skilled practitioner. This included the first successful shoulder joint amputation in Bristol (at least). JN moved to Bath in 1783, though he struggled to get his practice going. In 1788 he played a significant part in establishing the new Casualty Hospital and was appointed as the first surgeon. JN retired in 1816, though his son (**G. Norman, senior**) subsequently held the post.

Nugent, Dr Christopher, FRS; b. 1698, Ireland – d. 1775, London; physician; medicine; *DNB*.
Studied medicine in France and started a successful practice in Bath. Wrote a text on hydrophobia in 1753. Elected LRCP in 1765.

Oliver (senior), Dr William, FRS; bap. 1658, Launceston (Cornwall) – d. 1716, London; soldier, surgeon and physician; medicine; *DNB*.
Studied medicine at Leiden University. A Royalist, WO served the Duke of Monmouth's troops as surgeon in 1683 and William III as an officer in 1688. Qualified as LRCP in 1693 and lived in Bath and London. It is unknown whether or not he practised in Bath, though it seems likely as he published *A Practical Dissertation on Bath Waters* which ran to five editions. Uncle of **W. Oliver (junior)**, WO never married.

Oliver (junior), Dr William, FRS; b. 1695, Ludgvan (Cornwall) – d. 1764, Bath; physician; medicine; *DNB*.
Lived at: Queen Square (site now occupied by BRLSI).
Worked at: MWH.
Moved to Bath in 1725; became a leading physician and one of the founders of the MWH. Investigated the mineral water composition. Invented the 'Bath Oliver' biscuit. Studied at Cambridge, Oxford and Leiden Universities. Nephew of **W. Oliver (senior)**. Buried at Weston, with a plaque in Bath Abbey.

Padmore, John; fl. 1710-1739; civil and mechanical engineer; transport.
Possibly trained as a mason. In 1731, JP designed and built the tramway between Ralph Allen's quarries and the wharves at Dolemeads. He worked on the scheme to make the Avon navigable. JP also designed cranes and carried out much work in Bristol including building the docks at Sea Mills. Died by 1739/40.

Parry, Dr Caleb Hillier, FRS; b. 1755, Cirencester (Glos) – d. 1822, Bath; physician; medicine, agriculture and geology; *DNB*.
Lived at: 13 Catherine Place; 27 The Circus; Summerhill (Park); 7 Sion Hill Place.
Worked at: MWH, Bath Casualty Hospital.
Attended Cirencester Grammar School with Edward Jenner. Trained as a physician at Edinburgh University, and came to Bath in 1779. CP set up an experimental farm at Weston and his medical and agricultural experiments including sheep cross-breeding and the medicinal effects of rhubarb. CP was the first to describe thyrotoxicosis (Parry's disease) and discovered the origins of angina. First in the west to launch a hydrogen balloon (unmanned) in 1784. An avid fossil collector from an early age, he became a founding member of the GSL. Suffered a stroke in 1816.

Peirce, Jeremiah, FRS; b. 1696 – d. 1767; surgeon; medicine.
Lived at: Lilliput Villa (renamed Battlefields), Lansdown.
Worked at: MWH.
One of the founders of the MWH and became senior surgeon. Elected to the Royal Society in 1742.

Peirce, Dr Robert; baptised 1622, Combe Hay, near Bath – d. 1710, Bath; physician; medicine; *DNB*.
Lived and worked at: Abbey House.
Attended King Edward's School and Oxford University. Set up a practice at home in Bath in 1653. Elected FRCP in 1688 in honour of his many original medical observations including acute rheumatism following scarlet fever and repetitive strain syndrome (from carrying a heavy falcon). Buried in Bath Abbey.

Pigott, Edward; b. 1753, ?Brussels – d. 1825, Bath; astronomy and botany; *DNB*.
Lived at: 31 Rivers Street; 15 Belmont, Lansdown Road.
Settled in Bath in 1796. Discovered a number of variable stars and corresponded with **W. Herschel** regarding observations of comets. Corresponded with **Stackhouse** about seaweeds.

Pitt, Robert; b. 1818, London – d. 1886, Bath; mechanical engineer; heavy machinery and steam engines.
Lived at: 5 Widcombe Terrace, 7 Miles' Buildings
Worked at: Newark Foundry, Horse (now Southgate)/Philip/Newark Street area.
RP joined Stothert's as a 16-year-old apprentice in 1834. Went into partnership with **H. Stothert** (along with **Rayno**) in 1844 aged 26. The company traded as 'Stothert, Rayno & Pitt', but their products were labelled simply as 'Stothert, Bath'. When Rayno retired in 1855, the company became 'Stothert & Pitt' and soon moved to Lower Bristol Road. RP held patents, including one (with Stephen Cox of Bristol) for machinery to dramatically reduce the time taken to tan hides. The device won a silver medal at the 1867 Paris Great Universal Exhibition. Their company eventually became a world-leading firm for cranes and heavy lifting gear, though it eventually closed in 1989.

Pratt, Samuel Peace, FRS; b. 1789, Enfield – d. 1864; geology.
Lived at: 3 Lansdown Place West.
Although he is not well known now, his proposers for election to the Royal Society (1842) were some of the greatest geologists of all time. He most important work was showing that the chalk marl in Normandy was the same as that in England. SP arrived in Bath in 1823 and stayed for 16 years. He was active in BRLSI and was elected FGS.

Priestley, Dr Joseph, FRS; b. 1733, Leeds – d. 1804, Pennsylvania (USA); cleric and teacher; chemistry and physics; *DNB*.
Lived at: Calne (Wilts); ?Pierrepont Street.
Worked at: Bowood House, Calne (Wilts).
Employed as library companion to Lord Shelburne between 1773-1780. Discovered oxygen when at Calne, and went on to identify ammonia, sulphur dioxide, and nitrous oxide. Collaborated with **Falconer** on treating patients with various gases. Worked closely with **Warltire** and carried out early experiments into photosynthesis in plants. He worked out how to dissolve carbon dioxide in water which he intended to be an artificial replacement for some naturally aerated mineral waters, thereby inventing the fizzy drinks industry. JP was awarded a doctorate by Edinburgh University in 1764, and elected FRS in 1766 for his work on electricity and electrostatics. A founding member of the 1st BPS, and vice-president of the BAS. Sometime lodger with the Linleys in Bath and a close friend of the **Herschels** and **Watson**. Popularised and promoted the work of **Hartley**.

Pring, Daniel; b. 1789 – d. 1859; surgeon; medicine.
Lived at: 9 then 17 Russell Street; 8 Walcot Parade; 36 Rivers Street.
Worked at: BCID.
Pioneer of colostomy surgery.

Rack, Edmund; b. c.1735, Attleborough (Norfolk) – d. 1787, Bath; draper; agriculture and botany; *DNB*.
Lived at: 5 St James's Parade.
Retired to Bath in 1775 and wrote on agriculture. Published poetry, essays etc. Undertook much of the research for Collinson's three-volume *History of Somerset*. Founder and Secretary of BAS, and founding member and Secretary of the 1st BPS.

Rayno, George; fl. 1831-1855; mechanical engineer; heavy machinery and steam engines.
Lived at: 4 St Mark's Place; Leicester Cottage, Prior Park Road.
Worked at: Newark Foundry, Horse (now Southgate)/Philip/Newark Street area.
Started work for **H. Stothert** in 1831 and rose to become chief engineer by 1836. GR was taken into co-partnership (along with **Pitt**) in 1844. The company traded as 'Stothert, Rayno & Pitt', but their products were labelled simply as 'Stothert, Bath'. GR retired in 1855 due to ill-health.

Ribright, Thomas; fl.1780-1790; engineer; scientific instruments.
Worked at: 18 Bridge Street; Green Street; 10 [Old] Bond Street.
Came from London where his family had an instrument-making business. TR specialised in optical instruments. TR and **B. Smith** started their business in Bath in 1777, though he was forced to return to London on the death of his father c.1784.

Richardson, Rev Benjamin; b. 1758 – d. 1832, ?Bath; cleric; geology.
Lived at: Farleigh Rectory, Farleigh Hungerford; Lisbon Terrace.
Fossil collector and life-long friend of **W. Smith**. BR was one of the earliest members of the GSL.

Considered to have great knowledge, but he wrote little. BR gave away all his fossil collections. Wrote down Smith's dictation of *The Order of the Strata* at **Townsend**'s house.

Roberts, Richard, FRS; b. 1943, Derby; industrial researcher; biochemistry.
Moved to Bath aged four. Attended City of Bath Boys' Grammar School (now Beechen Cliff School). Shared the 1993 Nobel prize for medicine for his work on genetics. Lives and works in the USA.

Robins, Benjamin, FRS; b. 1707, Bath – d. 1751, Madras (India); teacher and engineer; mathematics; *DNB*.
Came to prominence by refuting Bernoulli's theory of elastic collisions. Turned to engineering and built mills, harbours and bridges. Invented the ballistic pendulum for measuring the velocity of gun projectiles and made important calculations to include the effects of air resistance on them. His seminal book on projectiles was translated and extended for Frederick the Great by the brilliant mathematician Leonhard Euler. BR was awarded the Royal Society's Copley medal in 1745.

Rudge, John Arthur Roebuck; b. 1837, Bath – d. 1903, ?Bath; electrical and mechanical engineer; scientific instruments.
Lived and worked at: 1 New Bond Street Place.
Inventor of the 'phantascope' and 'bio-phantascope' for projecting sequences of lantern slides. Created much of the mechanism recognised as important to cinematography. Friend and collaborator of **Friese-Greene**.

Salmon, Frederick; b. 1796, Bath – d. 1868, Ombersley (Worcs); surgeon; medicine.
Lived at: St. George's Hill House, Bathampton.
Worked at: Bath Casualty Hospital.
Although apprenticed to another Bath surgeon, FS was possibly a pupil of **J. Norman**. He conducted work with **White**. He moved to London in 1817, was made MRCS a year later, and went on to become a pioneer of rectal surgery. FS published several texts (including papers in *The Lancet*). He developed several influential treatments; however, one of his ideas was later dismissed. His interests as a medical reformer, and his dissatisfaction with the ways of the RCS, led him to found (in 1835) what became St Mark's Hospital. Perhaps his most notable patient was Charles Dickens. FS retired to Worcestershire in 1857, but is buried in Kensal Green cemetery in London.

Saumarez, Richard, FRS; b. 1764, St Peter Port (Guernsey) – d. 1835, Bath; surgeon; medicine; *DNB*.
Lived at: 21 The Circus.
Retired to Bath in 1818 following a successful and lucrative career in London. Campaigned vigorously to improve medical education. RS was a proponent of investigating disease by considering the interdependency of internal organs and viewing the body as a single system. Made FRS (Edinburgh) in 1822 and FRS (London) in 1834. Attended the 1833 British Association for the Advancement of Science meeting at Cambridge. Wrote a text on the *Physiological and Physical Sciences*; his grasp of other peoples' work in physics was acceptable given his time, but his own new theories were less so.

Sherwen, Dr John; baptised 1748, Workington (Cumbria) – d. 1826, Enfield; surgeon and apothecary; medicine; *DNB*.
Lived at: 18 Great Stanhope Street.
Worked at: BCID.
Served a five-year apprenticeship in Penrith; studied medicine at Aberdeen University. Won a silver medal from the Medical Society of London for his contributions to various medical journals. Set up practice in Bath in 1805.

Sibthorp, Prof John, FRS; b. 1758, Oxford – d. 1796, Bath; scholar; botany; *DNB*.
Graduated from Oxford University where he became the Sherardian professor of botany in 1783 after his father had resigned the same post in his son's favour. Travelled extensively throughout Europe and started on a mammoth work on the botany of Greece. JS fell ill when returning from his Greek trip and went to Bath for convalescence. Died of tuberculosis and was buried in Bath Abbey, where he has a delightful wall memorial that includes a view of the entrance arch of the Oxford Botanic Garden.

Skinner, Rev John; b. 1772, Bath – d. 1839, Camerton, near Bath; cleric; archaeology; *DNB*.
Lived at: Old Hall, Claverton; The Rectory, Camerton.
Graduated from Oxford University. Arrived in Camerton c.1800. His interests and observations of Iron-age and Roman remains at Camerton and Bathampton filled 146 volumes, though debate continues about the soundness of his observations and conclusions.

Skrine, Colonel H.D.; d. 1901, ?Bath; soldier; archaeology.
Lived at: Claverton Manor; Warley Manor, Bathford.
Most interested in the archaeology of North Somerset. Founder and President of the Bath branch of the Selborne Society and sometime President of the BAFC.

Smith, Benjamin; b. 1753 – d. 1813, Bath; engineer; scientific instruments and physics.
Worked at: 18 Bridge Street; Green Street; 10 [Old] Bond Street.
Specialised in optical instruments, but is known to have made planetaria and other precision mechanisms. BS and **Ribright** came to Bath and started their business in 1777. After Ribright returned to London c.1784, BS continued on his own until 1809. He certainly conducted experiments on electricity and gases with **W. Herschel**, and probably **Arden** and **Bryant**, too. Founding member of the 1st BPS.

Smith, William; b. 1769, Churchill (Oxon) – d. 1839, Northampton (Northants); surveyor; geology; *DNB*.
Lived at: Rugbourne Farm, High Littleton; 4 Bloomfield Crescent; Tucking Mill, Midford.
Worked at: 2 Trim Street.
Sometimes styled 'The Father of English Geology'. Surveyor to many mining companies and the Somersetshire Coal Canal Company. WS was the first to realise that rock was laid down in a consistent order, regardless of location and that fossils formed a signature of those strata. Created the first geological maps: *Five Miles Around Bath* (1799) and of England and Wales (1815). Inaugural recipient of the Wollaston medal of the GSL in 1831.

Snell, Edward; b. 1820, Barnstaple (Devon) – d. 1880, Saltash (Devon); mechanical engineer; engines.
Lived at: 7, The Paragon; 2 Great Stanhope Street; 12 Brougham Hayes Buildings, Twerton.
Worked at: Newark Foundry, Horse (now Southgate)/Philip/Newark Street area.
Arrived in Bath in 1835 as an apprentice to **H. Stothert** at the Newark Foundry. Rose to become deputy works manager at the GWR Swindon works. Emigrated to Australia in 1849, made a fortune via gold digging and railways, but returned to the UK in 1858 after making some engineering errors. Also an artist, diarist and chronicler.

Soden, John Smith; b. 1780, Coventry – d. 1863, Bath; surgeon and midwife; medicine.
Lived at: 13 then 29 Gay Street; 101 New Sydney Place.
Worked at: BCID; Bath Eye Infirmary.

Qualified c.1800 and went into the army as an assistant surgeon. Left in 1803 and moved to Bath. JS pioneered vascular surgery and in 1843 was elected as one of the original Fellows of the RCS. He was ambidextrous, which enabled him to become an immensely skilled eye surgeon, specialising in cataract removal. Went on to win the RCS Jacksonian Prize for his paper on rabies. Also interested in the effects of arsenic poisoning. Was an original member of the British Medical Association. JS amassed nearly 900 medical portraits; his son presented them to the Royal Society of Medicine.

Sole, William; b. 1741, Thetford (Norfolk) – d. 1802, Bath; apothecary; botany; *DNB*.
Lived at: 7 Trim Street.
A highly respected botanist specialising in mints and grasses. Had a botanical garden near the Avon at Kensington. Presented his exquisite folios to the BAS for their library (now at the University of Bath).

Stackhouse, John; baptised 1742, Trehane (Cornwall) – d. 1819, Bath; cleric; botany; *DNB*.
Lived at: 4 Edgar Buildings.
Published widely on botany, especially algae and the lower plants. Wrote a book on British seaweeds and corresponded on the subject with **Pigott**. Retired to Bath in 1804. Buried at All Saints, Weston.

Stothert (senior), George; b. 1755, Shaftsbury (Dorset) – d. 1818, London; ironmonger and entrepreneur.
Lived and worked at: 21 Horse (now Southgate) Street.
Worked at: 15 Northgate Street.
Arrived in Bath in 1779, took over an ironmongers in 1785 to supply mainly the domestic market. The company grew and expanded into supplying larger items such as steam engines. GS knew **W. Smith** well and subscribed to his famous 1815 geological map.

Stothert (junior), George; b. 1786, Bath – d. 1858, ?Bath; engineer and entrepreneur.
Lived at: 2 Richmond Hill.
Worked at: 15 Northgate Street; Newark Foundry, Horse (now Southgate)/Philip/Newark Street area.
Eldest son of **G. Stothert**. Probably much influenced and inspired by his tour through South Wales in 1804 under the guardianship of **Brough**, and aided by a letter from **W. Smith**. Started the Newark Foundry in Horse Street in 1815, which gradually expanded to occupy part of the site of the Southgate shopping centre. GS retired aged 40 and handed over the running of the foundry to his half-brother **H. Stothert**.

Stothert, Henry; b. 1797, Bath – d. 1860, Bath; mechanical engineer; heavy machinery and steam engines.
Lived at: 3, Perrymead; 4 Priory Place, Lyncombe.
Worked at: Newark Foundry, Horse (now Southgate)/Philip/Newark Street area.
Took over the Newark Foundry in 1827 from his half brother **G. Stothert (junior)** and took out the first 'Stothert' patent (relating to ploughs). Became a well respected engineer. HS expanded the company by starting a foundry in Bristol and by buying a company in South Wales. Importantly, HS appointed **Pitt** in 1834 as an apprentice. HS devised a scheme for turning London's sewage into useable manure (patented in 1852). Only some of the scheme was adopted, but he used the system at his home in Bath to grow vegetables.

Stothert, John Lum; b. 1829, Bath − d. 1891, Bath; mechanical engineer; heavy machinery, steam engines, and astronomy.
Lived at: 3 Widcombe Terrace; Mount-view, Newton St Loe; Audley Park Gardens.
Worked at: Lower Bristol Road.
Took over Stothert & Pitt from his father **H. Stothert** and was largely responsible for introducing heavy crane production. JS was Secretary of the 1888 meeting of the British Association for the Advancement of Science held in Bath and was a skilled astronomer, publishing four papers at the Royal Society.

Strachey, John, FRS; b. 1671, Chew Magna (Somerset) − d. 1743, London; attorney; geology; *DNB*.
Lived at: Sutton Court, Chew Magna.
One of the earliest English geologists to make observations and records rather than simply theorising. JS made some very important contributions to geology by observational stratigraphy, though his theories were rather fanciful. He made many detailed records of Somerset coal measures and his 1727 booklet on strata possibly influenced **W. Smith**.

Swinnerton, Prof Henry, CBE; b. 1875, Bungay (Suffolk) − d. 1966, London; teacher and scholar; zoology and geology; *DNB*.
Worked at: Kingswood School.
His research led to the first hatching of the New Zealand tuatara lizard *Sphenodon* in Europe. Doctorate on the cranium of the stickleback completed whilst working as a master at Kingswood School. Moved to Nottingham University and started the departments of Natural Sciences, and Geology and Geography. Served as President of the GSL (1938-40) and the Biological Sciences section of the British Association for the Advancement of Science (1940). Won the GSL Murchison medal in 1942.

Symons, John; d. 1811, ?Bath; surgeon and midwife; medicine and physics.
Lived at: Alfred Street; 22 Camden Place.
Practised in Bath between c.1766-1799. Conducted experiments in electricity and published on various medical topics. Founding member of the BAS and 1st BPS. Elected Mayor in 1795 and 1803.

Talbot, William Henry Fox, FRS; b. 1800, Melbury (Dorset) − d. 1877, Lacock Abbey (Wilts); mathematics and chemistry; *DNB*.
Lived and worked at: Lacock Abbey (Wiltshire); 4 The Circus.
Co-founder of photography, particularly worked on the chemistry of 'fixing' an image. Collaborated extensively with Sir John Herschel. Sometime MP for Chippenham. Was elected FRS for his contributions to mathematics, especially geometry and calculus. Won the Royal Society's Royal and Rumford medals in 1838 and 1842, respectively. Died of heart disease.

Thomas, Sir Noah, FRS; b. 1720, Neath (Glamorgan) − d. 1792, Bath; physician; medicine; *DNB*.
Lived at: The Paragon.
Very well respected as a physician, but not known to have published anything. Graduated from Cambridge University and worked mostly in London. Elected FRCP in 1757 and served George III as physician from 1763. Lived in Bath between 1780-1790.

Thuillier, Sir Henry E. Landor, FRS; b. 1813, Bath − d. 1906, London; Soldier and surveyor; cartography; *DNB*.
Lived at: ?19 Paragon Buildings.
Rose to become surveyor-general of India. Implemented, and perhaps developed, new printing techniques for maps.

Townsend, Rev Joseph; b. 1739, London – d. 1816, Pewsey (Dorset); cleric; geology; *DNB*.
Lived at: 29 Great Pulteney Street.
Friend of **Richardson** and **W. Smith**, who dictated *The Order of the Strata* at his house. JT built up one of the largest fossil collections in Britain. Member of the 2nd BPS. His views on population influenced **Malthus**. Proponent of, and shareholder in, the Kennet & Avon Canal. Educated at Cambridge and Edinburgh Universities.

Tudor, William; b. 1769 – d. 1845, Bath; surgeon; medicine.
Lived at: Kelston Knoll, Kelston.
Joined the 2nd Dragoon Guards as surgeon in 1791 and later served under the Duke of York. Saw action on the continent. Became Assistant, then Deputy Inspector of Army Hospitals. Retired in 1821 and became Inspector of Army Hospitals. Elected FRCS in 1844.

Turner, Rev Dr William; b. 1509/10, Morpeth (Northumberland) – d. 1568, London; physician and cleric; natural history; *DNB*.
Eventually became Dean of Wells. Published extensively on botany and was known as 'The Father of English Botany'. WT's 'herbal' was both the first British one and the first to be written in English; arguably it helped to revive Bath as a spa. It contained details of 238 native plants with 12 of the rarer ones collected from the Bristol/Bath area. WT was probably the first British botanist to use scientific criteria to discriminate between plants. Also knowledgeable about birds.

Venner, Dr Tobias; b. 1577, N. Petherton (Somerset) – d. 1660, Bath; physician; medicine; *DNB*.
Worked at: Bellot's Hospital, Beau Street.
Practised as an independent physician, and as Bath's first hospital consultant became a leading early expert on public health. Wrote extensively on the mineral waters and was the first to write exclusively on Bath's spa. TV advocated eating bran and the regularly cleaning of teeth. He chastised regular smokers and warned against drinking water piped through lead. Buried in Bath Abbey.

Voelcker, Dr (John Christopher) Augustus, FRS; b. 1822, Frankfurt (Germany) – d. 1884, London; chemist; agriculture; *DNB*.
Worked at: BAS.
Appointed as consultant chemist to BAS in 1855, bringing scientific rigour to assessing the value and state of fertilizers and soils by analysing their chemical composition. In 1849 AV had been the first Professor of Chemistry at the Royal Agricultural College at Cirencester, which is where he carried out most of his Bath-related analytical work. A pioneer of applying scientific principles to cheese-making.

Walcott, John; b. 1754, Cork (Ireland) – d. 1831, Bath; land-owner; natural history; *DNB*.
Lived at: Bathford; Great Pulteney Street.
Also a fossil hunter, JW's drawings were the first ones to accurately depict Bath specimens. Later cited and respected by **Moore**, **Parry** and **W. Smith**. Founding member of both the 1st BPS and the BAS. Strongly promoted Linnaeus and his classification system.

Warltire, John; b. 1725/6, Switzerland – d. 1810, Tamworth (Staffs); lecturer and chemist; chemistry; *DNB*.
Lived and worked at: Calne (Wilts).
JW arrived in Bath in 1776 and lectured on the new science of gases. He was a skilled experimenter

and collaborated with **Priestley**, making significant contributions to understanding the composition of water. JW was highly respected by many major scientific figures of the time. He was the first to observe that Exeter was sited on an extinct volcano, and made attempts to obtain a soft metal from manganese. Sometime tutor to the children of Josiah Wedgwood and Erasmus Darwin.

Warner, Rev Richard; b. 1763, London – d. 1857, Chelwood (Somerset); cleric; archaeology, history and cartography; *DNB*.
Lived at: 3 Duke Street; Widcombe.
Worked at: All Saints, then St James's Bath.
Although not a graduate (he only completed eight terms at Oxford University) he received ordination. RW held a variety of posts around Britain, arriving in Bath in 1794. An esteemed cleric and a prolific writer. Although he left the city in 1817, RW remained in nearby villages. As a friend and colleague of **W. Smith**, he helped him get his first map published. Created and published a 'fossilogical map' of five miles around Bath in 1811 to show the deposits identified by Smith.

Watson, Sir William, FRS; b. 1744, London – d. 1824, Bath; physician; physics and natural history; *DNB*.
Lived at: 21 Great Pulteney Street.
Close friend and correspondent of **W. Herschel** and instrumental in getting the Herschels' early work recognised by the Royal Society. Founding member of the 1st and active in the 2nd BPS. Published on blue sharks, but also worked on electricity. Collaborated with W. Herschel in measuring the hill heights around Bath. Became the city's mayor in 1801.

Weaver, Thomas, FRS; b. 1773, Gloucester – d. 1855, London; surveyor and mining consultant; geology; *DNB*.
Lived at: 1 Percy Place; 3 Hanover Place; 7 Vineyards; 3 Paragon Buildings; 7 Upper Camden Place.
Studied mining at Freiberg (Germany), then became a manager in an Irish copper mine. TW took a post at the Royal Dublin Society and started his work on Irish geology which included creating a geological map of much of Ireland. This work got him elected to the Royal Irish Academy. On returning to Gloucestershire TW was one of the first to study the Lower Palaeozoic rocks there. Published extensively and carried out the work which led to the naming of the Devonian geological period.

Wheatcroft, Lucy; fl. 1890-1910; artist; natural history.
Lived at: 6 Widcombe Terrace; 27 Rivers Street.
Worked at: 1 Lower Church Street; Bath and County Art Studios, 6 Rivers Street Place.
Sometime Secretary of the Bath branch of the Selborne Society. Her husband, William, wrote the botany chapter for the *Handbook* to the 1888 Meeting of the British Association for the Advancement of Science.

White, William; b. 1762 – d. 1826; surgeon and apothecary; medicine.
Lived at: 36 St James's Parade; 15 Westgate Buildings.
Worked at: BCID.
In 1798 WW demonstrated that English broad-leaved willow bark was just as efficacious as a fever treatment as the increasingly expensive alternatives. Together with **Ewart** and **James Nooth** built apparatus to apply carbon dioxide gas to ulcerated cancerous tissue.

Wilkinson, Charles Hunnings; b. 1763/4, ?London – d. 1850, Bath; surgeon; physics and medicine.
Lived at: 5 Burlington Street; 11 Old Sydney Place; Kingston House, Kingston Buildings; 55 Great Pulteney Street.
Worked at: Kingston Baths, Abbey Street (site of the Roman Baths).
Moved to Bath c.1806 and soon referred to himself as 'Doctor'. However, no record of his claimed MD has been found, though he certainly qualified as a surgeon in 1791. Wrote on medicine and electricity and purchased the Kingston Baths where he continued promoting and practising galvanic medical therapy. Conducted experiments which determined that fish air-bladders were solely for buoyancy control. CW became superintendent of the Bath Gas Light and Coke Company and was instrumental in introducing gas lighting to Bath in 1819. May have been an inspiration to Mary Shelley when writing *Frankenstein*, particularly his account of the new science of 'galvanic chemistry'. Mastermind of the 3rd BPS and was Honorary Secretary and Chemical Professor to the BAS c.1820.

Winwood, Rev Henry Hoyte; b. 1830, Bristol – d. 1920, Bath; cleric; geology.
Lived at: 4 then 11 Cavendish Crescent.
Part of a family with a long history of iron-founding in Bristol. Graduated from Oxford University, but only held a curacy for three years. He travelled extensively to study geology including to Greece, Syria, Italy and Canada. Close friend and obituarist of **Moore**. As honorary curator to BRLSI from 1882 (with **Broome**), HW extensively re-organised the Moore collection. Very active in the BAFC. Presented his work on local geology and metrology at the 1888 meeting of the British Association for the Advancement of Science held in Bath. Elected FGS and twice as vice-president of the GSL, and sat on GSL Council for 20 years.

Woods, Henry; fl. 1819-1826; surgeon; natural history.
Lived at: 7 North Parade.
Worked at: Bath Eye Infirmary.
One of the principal proponents, and first secretary, of BRLSI.

Young, Alfred, FRS; b. 1873, Widnes (Lancs) – d. 1940, Saffron Walden (Essex); cleric; mathematics; *DNB*.
Attended Monkton Combe School, winning a scholarship to Cambridge University; briefly lectured before taking holy orders. Even though he was not a professional mathematician, he was able enough to make important discoveries in algebra.

Authors

Colin J. Axon, who works on sustainable energy use and technologies in Oxford University's Department of Engineering Science, led a team from the Bristol and Bath branch of the British Association that created the Bath Scientific Heritage Trail in 1997.

Prof. R. Angus Buchanan is both Emeritus Professor of the History of Technology at the University of Bath and Honorary Director of the University's Centre for the History of Technology. He has written on industrial archaeology, engineering history, and I.K. Brunel.

Stuart L. Burroughs, Director of the Museum of Bath at Work, is Chairman of the Bristol Industrial Archaeology Society. He has lectured widely on the commercial and industrial development of Bath and is a co-author of *Stothert and Pitt: Cranemakers to the World*.

Michael C. Chapman, Historic Landscape Surveyor and former Cartographic Surveyor (Royal Engineers), produces guides and articles on the topographical history of Bath, published by the Survey of Old Bath.

Robert C.J. Draper, Experimental Officer in the Department of Physics at the University of Bath, devotes considerable energy to the day-to-day running of BRLSI. He received an MBE for 'services to the Bath Royal Literary and Scientific Institution' in the 2005 New Year Honours List.

Trevor Fawcett, a former university librarian, has published widely on art history, librarianship, and local history – especially that of Norwich and Bath.

Dr Peter J. Ford, recently retired from the Physics Department of the University of Bath, is Chair of the History of Physics Group of the Institute of Physics and of The William Herschel Society. He received an MBE for 'services to higher education and to science' in the 2008 New Year Honours List.

Marek J. Lewcun worked for Bath Archaeological Trust for 23 years, employed on many different excavations in and around the city. He is an independent consultant, a specialist in clay pipes, and a senior archaeologist for the Museum of London.

Robert D. Randall, a former systems analyst, is chair of the collections sub-committee at BRLSI and has a lifelong interest in natural history.

Prof. E. Francis J. Ring, Professor of Imaging Science at the University of Glamorgan, is a long-serving former chairman of The William Herschel Society and a trustee of The William Herschel Museum of Astronomy. He is a specialist in infrared thermal imaging, keenly interested in the history of science and of medicine.

Dr Roger L. Rolls has written and edited books and articles on the history of medicine. He is a retired general practitioner with a particular interest in the history of medicine in Bath.

Dr Peter J. L. Wallis, retired Reader in Computing from the University of Bath, edited an academic journal and several previous books, mostly concerned with aspects of computer software.

Roger C. Watson is Curator of the Fox Talbot Museum in Lacock, Wiltshire, and a recognised expert on the early history of photography, in particular the simultaneous invention of photography in England by William Henry Fox Talbot and in France by Louis Jacques Mandé Daguerre.

Matt Williams, Collections Manager at BRLSI, is a natural history curator specialising in palaeontology. He has a masters degree in palaeobiology from the University of Bristol.

Index

Subscribers

Laurence Anslow
John T. Appleby
Mr J. & Mrs B. Axon
Mr Edward Barham
Lyn Barham
Mrs S.E. Barrett
Keith Batten
Philip Bayliss
Dr George Beckmann
Hedda & Wolfgang Beese
Patricia C. Bennett
Gordon Bevans
Rodney Frank Bickley
Mrs I. Blackburn
Tom Boden
Bruce Boswell
David R. Boswell
Mr R.J. Brake
John & Jean Brushfield
Amy Burgess
Dr D. Cameron
Dr Suzanne Campbell-Jones
Simon Carpenter
Nancy & Geoffrey Catchpole
Peter Chapple
Douglas Clark
Mrs Y. Clemenson
John Coates
Terry Coles
A.T.F. Comer
Ken Cookes
Ruth Rose Corbett
Mr R.A. Cross
Dr Richard Crossley
Professor J. John Davies
Tony Davies
Peter & Christine Davis
J. De Normann
Marsali Dening
Dr Dixon
Dr David Dunlop
J.D. Ede
Stan Eling

Dr P.J. Ford
Don Foster MP
Robert Gardiner
Mr John A. Garrett
Professor P.J. Gates
Professor David Gooding
Dr William Gosling
Lyndon G. Greedy
Mrs Richard W. Hamming
Mr & Mrs William Hanna
Mr & Mrs J. Herschel-Shorland
Letitia C.K. Holt
Mr Barry R. Horton
Mr Mark Hurn
R.A. Hutchings
Norman L. Hyde
M. Jefferies
Dr Charles Johnson
Bernard Kelly
Steve Kimmins
Michael King
Dave Ladbrook
Richard Lawrence
Dr Evelyn L. Lewis
Nicholas Lewis
Professor Stephen Lillicrap
Mr Neil Lilly
Geraldine Lindley
D.R. Lovell
Marie-Louise Luxembourg
Felicity A. McAvoy
David Charles Mander
Judith Marsham
Peter Martin
Dr Richard Mawditt OBE
C. Miles
Roger Morgan
Eve Moseley
Dr Roger Moses
P.J. Nind
Richard J.M. Norris
Janet Parr
F.H. Pearson

Debonnaire Perceval
Richard Phillips
Göran Pilbratt
Felix Pole
Nigel E. Pollard
Huw Price
Dr Michael Purshouse
Ralph Allen School
Professor Francis Ring
Brian Robertson
Arthur John Rostron
Dr Michael Rowe
District Judge Rutherford
Fred Schlesinger
Prudence Shorland
Barry Smith
Roger Southgate
David Stevenson
Betty Suchar
Anthony Symes
Dr Tom Szabo
Michael Tabb
Jacqueline M. Thompson
Mr Alex J. Thomson
Dr Christopher Toland
Rodney Tye
Dr Rex Valentine
Brenda Vickery-Finch
Julian and Liz Vincent
Daniel Wall
Professor P.N.T. Wells
Timothy Wheeldon
R.J. Whitaker MBE
Martin A. Wilkinson
Mr & Mrs D.P. & C.M. Williams
Keith V.H. Williams
Mr Roger B. Wiseman
W.R. Withey
Des H. Woolley

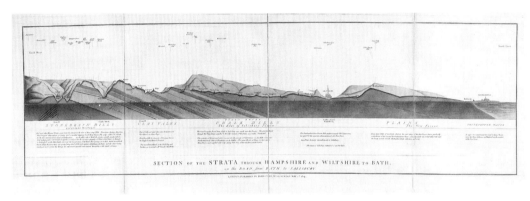

A monochrome reproduction of the complete section by William Smith
from which the detail on the front cover is taken.
(© *Natural History Museum*)